VIRGINIA WOOLF
"THE HOURS"

VIRGINIA WOOLF
"THE HOURS"

THE BRITISH MUSEUM MANUSCRIPT OF *MRS. DALLOWAY*

TRANSCRIBED AND EDITED BY
HELEN M. WUSSOW

PACE UNIVERSITY PRESS

One Pace Plaza
New York NY 10038

IBSN for hardcover edition (1996) 0-944473-29-6
ISBN for paperback edition (2010) 978-1-935625-01-8

The paper used in this publication meets the minimum requirements of American National Standard for information Sciences—Permanence of Paper for Printed Library Materials, ANSI Z39.48—1984

TABLE OF CONTENTS

Acknowledgments	vii
Introduction	ix
Principles of Editing	xxvii
A Chronology of "The Hours"	xxix
"The Hours" Notebook One	1
"The Hours" Notebook Two	145
"The Hours" Notebook Three	292
Appendix One	404
Appendix Two	408
Appendix Three	488

Acknowledgments

A project such as this could only have come about through the help and generosity of many individuals and institutions. For permission to transcribe and publish the manuscript of "The Hours" and related materials, I wish to thank Professor Quentin Bell, Angelica Garnett, the Trustees of the British Library, the Henry W. and Albert A. Berg Collection of English and American Literature, The New York Public Library, Astor, Lenox and Tilden Foundations, Ms. Roma Woodnutt of the Society of Authors, Hogarth Press, and Harcourt Brace Jovanovich.

The University of Memphis provided generous support for my research in the form of two Faculty Research Grants during the summers of 1990 and 1991. The University's College of Arts and Sciences also provided financial assistance. Travel to the Berg Collection of the New York Public Library was made possible by a grant from the National Endowment for the Humanities.

I would like to extend my gratitude to several individuals for their advice and support during the course of my research. Andrew McNeillie provided encouragement at a crucial period. I am indebted to the staff of the British Library and the Berg Collection, particularly, Stephen Crook and Philip Milito. Dr. Mark Hussey, of Pace University Press, brought patience, perspective, and his notable talents as a Woolf scholar to a text that, at times, seemed to evolve on its own terms. Thanks, too, to Michelle Folster and Dawn Roode for efficiently typesetting and processing the multiple sets of proofs. I would especially like to thank friends whose hospitality made this transcription possible: in London: Rachel Cooke, Yoko Nakano, and Penny Walker; in New York: Ann, Jack, and John Maidman, Margaret Morth, and Chris Rude.

Finally, I wish to express my gratitude to my parents. Their foresight and generosity are responsible for this as well as many other endeavors.

Introduction

> But how does one make people talk about everything in the whole of life, so that one's hair stands on end in a drawing room? How can one weight and sharpen dialogue till each sentence tears its way like a harpoon and grapples with the shingles at the bottom of the reader's soul?
>
> *Letters* 3: 36

Woolf's letter of May 13, 1923 to Gerald Brenan refers to the novel she was currently writing. Called, among other titles, "At Home," "The Party," "Mrs. Dalloway," and "The Hours," her work takes place, for the most part, in one drawing room or another, places where her characters grapple with issues of life, love, and death, matters of concern to her readers as well.

"The Hours" represents what might be termed the first full-length draft of *Mrs. Dalloway* (1925). Yet "The Hours" is more than an incident on the road towards *Mrs. Dalloway*'s eventual publication. It is part of the multiple text that is Woolf's novel. "The Hours" relates intertextually with the many versions, the many texts of itself. The result of this dynamic interrelation is yet another work, another version of what we call *Mrs. Dalloway.* This version is not "final," but is created from constant dialogue as it speaks to and out of its associate texts. The ambiguity surrounding the finality of *Mrs. Dalloway* is best evidenced through the confusion encompassing the status of the corrected proofs, a topic discussed below. The lack of closure, the open-endedness of the ever-constructing work reveals the fluctuating textual boundaries of *Mrs. Dalloway*, a situation that defies delineation in this age of definitive editions.

Donald Reiman argues that the practice called "versioning" provides a "complete" literary text without silencing any stage of composition. "Versioning" does not insist that there is an ultimate or "final" text worth more than the texts preceding it (169-70). This concept of multiple, co-existing texts is expanded by Brenda Silver in "Textual Criticism as Feminist Practice: Or Who's Afraid of Virginia Woolf Part II." Silver reworks Donald Pizer's definition of a "palimpsest," a text he describes as a "record of our civilization in the different ways that other men at other times have read it" (155-56). For Silver, the term also refers to a text, the boundaries of whose versions blur and thereby create another work, one that is no longer single, but rather "multiple, intertextual" (206). "The Hours," as we will discover, provides excellent palimpsestic reading.

i

"Mrs. Dalloway in Bond Street" and "The Prime Minister," written approximately between April 14 and October 21, 1922, together are the first textual layer of *Mrs. Dalloway.* The manuscripts and typescripts for both these stories may be found in the Berg Collection of the New York Public Library. The stories are published in *The Complete Shorter Fiction of Virginia Woolf* (1989), edited by Susan Dick. "Mrs. Dalloway in Bond Street" was originally published in the July 1923 issue of *Dial* and was subsequently published by Stella McNichol as part of a collection entitled *Mrs. Dalloway's Party* (1973). The story is similar to the section in the published narrative in which Mrs. Dalloway walks across Westminster to Miss Pym's in order to check on the flowers for her party (in the short story she is in search of gloves) (*Mrs. Dalloway* 3-14). "The Prime Minister" was never published separately in Woolf's lifetime, though like "Mrs. Dalloway in Bond Street" it functions as a complete, independent narrative. The story opens with a description of a sudden explosion, followed by the introduction of one Septimus Smith, and ends as Septimus and Mrs. Dalloway look at the sky to observe an airplane writing letters in the sky (*Mrs. Dalloway* 14-29). Eventually, versions of "Mrs. Dalloway in Bond Street" and "The Prime Minister" reappear as the first two sections of *Mrs. Dalloway.*

Also in the Berg Collection are two notebooks, one dated March 12, 1922 and another dated variously from November 9, 1922 to August 2, 1923. These notebooks contain Woolf's plans for her novel, her speculations on its title and the nature of its central characters, along with an extended section of dialogue between Clarissa Dalloway and Peter Walsh. The text of this conversation antedates a similar one in "The Hours" by well over half a year. Another notebook in the Berg, dated January 7, 1924, contains five folio pages given over to a bitter internal commentary by Peter on Clarissa. All of this material can be found in Appendix 2 of this volume, with the exception of "Mrs. Dalloway in Bond Street" and "The Prime Minister," the texts of which can be found in the aforementioned volumes edited by Susan Dick and Stella McNichol. Any references to manuscript material in this Introduction, including the manuscript of "The Hours," will give the folio, or holograph, page numbering assigned by curators at either the Berg Collection or the British Library. Folio numbers will be preceded by an "f" in order to differentiate them from conventional page numbering. In the transcription, the folio numbers are placed in square brackets and centered at the bottom of the page.

Just as "The Hours" and *Mrs. Dalloway* are composed of several earlier texts, they also participate in several later works. Six of the seven stories collected in *Mrs. Dalloway's Party*, along with "Happiness" and "A Simple Melody," in *The Complete Shorter Fiction*, provide a channel from *Mrs. Dalloway* to *To the Lighthouse* (1927), a corridor similar to that formed by the "Time Passes" section in the latter novel. These several stories, written during the first half of 1925, create a tunnel of time through which we can translate the past into the present. Some of the stories, such as "The New Dress," were written while Woolf worked on *To the Lighthouse.* Through them, Woolf extends the "party consciousness, the frock consciousness" of "The Hours" and *Mrs. Dalloway* into her fifth novel (*Diary*

3: 12). As John Hulcoop has suggested, the stories may tell us as much about *To the Lighthouse* as about its predecessor (4). To travel among "Mrs. Dalloway in Bond Street," Woolf's writing notebooks, the manuscript of "The Hours," *Mrs. Dalloway*, and *To the Lighthouse*, whether vertically or horizontally, is to explore a vast palimpsestic text in which the texts of the past are read through those of the present, and vice versa. Such a process reveals the the act of reading as palimpsestic, as each encounter with one of the many works comprising *Mrs. Dalloway* adjusts previous interpretations and earlier readings while informing the present.

Mrs. Dalloway is the story of displacement; its setting in post-war London illustrates the exchange of one world order for another. Its characters are the victims of change. For Septimus Warren Smith, transformation is synonymous with violence. Woolf's characters are aware of change in themselves and in others. Yet it is the text itself that shifts most dramatically. The modifications made in each text and between each version reflect and enact the fluctuations Woolf's characters anticipate and fear.

ii

Three weeks after writing to Brenan, Woolf offered two stories to T.S. Eliot for publication in the *Criterion*. One story was "Mrs. Dalloway in Bond Street." The other may have been "The Prime Minister." She had been working on both these stories off and on for nearly a year. On April 14, 1922, she wrote to Eliot and mentioned she was trying to "finish off" a long story, one which possibly could have been "Mrs. Dalloway in Bond Street" (*Letters* 2: 521). By September the story was completed, and she was able to turn to "The Prime Minister." In the March 12, 1922 notebook, Woolf, in an entry dated October 6, 1922, outlined her plan for a novel called "At Home" or "The Party" which would contain both short stories. Later in the same notebook, on October 16, she sets forth "a possible revision of this book," and works on how the two stories could be expanded into a novel, a concept she describes in a diary entry for October 14: "Mrs. Dalloway has branched into a book; & I adumbrate here a study of insanity & suicide: the world seen by the sane & the insane side by side—something like that (2: 207). It may have been during this period that Woolf contemplated having Mrs. Dalloway commit suicide, an ending she suggests in the Introduction to the Modern Library edition of *Mrs. Dalloway* in 1928 (vi), but for which there is no textual evidence. Instead, her notebook entry of October 16 corroborates a complementary relationship between the two central characters: "M[rs] D. seeing the truth—S.S. seeing the insane truth" (folio 153). On November 7, 1922, Woolf writes in her diary that she is ready "to sketch out Mrs D. & [. . .] write the aeroplane chapter now [. . .]" (2: 211). Two days later, she sets forth yet another plan for her novel, this time in a small, bound, reddish notebook, now in the Berg Collection. Although Woolf later stated, in the Introduction to the Modern Library edition, that "the little note book in which an attempt was made to forecast a plan was soon abandoned" (viii), the "plan" actually runs from November 9, 1922 to August 2,

1923. The entry for November 9, in this notebook, once again concentrates on the relationship between Clarissa and Septimus: "Suppose the idea of the book is the contrast between life & Death. All inner feelings to be lit up. The two minds of Mrs D. & Septimus" (unnumbered folio). Woolf worries about her style which she fears is "too jerky & minute." She lays out a "Fuller plan," showing that the action will take place between 10 and 2 a.m. (unnumbered folios).

The following entry is dated November 19. Woolf concentrates on Septimus and the inner swing of his emotions. She considers that he "might be left vague—as a mad person is—not so much character as an idea" (unnumbered folios). Observers will sing around Septimus; the book will have no chapters but will be divided by "Possible choruses" (unnumbered folio). On February 26, 1923, in the same notebook, Woolf focuses on Clarissa's character, and notes that like Septimus, Clarissa "must be seen by other people," a group that will serve as critical chorus (unnumbered folio). One member of this "chorus" is Peter Walsh, whom Woolf mentions in a subsequent entry dated May 7: "There shd. now be a long talk between Mrs D. & some old buck" (unnumbered folio). Such an encounter would provide Woolf with the immediacy and essential dialogue she found lacking in the work at that time. On June 18, 1923, she continues to complain that her dialogue is "too thin & unreal somehow" (unnumbered folio). She finds comfort, however, that "the merit of this book so far lies in its design, wh. is original—very difficult" (unnumbered folio). She goes on to chart Peter Walsh's walk towards the Green Park. Nine days later, she begins writing the long manuscript she provisionally calls "*The Hours*?", opening with Peter's thoughts on Clarissa as the bells of Westminster chime around him. By July 22, she felt pleased enough with the progress of the novel to make a self-congratulatory entry in her small bound notebook: "seems as far as I can judge rather good" (unnumbered folio). In a subsequent notebook entry for August 2, she boldly sets out the underlying struggle between Septimus and his doctors: "There must be a reality which is not in human beings at all. What about death for instance? But what is death? Strange if that were the reality—but in what sense could this be so?" (unnumbered folios). The confidence and pleasure evident in these entries is juxtaposed by Woolf's comment in her diary on August 6. She describes "The Hours" as "sheer weak dribble" (2: 260), a condemnation she retracts on August 30, when the "beautiful caves" she finds "behind [her] characters" emerge to greet the hundredth page of "The Hours" (*Diary* 2: 263).

iii

On May 24, 1941, Leonard Woolf wrote to Vita Sackville-West to inform her that Virginia Woolf had left one of her manuscripts to her, with instructions that Leonard was to choose it. Leonard first offered Sackville-West *Flush* (1933) and then *The Years* (1937) (259). Instead, Vita asked for *The Waves* (1931), not realizing that this was the one manuscript besides the diaries Leonard particularly wanted for himself. He indicated that he had originally thought of offering her "*Mrs.*

Dalloway, but [he] could only find half of it and oddly enough the second half in two versions" (260). But by May 29, 1941, he had found the first volume. He sent the entire manuscript to Sackville-West on June 21, 1941, along with an advance copy of *Between the Acts* (1941). In August 1956, Leonard wrote to Frances Hamill, a rare book dealer from Chicago, indicating that he would be willing to sell "11 items" en bloc to either Harvard or Yale (499). Eventually these same manuscripts were purchased by the Berg Collection of the New York Public Library. The material found in Appendix 2 comes from some of the notebooks purchased by the Berg, and consists of Woolf's original outlines for the novel, along with drafts of extended dialogue, as described above.

The manuscript given to Vita Sackville-West, called "The Hours," was eventually purchased by the British Library with contributions from the Shaw Fund and the Friends of the National Libraries. The three notebooks of the manuscript are numbered Add. MSS. 51044-46, and total 467 folio pages. The paper is that consistently favored by Woolf for her notebooks, namely Chariot Cream Laid bound as large post quarto (8 1/4" x 10 1/2"; Leonard Woolf, vii). Most of the manuscript is written in the purple ink preferred by Woolf, although, upon occasion, she uses black and, more rarely, blue. Less frequent is her employment of blue or red crayon, and black or blue pencil. Pencil markings mainly appear as marginal comments or remarks on the back of pages, or short sentences at the end of a page that often serve as starting points for the next day's writing.

Leonard Woolf described the covers of the writing notebooks as being constructed from "coloured, patterned Italian papers which we frequently used for binding books of poetry published by us in The Hogarth Press and of which she was very fond" (vii). Each of the notebooks of "The Hours" has a different cover. Add. MS. 51044 has a cloth cover with a crimson background, upon which is a pattern of white circles with radiating lines. These lines connect with other lines from neighboring circles. The center four circles and their accompanying rays have been filled in with blue ink. Add. MS. 51045 is covered with stained, slick, dark purple paper. Upon the front cover is a white adhesive label with red borders which bears the inscription in blue pencil, "Mrs Dalloway 2." Add. MS. 51046 has a shiny cover of material similar to oilcloth covered with a rough crisscross pattern in white.

For the most part it is fairly easy to chart Woolf's progress on "The Hours;" she often begins her work by noting the date at the top of the page. This is fortunate, for Woolf marked Add. MS. 51045 "2" and Add. MS. 51046 "Volume II." Another opportunity for confusion rests in the fact that on folio 109 of Add. MS. 51045 (referred to henceforth as notebook 2), the visions of one "Bernard" Warren Smith are described while folio 110 opens with "Who was he talking to Sally asked?" What Woolf did was to move to Add. MS. 51046 (notebook 3), whose frontispiece bears the date of July 31, 1924, and there resume Bernard's conversation with Rezia. She continues to use this notebook until October 4, 1924. She then returns to notebook 2 and recommences Sally Seton's conversation with Peter Walsh, eventually concluding "The Hours" on Thursday, October 9, 1924 at 11:15 a.m. (f. 113). On October 20, she returns to this same notebook to rewrite the first chapter, a text which had its earlier incarnation in "Mrs. Dalloway in Bond Street" and "The Prime Minister."

Thus, while the palimpsestic text may be read vertically, "The Hours" is also circular, a text that at once completes and repeats itself. Its conclusion provides a lens through which its past can be read and interpreted. In so doing, "The Hours" recreates itself. This concurrent intertextuality is best exemplified in the corrected proof pages of *Mrs. Dalloway*.

iv

Although the typescript for *Mrs. Dalloway* is no longer available, two out of three sets of the corrected proof pages are still extant. In a letter of November 30, 1924 to Violet Dickinson, Woolf writes that she has "just finished a novel—all except copying out the last chapter" (3: 147). Woolf usually created her final draft on the typewriter, revising her holograph manuscript, in this case "The Hours," as she went along. She congratulates herself on December 13 for the speed with which she is rewriting while retyping the entire novel, a process she terms a "good method" (*Diary* 2: 323). On December 21, she remarks that she is "putting on a spurt to have Mrs D. copied for L. to read at Rodmell" (2: 325). The Woolfs stayed at Rodmell over Christmas, and it was there that Woolf made her final revisions before sending the typescript to her printer, R. & R. Clark Ltd. in Edinburgh (*Diary* 3: 4).

The returned proofs were dated January 9-13, 1925 by Clark. E. F. Shields and Glenn P. Wright have exhaustively charted the many complexities surrounding the proofs of *Mrs. Dalloway*. I will, however, briefly describe what appear to have been Woolf's working methods regarding the proof corrections. Woolf was faced with the disagreeable task of correcting three identical proof sets. One set was for her own use, another for the Hogarth Press, and the last for her American publisher, Harcourt Brace. One would expect Woolf to make identical corrections on all three sets. But a severe bout of influenza coupled with the tedium of the work and time constraints created a situation where Woolf was hard pressed to keep up with the minutiae of the process. Furthermore, each set of proofs served a distinct purpose and, consequently, resulted in a distinct text. On January 24, 1925, Woolf wrote her friend Jacques Raverat, offering him corrected proofs of *Mrs. Dalloway* (*Letters* 3: 154). Woolf's illness intervened, and she wrote Raverat on February 5 apologizing for the delay: " . . . I should have sent off my proofs before but they were muddled up, and influenza makes me like a wet dish cloth—even to sort them was beyond me" (3: 163). Although she assures Raverat she will send a set the next day (February 6), the pages were not mailed until some time in mid-February, leaving Raverat's wife, Gwen, only a short time to read the work to him before he died on March 7 (Wright 244). After sending a set of the proof pages of

Mrs. Dalloway to Raverat, Woolf continued correcting proof sets of both *Mrs. Dalloway* and *The Common Reader* for her British and American publishers. Corrected proof pages of both works were sent to Edinburgh and Harcourt Brace by mid-March, although Wright argues that Woolf continued to mark the Edinburgh set after mailing the other to the States (248). The discrepancies between the British and American editions, when compared to the Raverat proofs, can be explained by the fact that the Raverat set was mailed in mid-February, while Woolf had until mid-March to continue work on the remaining two sets. The proof pages for the British edition no longer exist. But Wright argues that Woolf continued to mark them after sending a corrected set to the States, since there are various corrections in the British edition not found in the American, most importantly in the number of section breaks (248). The Woolfs left for France on March 26 (*Diary* 3: 172), and it is doubtful that any additional marks on the Edinburgh set were made after that date. Given her previous work habits, it is doubtful whether Woolf would have taken a holiday had the corrections not been completed (Wright 248).

V

The complexities involved in reading the two sets of extant proof pages in conjunction with the first British and American editions of *Mrs. Dalloway* illustrate how rich and rewarding a palimpsestic text can be. In "The Hours" there are additional textual layers, namely the several reviews and essays Woolf was writing simultaneously with her novel, many of which appear in *The Common Reader* (1925). Woolf worked on "The Hours" and *The Common Reader* concurrently, as is dramatically evidenced by the essays interspersed among the scenes in the manuscript. She outlined her work habits in a diary entry for August 16, 1922. After writing four thousand words of what became "The Pastons and Chaucer" (*Common Reader* 3-22), she "break[s] off, according to [her] quick change theory, to write Mrs D." (2: 189). Woolf's composition of one text within another is at the heart of "The Hours." Often a scene will be interrupted in mid-sentence, as on folio 84 of notebook 1, where Woolf suddenly comments on Electra's relationship with Clytemnestra, a passage found later in "On Not Knowing Greek" (*Common Reader* 23-38). On folios 22 and 23 of notebook 2 is a portion of the familiar "Mr. Bennett and Mrs. Brown" (*Captain's Death Bed* 94-119). On folios 33-38 is "Nature at Wembley," later published as "Thunder at Wembley" in *Nation & Athenaeum* on June 28, 1924. Also in notebook 2 is "Nurse Lugton's Golden Thimble" (ff. 104-06), accompanied by a list of possible four-legged characters on the *verso* of folio 103. A similarly delightful sketch appears on reversed folio 130 in notebook 3, where a porpoise named Peter cavorts in his tank at Brighton.

Woolf used the reversed pages of notebook 3 to set out the structure and draw up several of the essays in *The Common Reader*. By simply turning her notebook upside down she could use the same volume for both fiction and criticism. The date given on reversed folio 178 (counting back to front) is August 3, 1924, while the frontispiece of the same volume is marked July 31. This volume exemplifies Woolf's method of the "quick change"; she could literally flip from one genre to another without so much as changing notebooks. A list of the essays and reviews on the reversed pages of notebook 3 may be found in Appendix 3.

This practice represents on a small scale the overall blurring of boundaries between the many texts that comprise what we call *Mrs. Dalloway.* On the same day Woolf makes the first entry for *The Common Reader* in notebook 3 of "The Hours," she discusses the essays in her diary:

> . . . my 250 words of fiction first & then a systematic beginning, I daresay the 80th, upon the Common Reader, who might be finished in a flash I think, did I see the chance to flash & have done with it. But there's a lot of work in these things. It strikes me, I must now read Pilgrim's Progress: Mrs Hutchinson. And should I demolish Richardson? whom I've never read. Yes, I'll run through the rain into the house & see if Clarissa is there. But thats a block out of my day, a long long novel. Then I must read the Medea. I must read a little translated Plato. (2: 309)

Side by side in her mind, in her diary, and in her notebooks, "The Hours" and *The Common Reader* complement and expand one another. Through both books we learn again how to read, how to interpret a multiple, multi-faceted text. When Clarissa Dalloway speaks of the difficulty of knowing the other, she gives voice to concerns aired in essays such as "The Elizabethan Lumber Room" (*Common Reader* 39-47) and "Modern Fiction" (146-154). The personalities in *The Common Reader* are as striking as those of Clarissa, Peter, or the inimitable Hugh Whitbread. Montaigne, Charlotte Brontë, and the Duchess of Newcastle, all reside in the "beautiful caves" Woolf creates behind her characters. They possess the "humanity, humour, depth" of the characters in "The Hours" (*Diary* 2: 263). The famous passage in her diary about her "tunnelling process" in which she tells "the past by instalments, as I have need of it" (2: 272) is usually applied to *Mrs. Dalloway*, rarely to *The Common Reader.* Yet in both works Woolf excavates the past in order to reveal and explain character. Two parts of one work, "The Hours" and *The Common Reader* are connected by a tunnel through which both works communicate back and forth, informing and reworking one another. Woolf's exacavating technique creates an awareness of past time, time present, and time passing. This dynamic is part not only of "The Hours" and *The Common Reader*, but also of the reader's participation in the ongoing re-creation of multiple texts, texts brought together to form what we name *Mrs. Dalloway.* In reading "The Hours," the reader burrows into the texts of present and past, shaping them into works that will, in turn, be read, reread, criticized, and reinterpreted in the years to come.

vi

The first notebook of "The Hours" is dated June 27, 1923 and opens with Peter Walsh walking across Westminster as the bells of the Abbey and St. Margaret's toll half past eleven in the morning. The vibrations of time merge into a woman's voice, a voice that turns Peter's thoughts to love, Clarissa, and his inability to succeed in life. His failure to take hold of life is in contrast to the seeming purposefulness of a group of young boys on their way back from the Cenotaph, where they have placed a wreath. On folio 8, it becomes plain that Peter's meditations occur after seeing Clarissa and being invited to her party. Woolf begins again under the heading "III" on folio 10 (marking what was to become the third section of *Mrs. Dalloway*). In "The Hours" this third section opens not with Clarissa's cry, "Remember my party, remember my party" (*Mrs. Dalloway* 48), but with a chorus of bells. Time is precedent; the hours speak to "desultory women" who ask "What?" and "Why?" (f. 1: 10). The hours, too, are women, who alternately scurry or browse, as if on a shopping trip down Oxford Street. In the mind of Peter Walsh, Clarissa's voice mingles with the chimes of Big Ben. Like the shopping women, Peter indulges in comparison as he reviews his life in light of Clarissa's. In the center of his reflections rests the as yet unrevealed truth that Clarissa had once refused him.

"Ah, said St. Margaret's," like a hostess eager to swing the conversation away from painful teatime topics (*Mrs. Dalloway* 49). As in *Mrs. Dalloway*, the chimes of "The Hours" contain a sense of loss, and the sound "glides into the recesses of the heart" (f. 1: 12). There Peter discovers Clarissa in white, presumably at Bourton. She is the bell, the hour, but as the sound withdraws Peter fears her death, the threatened absence amidst all this clamor and life.

Peter's fears reflect his own apprehension at growing old, and again his thoughts march with the young boys traveling away from and into death. Yet as Peter walks through London he gains time. A young woman is the object of and inspiration for his new found vitality. Influenced by time's female voice and his memories of Clarissa, Peter quests for a new lease on life. Woolf opens "The Hours" with new beginnings, beginnings that contain the plots of their own conclusions. Bell-like, the unknown woman calls to Peter amidst the shops of Cockspur Street. Moving like the sound of time among the streets of London, she hesitates, lingers. A talisman of time passing, she encourages and mocks Peter to recklessness despite age and failure.

In "The Hours," Peter half opens "the main blade of his knife" and stealthily follows the young woman (f. 1: 16). In *Mrs. Dalloway*, Woolf makes the image of the knife more covertly sexual; there, Peter "stealthily finger[s] his pocket-knife" (45). The image of the knife is used earlier in a version of dialogue between Clarissa and Peter. In the notebook dated March 12, 1922 is an entry in which Clarissa comments upon Peter's surreptitious habit.

> [. . .] there was something—how could she define it?—egotistical about Peter which made him do things like opening & shutting a knife without noticing how ~~they~~ <it> got on people's nerves. (f. 187)

Private, and yet disturbingly public, Peter's obsessive behavior signifies his thwarted desires and his need to impose them, however symbolically, on others.

Peter's dream of the solitary traveller in "The Hours" is in several respects more active, although less cohesive, than the version in *Mrs. Dalloway*. Images of sirenic jellyfish metamorphose, through Woolf's rewriting, into visions that murmur "like sirens lolloping away on the green sea waves" (f. 1: 27). On August 2, 1923, Woolf returns to the passage, and the jellyfish "rise to the surface like pale faces which fishermen flounder through floods to embrace" (f. 1: 29). By August 13, 1923, the dream concludes and Peter awakes "with extreme suddenness" (f. 1: 32) at the beginning of part "IV." (section 5 in *Mrs. Dalloway*). Half-dreaming, Peter recollects "Sally ~~Silcox~~ Seaton" (f. 1: 32). He recalls the terrible evening when Richard Dalloway took "Molly Seaton" (f. 1: 35) and Clarissa boating while he feigned to prefer the company of old Miss Parry. The "final scene, the terrible scene" (*MD* 63) is somewhat truncated in "The Hours," and the unintentionally irritating Mr. Breitkopf makes his first appearance under the name of "Breachhammer" (f. 1: 41).

What would be section 6 of *Mrs. Dalloway* begins on an unheaded page in "The Hours," so it is difficult to tell if Woolf intended a section break in the manuscript. But as in *Mrs. Dalloway*, this portion of "The Hours" begins with Peter's proclamation, "It was awful" (f. 1: 42). His reveries, watched over by a suddenly "elderly" nurse (f. 1: 42) are interrupted by "little Elsie Mitchel" (f. 1: 42), who runs away from the intense-looking, middle-aged man towards Rezia (the first mention of her in "The Hours"). Rezia recognizes that "'Everyone is afraid'" (f. 1: 42).

Rezia's observation leads not to Septimus' delusions, but to Clarissa's thoughts, which parallel and expand those of Peter. She fondly remembers her friendship with "Sally Seaton," and Sally's anarchic ways compared to her own middle-class upbringing. Clarissa ponders "this question of falling in love—of women" (f. 1: 43). She, or rather the narrative voice that appropriates her perspective, considers her feelings for Sally. These emotions exclude Peter, who, suspecting what is happening, jealously attacks Clarissa in the hearing of poor "Mr. Breitkopf" (f. 1: 51).

Following this "vision of strife" (f. 1: 52), Clarissa contemplates her friendship with Peter, a topic Woolf cuts short on October 1, 1923, when she returns to Rezia and "Elsie Mitchell" in Regents Park (ff. 1: 54-6). Turning towards the seated Septimus, Rezia recollects how at Hampton Court he proclaimed, "'Now we will both kill ourselves'" (f. 1: 56). As in *Mrs. Dalloway*, Rezia's removal of her wedding ring segues into Septimus' visions. On May 1, 1925, Woolf commented to Gwen Raverat on the difficulties she experienced while writing about Septimus and his illness: "It was a subject that I have kept cooling in my mind until I felt I could touch it without bursting into flame all over. You can't think what a raging furnace it is still to me—madness and doctors and being forced" (*Letters* 3: 180). Yet these tensions are barely evident in the physical appearance of the manuscript. The textual cancellations and insertions diminish slightly at this point in the manuscript, suggesting either a rush to complete a task, the painful nature of which drained Woolf, a burst of creativity, or both. From October 1 to December 13, 1923, Woolf wrote thirty-one pages; fourteen concentrate on Rezia and her husband, while the remaining seventeen are given over to Peter and his recollections (ff. 1: 54-85). On folio 60 of notebook 1, Woolf notes that 28,000 words are now complete. On October 15, in her diary, she mentions that she can write 50 words a morning of the "mad scene in Regents Park . . . by clinging as tight to fact as I can" (2: 272). Such a pace might account for the relative clarity of the manuscript. Calculations in the margins of this section of "The Hours" further reveal Woolf's impatience to conclude the episode.

Respite from the "mad" scene comes in the form of "a man in a grey check suit," whom Septimus takes to be Evans (f. 1: 66). The focus shifts, and now Peter Walsh's voice comments upon the "freshness" of the passing women (f. 1: 69). He considers Richard Dalloway, and what Richard and Clarissa have in common. Peter resents Dalloway's priggishness over Shakespeare and outmoded marriage laws, and condemns Dalloway's association with Hugh Whitbread, a man disliked equally by Sally Seton.

Woolf begins to rewrite Peter's musings on December 13, 1923. Walsh now calls Dalloway "a thorough good sort" (f. 1: 89). Again, Peter contemplates the "bonds between Sally & himself" (f. 1: 91); however, now he concludes that it is Clarissa who has "that woman's gift" of "making life wherever she happened to be" (f. 1: 91). The reservations Peter reveals in *Mrs. Dalloway* about Clarissa's parties, her politeness, and public-spiritedness are found in this section of "The Hours." Interestingly, his opinions about Clarissa's domestic arrangements are accompanied by Woolf's sketch of a houseplan on the *verso* of folio 94. The drawing is probably of 52 Tavistock Square, the lease of which she bought on January 9, 1924.

On January 3, Woolf begins her morning of writing on "The Hours" by describing an elderly woman singing near the Regents Park tube station. Rezia and Septimus pass by, while the narrative voice assesses Septimus as being "a clerk of the better sort" (f. 1: 100). His pedigree is somewhat different in "The Hours." "The outline of an ordinary case" (f. 1: 101) is longer and more pedestrian in nature than in *Mrs. Dalloway*. As in the published version, Mr. Brewer urges Septimus to take up football. The description of Brewer in "The Hours" portrays him as a failed prophet, an ineffectual astrologer whose readings are disastrously out of touch with reality (f. 1: 106). Septimus travels to France, meets and loses Evans, and proposes to Rezia "in a moment of fear" (f. 1: 107). Septimus' appreciation of Dante and Aeschylus here extends to Swift as well (f. 1: 111), thereby underscoring his disillusionment with humanity. As in *Mrs. Dalloway*, Rezia begs to have children while Septimus refuses to populate the world with "Tom's & Berties" (f. 1: 113). The "seedy-looking nondescript man" on page 28 of *Mrs. Dalloway* is echoed by the man in "The Hours" whom Septimus sees feeding pigeons at St. Paul's while riding at the top of an omnibus (f. 1: 114). Septimus' comments come to a close when, with a "melodramatic" gesture, he collapses on a "green baize tablecloth," and Dr. Holmes is called (f. 1: 115).

The tension in Woolf's hand and compositional style noticeably increases during the exchange between Septimus and his doctor. Marginal insertions abound, as do lengthy deletions, indications of Woolf's misgivings over the dialogue. "Human nature" is now upon Septimus (f. 1: 119). In "The Hours," Septimus' sense of paranoia is emphasized as the narrative voice portrays others' views of him, particularly at the office, where he creates an "unpleasant impression" (f. 1: 120).

Folio 124 bears the inscription "52 Tavistock Sq$^{re.}$" The introduction of a new address marks the introduction of Sir William and Lady Bradshaw. This section corresponds to section 8 of *Mrs. Dalloway*. In "The Hours," Septimus' first encounter with Bradshaw consists of a conversation centering around questions and answers (ff. 1: 126-27). At the end of the dialogue, Septimus accuses Bradshaw of desiring Rezia, an accusation Bradshaw does not deny. Left alone, Septimus compares himself, as outcast, to Christ, and seeks to confess his greatest sin: that he had lied. When Bradshaw returns, Septimus asserts that *he* is the real enemy, and the two engage in a desultory conversational to and fro. Septimus makes his familiar sneering reference to "Holmes's homes" (f. 1: 132) during the verbal duel. He selects this moment to speak the truth of "universal love" (f. 1: 134), which leads, ironically—as Sir William is quick to point out—to an imprecation against Holmes and Bradshaw. Rezia is again sent from the room and another heated dialogue between patient and doctor ensues. Intellectual sparring becomes, for Septimus, a bloodthirsty pursuit with himself as prey. He seeks "caverns, recesses" in which to hide from the Sir Williams and Mr. Brewers of this life (f. 1: 136). In the middle of writing Septimus' fears, Woolf switches to Bradshaw's desire "to master this sceptical spirit" (f. 1: 137). Struggling, for the second time, to convey that "communication is life, communication is health" (f. 1: 137), Septimus is silenced by Sir William's abrupt conclusion of the interview. As in *Mrs. Dalloway*, Woolf ends this section with a condemnation of the Bradshaws of the world. But the passage in "The Hours" is curter; here Sir William is "the judge, the saviour, the super man, in whose hands powers of life & death were lodged; torture, isolation; the great gaoler" (f. 1: 139).

The concept of imprisonment is carried over into the first words of notebook two, dated April 18, 1924. Woolf is determined to escape restrictions of style and subject: "(a delicious idea comes to me that I will write anything I want to write)" (f. 2: 2). The gesture expresses both confidence and fear over what has been accomplished and what is yet to come. In the margin, she calculates that "The

Hours" is now 40,000 words long. The new notebook opens with a portrait of Sir William as prophet of proportion, "divine proportion" (f. 2: 4). Conversion is sovereign in Bradshaw's pantheon, and her bounty is Lady Bradshaw. On the *verso* of folio 6, Woolf considers, in pencil, that "it is for the purpose of giving character that the form of the novel has been devised," an intriguing contrast to Bradshaw's determination to eliminate the characters of others.

As in *Mrs. Dalloway*, Hugh Whitbread here illustrates proportion in action. Yet in "The Hours" Hugh displays rather *avant-garde* qualities. He evinces a dangerous interest in Freud and Stravinsky compared to the safer pursuits of "dead languages" and "the protection of owls" enjoyed by him in *Mrs. Dalloway* (103).

On May 20, 1924, Woolf begins Lady Bruton's assessment of Clarissa and Peter. In the manuscript, Lady Bruton's post-luncheon nap is interrupted by a review of "*Robert Smith Surtees* by himself" (f. 2: 29), which in turn is followed by Richard's selection of flowers for Clarissa; "deep black & [. . .] blood red tulips" (f. 2: 30) are replaced by carnations and evolve, finally, into roses (f. 2: 48). Richard's progress home and his speculations on brown bag lunches in the Green Park are echoed in an accompanying draft of "Nature at Wembley" (ff. 2: 33-38). Throughout notebook 2 of "The Hours" Woolf turns from her work on the novel to writing criticism, and vice versa, a practice continued in notebook 3, where the manuscript of "The Hours" exists next to drafts of essays included in *The Common Reader*.

In "The Hours," Ellie Henderson appears as Milly (f. 2: 48) and, briefly, Doris Kilman is called Dora (f. 2: 43). Woolf twice drafts the passage in which Clarissa complains to Richard about not wanting to invite "Milly" Henderson to her party. Clarissa's concern over her party is quite pronounced in "The Hours," and her conviction that her parties are a form of art is central to her definition of life.

On the *verso* of folio 53, headed, and later deleted, "Whitmonday, June 9th.," Woolf outlines the scenes remaining to be written:

> *4 or 5* scenes more.
> Kilman & Elizabeth.
> The Warren Smiths.
> Peter.
> London.
> The party.

This plan supplements her earlier schedule, drafted on May 5 in her diary:

> But my mind is full of The Hours. I am now saying that I will write at it for 4 months, June, July, August & September, & then it will be done, & I shall put it away for three months, during which I shall finish my essays; & then that will be—October, November, December—January: & I shall revise it January February March April; & in April my essays will come out; & in May my novel. (*Diary* 2: 301)

Woolf adhered to both the above schedule and her later plan. Her marginal calculations in "The Hours" reveal a writer keeping herself on schedule, as well as estimating how much of her novel remains to be written.

"Love & religion [. . .] which is worst?," speculates Clarissa as her daughter departs for the Stores with Miss Kilman (f. 2: 67). Thrice Woolf drafts the scene in which Clarissa watches the old woman in the neighboring house. As in *Mrs. Dalloway*, Clarissa's speculations about religion and human isolation, which Woolf drafts twice, are juxtaposed by Miss Kilman's denial of the flesh, a notion shattered by the bells of Big Ben as they measure out portions of human mortality. Miss Kilman's selection of petticoats is brief, but in recompense she gets to eat her pink cake, even if denied yet another. While Miss Kilman savors her "sugary cake," her only luxury, Woolf contemplates what the title of her work is to be. Her proposed titles are in sharp contrast to her character's situation and personality: "A ladies portrait. A lady of Fashion." "M[rs.] Dalloway" is presented but then deleted (f. 2: 82).

Elizabeth's journey around London is marked, in turn, by various milestones for Woolf. While Elizabeth stands waiting for a bus on Victoria Street, Woolf calculates that she has now completed 56,000 words (f. 2: 90). At the point Elizabeth reaches Fleet Street, Woolf notes emphatically, "*Mrs. Dalloway.*," a title she will later equivocate (f. 2: 95). Elizabeth loses her sense of direction; she "hesitated: [. . .] finally turned; & could be seen [. . .] zigzagging her way tentatively" (f. 2: 97). At this juncture, Woolf draws the points of the compass in the margin of the manuscript, as if to aid Elizabeth and her own memory.

When Elizabeth disappears, "Bernard Warren-Smith" takes her place in the narrative (f. 2: 98). His vision of "high mountains, death, revelations" (f. 2: 103) is interrupted by a revery of another sort, the story known as "Nurse Lugton's Golden Thimble." On the *verso* of folio 103, Woolf provides an enchanting array of birds and beasts, some of which figure in her letters as endearments, such as "marmot mandrill & mongoose." Following the story, "Bernard's" vision is reinstated and rewritten, ending abruptly, only for the narrative to begin again with the question, "Who was he talking to Sally asked?" (f. 2: 110).

In order to explain this change in narrative direction, we must turn to notebook 3, whose frontispiece is inscribed, "M[rs.] Dalloway, or The Hours, July 31st 1924." (f. 3: 1). It is here that Woolf returns to the scene between "Bernard" and Rezia, an episode that eventually evolves into "Bernard's" contemplation of suicide. The passage where "Bernard" is "left alone with the screen, the coal scuttle, & the chiffonier" (f. 3: 9) is drafted twice, the second version dated Monday, August 11, eight days after Woolf dated the frontispiece to *The Common Reader* on the reversed side of the same volume (f. 3R: 178). On the subsequent page, she begins another draft of the scene in which Rezia swears while hat-making, and this episode leads to her early memories of the now re-named Septimus. The *verso* side of folio 14 contains a sketch of the dialogue yet to come, ending with Septimus' suicide and Clarissa's "sense that they were one flesh." In "The Hours," Rezia affirms Septimus' death, saying "He has done right" (f. 3: 23). Twice Woolf drafts Rezia's lengthy reflections on her own education, comments mostly absent from *Mrs. Dalloway*. Septimus' body is removed while Rezia, in a morphia fog, dreams of the sea and flowers. The focus then shifts to Peter Walsh, who observes approvingly the efficiency of the ambulance swerving around the corner.

Peter sits down to dinner accompanied by multiplications indicating that the work has reached 65,000 words and that if the rate of 280 words a day continues for another month, an additional 9,400 will have accrued. Presumably anxious to complete the novel, Woolf begins the party scene on September 7, 1924, opening with Lucy straightening a chair cover in the drawing room before the guests arrive. Woolf twice writes the encounter between Peter and Clarissa. Poised at the top of the stairs, Clarissa hesitates as Woolf calculates that at 84,000 words she is ahead of schedule. Intriguingly, Peter's antipathy and boredom towards Hugh Whitbread is accompanied by a schedule of trains to and from Rodmell and Lewes, perhaps an indication that the author, too, found the encounter of little emotional interest.

At the bottom of folio 70, Woolf comments in pencil, "Now for the party!" The *verso* of the same page bears an outline of the basic movement of the concluding section, a guideline to which she adheres in both "The Hours" and *Mrs. Dalloway*:

> A general view of the world:
> The different groups:
> All sketched in.
> She makes her way gradually to the
> Bradshaw group.
> She is livid about Septimus. She
> visualises what happened.
> Goes into the little room. The clock striking her
> whole life
> Sees the old lady put her light out.
> Transition to Richard & Elizabeth, (They didn't enjoy
> themselves
> Then to Peter & Sally on the stairs
> Sally loved plants: a mother.
> But we haven't seen Clarissa.

Appropriately, the next page opens with the declaration, "She was for the party," as Clarissa and Woolf take on the scene at full tilt (f. 3: 71). The narrative then turns to various conversations around the room, such as those centered on "Sir John," who tells scurrilous stories in "The Hours" (f. 3: 71), Professor "Brierly" (f. 3: 73), and between Lord "Gazlin" and Miss Nancy Blow (f. 3: 75).

In *Mrs. Dalloway*, Septimus' malady is indirectly diagnosed as shell-shock through a discussion of a Parliamentary Bill by Richard Dalloway and Sir William

Bradshaw. During their corresponding conversation in "The Hours," the two men specifically discuss Septimus' suicide as a result of the condition (f. 3: 85). Clarissa's meditations on the significance of Septimus' death are quite a bit longer than the corresponding section in *Mrs. Dalloway*. Her inner tension over his suicide and her assessment of her marriage seems to affect Woolf, for on folio 94 Clarissa's evaluation of Richard's committee work disintegrates into long looping lines, lines embodying the end of a writer's creative tether. Yet on the following page, Woolf begins reconstructing Clarissa's comparison between herself and Lady Bexborough, a topic that leads Clarissa to comment positively on what she here calls her sense of personal "being" (f. 3: 96).

Four times Woolf sends the sound of Big Ben at midnight into the middle of Clarissa's thoughts. Peter's and Sally's conversation is also interrupted, not aurally, but textually. The last entry in volume 3 is dated October 4, 1924. To find the rest of their dialogue, we must return to folio 110 of notebook 2, where the two characters continue their deliberations over Dalloway's character. Only three pages later, Peter rises to speak with Richard and asks, as he feels the "moment" forming within him, "What is about to happen? By what name can I call it? This terror, this ecstasy? This Clarissa. For there she was" (f. 2: 113). It is with these words that Woolf concluded this version of "The Hours" on October 9, 1924, at 11:15 a.m.

Eleven days later, on October 20, she starts rewriting "The Hours," beginning with "Chapter One" (f. 2: 114). This opening chapter is a reworking of "Mrs. Dalloway in Bond Street." Instead of buying gloves, Clarissa now purchases flowers for her party. Her character has changed, too, from the earlier story. She is less brusque, more nostalgic. Although the memory of the Great War lingers on in "The Hours," it is referred to fewer times than in "Mrs. Dalloway in Bond Street." In this first chapter, Woolf twice writes Clarissa's comparison between Hugh Whitbread and Peter Walsh. Also drafted twice is the vibrant description of the flowers in Miss Pym's store. To readers of *Mrs. Dalloway*, the airplane episode will appear curtailed. Unfamiliar characters also appear, such as Mr. Scranton, who mourns for the past as he walks across Regents Park (f. 2: 151).

Notebook 2 concludes as Clarissa enters her house, only to discover that her husband is lunching at Lady Bruton's. Thus, the manuscript of "The Hours" ends near its beginning. In "The Hours," Woolf comes full circle. She returns to the beginning ("Mrs. Dalloway in Bond Street" and "The Prime Minister") in order to complete her story. Like its namesake, "The Hours" embodies change within repetition, difference within similarity. "The Hours" is more than simply the full-length draft of *Mrs. Dalloway*. It *is* what we will come to know as *Mrs. Dalloway* as well as being itself.

Works Cited

Hulcoop, John F. "McNichol's Mrs. Dalloway: Second Thoughts." *Virginia Woolf Miscellany* 3 (1975): 3-4 & 7.

Lewis, A.J. "From 'The Hours' to *Mrs. Dalloway*." *The British Museum Quarterly* 28 (1964): 15-18.

Pizer, Donald. "Self-Censorship and Textual Editing." *Textual Criticism and Literary Interpretation*. Ed. Jerome J. McGann. Chicago: U of Chicago P, 1985. 144-61.

Reiman, Donald. *Romantic Texts and Contexts*. Columbia: U of Missouri P, 1987.

Shields, E.F. "The American Edition of *Mrs. Dalloway*." *Studies in Bibliography* 27 (1974): 157-175.

Silver, Brenda R. "Textual Criticism as Feminist Practice: Or, Who's Afraid of Virginia Woolf Part II." *Representing Modernist Texts: Editing as Interpretation*. Ed. George Bornstein. Ann Arbor: U of Michigan P, 1991. 193-222.

Woolf, Leonard. *The Letters of Leonard Woolf*. Ed. Frederic Spotts. San Diego: Harcourt Brace Jovanovich, 1989.

Woolf, Virginia. *The Captain's Death Bed and Other Essays*. 1950. San Diego: Harcourt Brace Jovanovich, 1978.

———. *The Common Reader: First Series*. 1925. London: Hogarth Press, 1984.

———. *The Complete Shorter Fiction of Virginia Woolf*. 2nd ed. Ed. Susan Dick. San Diego: Harcourt Brace Jovanovich, 1989.

———. *The Diary of Virginia Woolf*. Ed. Anne Olivier Bell. Vols. 2 and 3. Harmondsworth: Penguin, 1978, 1980.

———. "The Hours." Add. MSS. 51044-46. British Library, London.

———. Introduction. *Mrs. Dalloway*. 1925. New York: Random House/The Modern Library, 1928. v-ix.

———. *The Letters of Virginia Woolf*. Eds. Nigel Nicolson and Joanne Trautmann. Vols. 2 and 3. London: Chatto & Windus, 1976, 1977.

———. *Mrs. Dalloway*. 1925. Foreword by Maureen Howard. 1981. San Diego: Harcourt Brace Jovanovich, 1990.

———. *Mrs. Dalloway's Party*. Ed. Stella McNichol. San Diego: Harcourt Brace Jovanovich, 1973.

———. Notebook. Dated March 12, 1922. Berg Collection. New York Public Library.

———. Notebook. Dated Nov. 9. 1922-Aug. 2, 1923. Berg Collection. New York Public Library.

———. Notebook. Dated Jan. 7, 1924. Berg Collection. New York Public Library.

Wright, Glenn P. [G. Patton]. "The Raverat Proofs of *Mrs Dalloway*." *Studies in Bibliography* 39 (1986). 241-261.

Principles of Editing

In this volume, the arrangement of the three notebooks that comprise "The Hours" follows the order of composition. For the most part, Woolf used the pages of her three notebooks in chronological order and often dated her entries at the beginning of the day's writing, so that it is possible to provide an accurate list of dates for the composition of the manuscript (see "'The Hours': A Chronology of Composition"). Appendix 1 contains passages from two reversed (or inverted) pages of notebook 3. After working on "The Hours," Woolf would turn notebook 3 upside down to work on essays that would later become part of *The Common Reader*. For a list of essays and reviews on the reversed pages of notebook 3, please see Appendix 3. Appendix 2 contains material from the Berg Collection in the New York Public Library. The Berg's curator assigned all *recto* (or right side) pages an odd number, in order to allow for pagination of any *verso* pages that contained writing. Appendix 2 follows the assigned pagination, as indicated by the centered numbers at the bottom of the page. The material, as described in the Introduction, comes from two notebooks and one small, bound book and is arranged chronologically, rather than by volume. Each new piece of material is introduced by a description of the notebook from which it comes, so as to avoid confusion over the source.

The general form of the transcription follows the methods used by S.P. Rosenbaum in his transcription of the manuscript versions of *A Room of One's Own* (1929), called *Women & Fiction* (1992). Also, the explanation of transcription practices relies heavily upon Rosenbaum's own clear prose. His transcription methods simplify earlier transcription practices used by J.W. Graham and Susan Dick in the editions of the holograph drafts of *The Waves* and *To the Lighthouse*, respectively (1976, 1982).

Virginia Woolf's spelling and punctuation are reproduced as they are in the manuscripts. Paragraphs, page divisions, and line arrangement are also reproduced as accurately as possible. When too long for the width of the page, the lines are doubled back and indented, as in the printing of poetry.

Woolf's holograph insertions above or below lines are represented in angle brackets. Insertions appear after the cancellations they replace, except when the sense is made clearer by putting them before the cancellations. Marginalia are represented approximately where they occur in the manuscripts, and in smaller print than the main text. It has not always been possible, however, to reproduce the line breaks in the marginalia precisely. Insertions within insertions have been transcribed as insertions. Comments on the backs of the manuscript pages are given as separate pages with a centered, bracketed page number and *verso* indication. Passages written in pencil or crayon have also been indentified.

Holograph cancellations are represented by struck-through characters. Vertical or oblique slashes cancelling entire passages have also been represented by struck-through characters. Various lines and squiggles have been indicated typographically whenever possible, or by bracketed descriptions. Cancellations within cancellations have been transcribed simply as cancellations. Woolf often cancelled punctuation marks, such as commas or quotation marks. Due to the limitations of typesetting, the cancellation may appear slightly above (;) or below (“) the mark.

Doubtful readings in the transcript have been followed with a question mark and enclosed in square brackets. A blank in square brackets marks an illegible word or phrase; a cancellation line in brackets indicates an illegible cancellation. The transcription of many words and phrases, cancellations and insertions depends on their context and must remain tentative. The occasional square brackets used by Woolf have been replaced by braces (wavy brackets).

~~example~~ = cancellation
<example> = insertion
<~~example~~> = cancelled insertion
[example?] = uncertain reading
[~~example~~?] = uncertain cancellation
[ ] = illegible
[———] = illegible cancellation
{example} = enclosed in square brackets by Woolf
[page number *verso*] = the back of the previous page

Page Numbering of "The Hours"

There are two types of page numbering. The numbers in the top margin sequentially number the pages of this volume. The numbers centered at the bottom of the page refer to those numbers assigned by curators at either the British Library or the Berg Collection to the manuscript pages. Each of the three notebooks of "The Hours" in the British Library is numbered separately. Thus, the centered, bottom page numbers begin sequentially three times. As indicated above, *verso* page numbers are indicated at the bottom of the page and refer to work written on the back of the previous page.

Collation of *Mrs. Dalloway* and "The Hours"

There are several editions of *Mrs. Dalloway*. Unfortunately, the Shakespeare Head Press edition published by Blackwell (1996) and the "definitive" collected edition published by the Hogarth Press (1990) are currently unavailable in the United States. As there are no chapter headings for *Mrs. Dalloway*, a useful system of collating by section number was not feasible. The most readily available edition for most U.S. readers is the paperback version reissued by Harcourt Brace Jovanovich in 1990, which includes a foreword by Maureen Howard. The numbers in the bottom margins refer to this edition. Readers unable to procure this particular edition of *Mrs. Dalloway* will find that the progress of "The Hours" is very similar to the published narrative. Anyone familiar with the text of *Mrs. Dalloway* should be able to compare the two works with relative ease, no matter which edition is used.

A Chronology of "The Hours"

14 April 1922	Woolf writes to T.S. Eliot concerning a story (possibly "Mrs. Dalloway in Bond Street").
28 August 1922	States in diary that she plans to finish "Mrs. Dalloway" by 2 September and start "Prime Minister."
6 October 1922	Devises a plan for a novel to be called "At Home: or The Party." (Appendix 2) Begins "Prime Minister." Sketches out a "possible revision of this book." (Appendix 2)
16 October 1922	Notes that Mrs. Dalloway and Septimus Smith will be central characters: "Mrs D seeing the truth. S.S. seeing the insane truth." (Appendix 2)
7 November 1922	Notes in her diary that she will shortly sketchout Mrs. Dalloway and write the aeroplane chapter.
19 June 1923	Use, in diary, of "The Hours" as possible title.
27 June 1923	Begins notebook 1 of "The Hours."
July 1923	"Mrs. Dalloway in Bond Street" published in *Dial.*
6 August 1923	Refers in her diary to "The Hours" as "sheer weak dribble."
23 January 1924	States, in her diary, that she is looking at "The Hours" "disconsolately."
9 February 1924	"The Hours" has now, in the diary, become a "very interesting attempt."
2 August 1924	Describes, in her diary, her depression over Septimus Warren Smith's death and the impending completion of the novel.
7 September 1924	Talks about the party scene in her diary. Refers to it as one of the "best of my endings."

17 October 1924	Notes in dairy that she wrote the last words of "The Hours" "a week ago yesterday"—really 8 October, as she later indicates.
30 November 1924	Writes to Violet Dickinson to say that she has just finished a novel, except for copying out the last chapter.
13 December 1924	States, in diary, that she is retyping.
6 January 1925	Notes, in diary, that she has finished revising and has sent typescript to printers.
13-19 January 1924	Proofs dated by printer in Edinburgh.
24 January 1925	Writes to Jacques Raverat and offers proofs of *Mrs. Dalloway.*
Early 1925	Begins writing seven short stories: "The New Dress," "Happiness," "Ancestors," "The Introduction," "The Conversation," "Together and Apart," "The Man Who Loved His Kind," "A Simple Melody," and "A Summing Up."
14 May 1925	*Mrs. Dalloway* published.

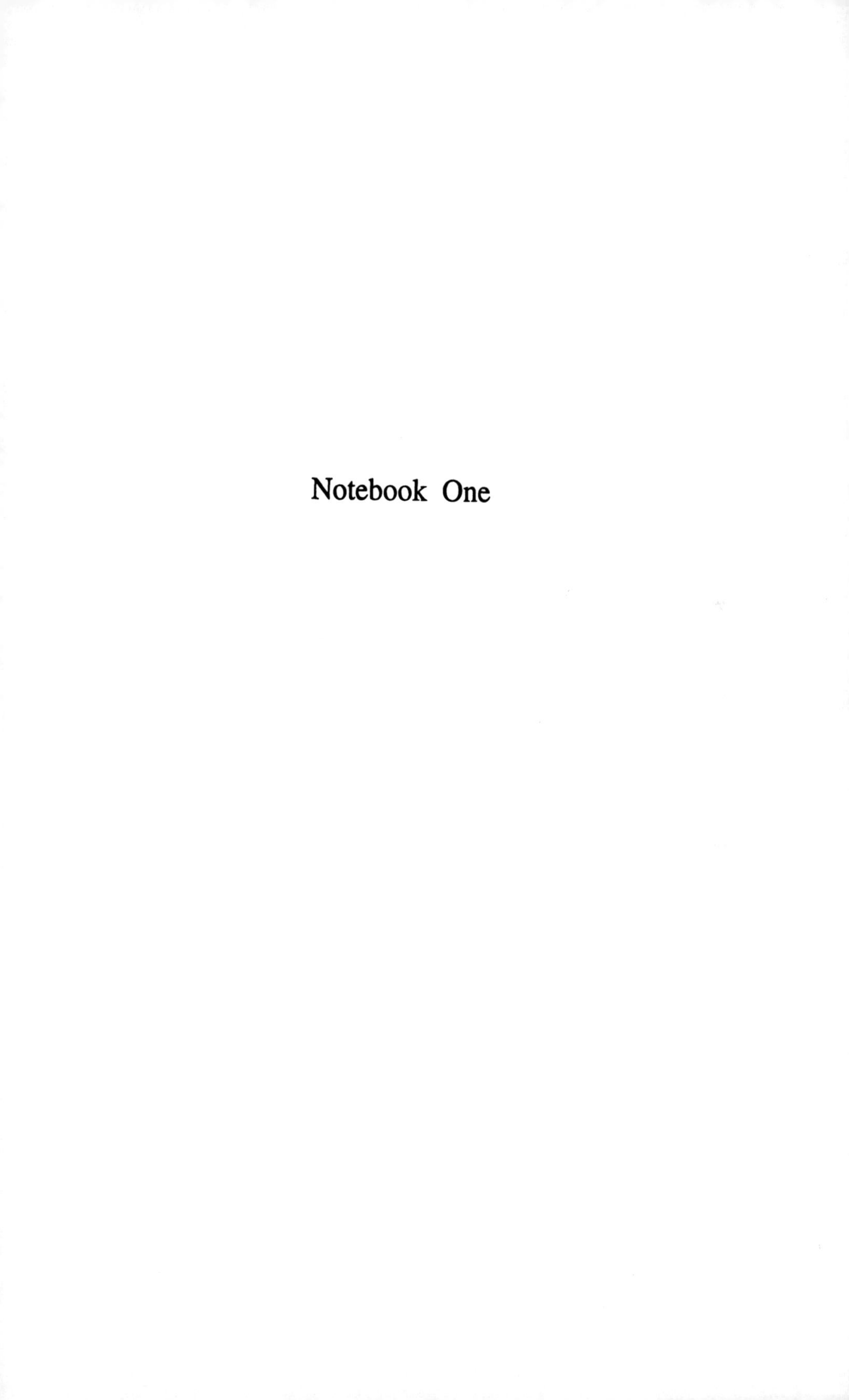

Notebook One

The Hours?

June 27th 1923.

June 27th 1923.

The Hours

In Westminster, where temples, meeting houses, conventicles,
& steeples of all kinds are congregated together, there is at all
hours & halfhours, a round of bells, ~~supplementing~~
<correcting> each
other, asseverating that time has come a little earlier, or
stayed a little later, here or here. Thus when M$^{r.}$ Walsh
walking with his head ~~a little~~ down, & his coat flying loose
came out by the Abbey the clock of St Margarets was
saying two minutes later than Big Ben that it was
half past eleven. But her voice was a womans <voice>, since
it is impossible to have anything to do with inanimate
objects without giving them sex, & the very stair rods have
character, & should fate send them to the old furniture shop &
their owners pass by their voices would be heard in their
own accents bringing back countless passages up & down
stairs, moments ~~to~~ of happiness, or despair, moments
not otherwise communicable, for there has attached itself
even to the stair rod, something that lies below words.
~~St Margarets'~~ spoke as a woman speaks, ~~with~~ <there was> a
vibration in
the core of the sound so that each word, or note, comes
fluttering, alive, yet <with some> reluctance to inflict its vitality,
some grief for the past which holds it back, some
impulse nevertheless to glide into the recesses of the
heart & there bury itself in ring after ring of sound,
so that M$^{r.}$ Walsh, as he walked past St Margarets,
& heard the bells toll the half hour felt ....

of all that surrounded it, of its futility. For he had never
married her. He had failed. But he now loved
more passionately than then. this girl in India .....
He had been sent down from Oxford. He had drunk too
much. He had been a socialist. But the future of the
~~Ho~~ civilisation lies, ~~he~~ in the hands of such young men.

of such young men as himself, he meant.
A patter, like the patter in a wood, came from behind, & with it
a ~~sound of feet mar~~ a rustling; a regular thudding, ~~as if~~
sound which as it overtook him, seemed to lift up his
thought & carry it on, up Whitehall ~~to Trafalgar Square.~~
Boys in uniform, carrying guns, marched, their eyes ahead of
them,
their arms stiff, their faces set upon vacancy, ~~& a likeness to~~
~~each other~~ which gave them a likeness one to the other which
was furthered by uniform & gesture. They displayed, as if
they carried a banner with a legend, ~~this <the> idea of~~
~~homage to the~~ one common purpose, for they had
left a wreath at the Cenotaph. ~~& now returning,~~ They
were ~~determined, should the ready to~~ <determined> ~~ready,~~ each
one of the
hundred; ~~to each ready at the sound of a bugle to wheel to~~
~~march to climb; read there was in them determined,~~
~~vigilant, severe.~~ they were vigilant; they were
severe. ~~Their~~ In an empty tomb, beneath
withered flowers ~~there~~ existed this ~~idea. of theirs.~~
~~Falling on their faces it stiffened them. &~~ purpose,
~~which issuing~~ This, thought Peter, beginning to keep step with
them, a very fine thing. The eldest was perhaps sixteen,
& ~~evidently~~ they were orphans, the sons of petty
officers, of able seamen, who ~~dying in the country's service,~~
~~had left this~~ had died, <or> ~~who~~ had been killed, ~~who had~~
~~or were unable, through illness to suppo~~ or fallen on evil days.
It is a ~~superb training for a young man" thought Peter.~~
~~very fine training,~~ thought Peter, a very fine training.
Not that they looked robust. They were weedy, for the most
part ~~pale~~. They had not the bluff look of trained soldiers.
They therefore carried on them ~~a~~ unmixed with sensual
pleasures the pale solemnity of this wreath, which they had
~~carried~~ <fetched> from Finsbury Pavement to the empty tomb.
~~Still~~
~~as they marched back again~~ ~~Death & its~~ They had
taken ~~this~~ <their> vow, ~~to~~ & therefore ~~the~~ The traffic made

way for them.

~~They are~~ I can't keep up with them, thought Peter Walsh, as they entered Trafalgar Square; & sure enough, on they marched, in their steady way, as if they had but one will ~~between them~~, ~~in all their~~ working all their arms & legs, & had renounced life, with its variety, ~~&~~ its temptations, had monuments & purposes, wreaths & guns, rhythm & order, control & discipline—~~So they marched.~~

There they go, thought Peter, ~~here~~ pausing on the ~~pav~~ edge of the pavement. And all the exalted statues, the black, the spectacular, the stone images of ~~men who had~~ great soldiers, stood looking straight ahead of them ~~into the sky, as if this strip of pavement on which their pedestals rested was as if it had been so for them too in their lives;~~ as if they too, ~~in their lives had~~ made the same renunciation, & secured by means of it an everlasting rest.

~~Peter Walsh~~ But then they are not old enough to know the troubles of the flesh, Peter thought. ~~They do not suffer as I suffer.~~ as the boys marched towards Charing Cross.

I have been a weak man, he thought. A wretched failure. he went on, looking at Gordon, with ~~its his foot raised,~~ his arms clasped, ~~as~~ & his foot raised, as though he trod under the frailties of the flesh.

Peter Walsh crossed the road, in a momentary exaltation of mood, for he had nowhere to go; no one knew him. Only Clarissa knew that he was in England He was

He heard Clarissa say "My party tonight" as he shut the door.
Her voice was ~~taken up~~ <overwhelmed> by the roar of ~~the~~
Westminster. It
became instantly refined & spiritual, ~~like~~ & very far away.
& ~~yet~~ it went on echoing in his head, as he walked, as
he passed a ~~very~~ man in a tail coat wearing a buttonhole,
~~as he~~ a very smartly dressed man, a despicable
specimen, thought Peter, ~~a~~ It must be Ascot, he thought;
& he became aware of all the towers which rise above
the little streets, the Abbey, the Houses of Parliament,
Westminster Hall. ~~There they sit, he thought,
thinking of the Government of Institutions, of settled ways
mumbling nonsense, he thought,~~ ~~H~~ "Remember my party
tonight" remember my party he went on saying to
himself. She's grown worldly—She's hard, he thought to
himself. ~~becoming more and more annoyed~~ Here is my
Elizabeth! he repeated. Elizabeth didn't like that.
~~She always was a little sentimental~~ Remember my
party, he repeated. ~~until~~, sarcastically, until outside
~~We~~ St Margarets, suddenly the clock tolled the half hour
& as each note came fluttering down, alive, yet within
some reluctance to inflict its vitality, some grief for the past
which held it back, some impulse nevertheless to glide into
the heart & there bury itself in ring after ring of sound.
Clarissa herself seemed ~~to be~~ with him. She had been ill,
he thought, & the sound expressed languor and suffering.
It was her heart, he ~~thought~~ remembered, & the bell tolled
for death that surprised in the midst of life. Mournfully,

He ~~heard Clarissa~~ say "~~My party tonight~~" as he shut the ~~door;~~ & her voice, overwhelmed by the roar of Westminster, & the sounds of all the clocks, became ~~instantly~~ refined—spiritual & very far away, as ~~Mr~~ <Peter> Walsh shut the door.

.III.

It might have been the seat of time itself, this island of
Westminster, the forge where the hours were made,
of studious & sent out, in various tones & tempers, to ~~be~~ glide into the
workers lives of the foot passengers, <~~of stud~~> ~~of the~~ desultory women
<withindoors>, who coming
to the window looked up at the sky as the clock struck,
as if to ~~ask~~ <ask> say, ~~yes? Well?~~ <What> ~~What next?~~ <or>
Why?
~~to which questions~~ ~~of studious workers, of~~ ~~to which questions~~
~~there And~~ They had their choice of answers; ~~they could~~
~~select~~ from the different sounds ~~they could now colliding~~ or
colliding, or running side by side, melting into each other,
forming, ~~a~~ for the moment, a trellis work of sound
~~over the roofs,~~ which, as it faded away, was suddenly
renewed from some other steeple; St Margarets, for
example, ~~supple~~ saying two minutes after Big Ben
how now, really & indeed, it was half past eleven, ~~though~~
~~in~~ Yes, it was half past eleven, S[t] Margarets said, in her
sad voice, ~~her woman's voice,~~ upon hearing which, ~~of course it~~
was necessary to make haste, or again to loiter; or
~~perhaps some there might be some mistake about it.~~
to attempt some kind of comparison. ~~Half past eleven~~
or to think how ~~very queer it was~~, not merely that ~~the~~ time
~~should differ, but that the voices of these clocks,~~ differed but that
the tone of it was possessed of the strangest power; ~~was~~
now militant & masculine; now ~~n~~ curtly prosaic, & now in
the voice of S[t] Margarets ~~had the power to brush every leaf &~~
~~flower in the mind,~~ & had the power, like some breeze
which visits a garden at dawn, to brush every flower &
leaf in the minds territory, ~~to set stirring & flashing~~
lifting, stirring, strangely, very strangely.

Remember my party, remember my party, said
Peter Walsh as he stepped down the street, with the sound
~~swing~~ of Big Ben in his ears; swinging down right

direct, ~~vigorous, like the punch of a young man striking out~~
~~ever so lustily this way & that, with irresistible vigour,~~ &
~~left on the~~ rhythmically in time with the flow of the sound
the direct downright sound of Big Ben striking the half hour;
~~Clarissa's parties, he thought—~~ Why does Clarissa give
parties? ~~he thought,~~ Not that he blamed her. He
blamed nobody. Only he was glad to be himself. And he
saw himself advancing in the plate glass window of a motor
car manufacturer, like a figure which has escaped. All
India lay behind him—its plains & mountains, the epidemics
which he had mastered, the decisions he had made alone, by himself,
affect~~ing~~<ed> the lives of thousands; ~~while here, he thought they~~
Clarissa ~~She~~ had grown hard, he thought, & a trifle sentimental he
thought,
& he stopped in front of the window, looking at the great motor
cars. He had a turn for mechanics. He had invented a
plough in his district, & ordered wheelbarrows from England,
but the coolies wouldn't use them. The way she said,
"There is my Elizabeth!"—that annoyed me, he thought.
And Elizabeth didn't like it either,—Still the last
& liked them; tremors of the great voice of the clock shook the air round
him, ~~& stirring~~ For he understood young people; young
~~men, young women—Clarissa was always cold,~~
there was always something cold about Clarissa, he
thought. She had always, ~~a~~ even when I first knew her, a sort
of timidity. ~~of mind—&~~ <which> in middle age, ~~he thought~~,
~~that kind of~~
becomes conventionality, & then its all up, its all up!
he thought, looking rather drearily into the glassy depths,
& wondering whether ~~somehow~~, by his appearance, or calling
at that hour, he had annoyed her? ~~Like a~~ With the
same ~~effect as~~ <suddeness that> a cloud ~~has~~ on a summers day,
cross~~ing~~<es> the
sun, silence falls on London; & falls on the mind, &
all effort ceases. Time flaps on the mast. Rigid, like a
skeleton, ~~only~~ the skeleton of belief <alone> upholds the human
frame.
Blankness ~~& indifference~~ yawns from pavement from
plate glass windows. ~~blankness & indifference.~~ She

refused me, he thought.

Ah, said St Margarets, like a hostess who comes into
her drawing room ~~a~~ on the very stroke of the hour, & finds
her guests there already, I am not late. No, it is precisely
half past eleven. ~~she says like a And~~ <But> ~~her voice~~
<al>though she is
certainly perfectly right, her voice is somehow reluctant to inflict its
~~<vitality> vitality~~, some grief for the past holds it back; some concern
individuality; ~~& sensitiveness perhaps, for feeling~~ for the present. It is
half past eleven she says, ~~&~~ the sound glides into the
recesses of the heart & buries itself in ring after ring
of sound, ~~flattering~~ like something alive which wants to
confide itself, ~~to~~ to ~~dissipate~~ <disperse> itself, to be, with an
~~exquisite~~ tremor of delight, at rest. ~~So Mr Walsh
felt as if Clarissa, were with him. leaving her
drawing room,~~ like Clarissa herself, thought Peter Walsh
~~coming out in by the~~ coming ~~along the lawn with her
hands full of something to~~ after ~~him~~ <me>, in white, ~~alto~~
For ~~She came back, as a whole, much more truly like this.
As if years ago there had~~ come in to some room
~~where they sat together~~ This is Clarissa, he thought,
with ~~an e~~ a deep emotion, & an extraordinary clear
yet puzzling recollection of her, as if this bell had come into the room,
years ago, where they sat, at some moment of
& felt laden great intimacy, & had n had <had> ~~kept it under keeping, & now~~
with the most & had gone from one to the other, & ~~then now poured~~
But what room? & what moment? And then as the
sound withdrew ~~he thought~~ She has been ill, & the
sound expressed languor & suffering. It was her
heart, he remembered, & the sudden loudness of the bell
tolled for death that surprised in the midst of life,
Clarissa falling where she stood, in her drawing room.
No, no! he cried, she is not dead. I am not old.
He was glaring ~~with~~ almost ferociously at the statue
of the Duke of Cambridge.

And he looked ~~a he~~ up Whitehall as if his future were spread
before him, & ~~he had only to step out briskly towards it~~.
He was not old, or set, or shrivelled, & as for caring what
people
said here in England, he cared not a rap, he cared not a
rap. So squaring himself with his cheeks all in a
wrinkle, he glared at the ~~statue of the~~ Duke of Cambridge.
~~ending~~ It was true that he was a failure. He had been
sent down from Oxford. He had drunk too much. He had
been a socialist. Still the future of civilisation lies,
he thought, in the hands of such young men. Of such
young men as himself, he ~~thought.~~ meant, thinking,
as no one else ~~can~~ <could> possibly think, of how ~~right~~ he
had been, <right & holy,> & courageous, & ~~how, though a
outwardly~~ unstable,
he had <always> kept up his faith in science & <& in>
knowledge & read
in mathematics.

with their courage, their loneliness, their passion for scientific truth.

A patter like ~~that~~ the patter of leaves in a wood, came
from behind, & with it a rustling, a regular thudding
sound which, as it overtook him, seemed to lift up his
~~what he was thinking~~ about young men & ~~civilisation~~
<mathematics &> &
to carry it all on up Whitehall. Boys in uniform
~~carry m~~ carrying guns marched with their eyes ahead of
them, their arms stiff, & an expression on all their faces,
~~which was like a banner the legend in a banner,~~
~~for they had left a wreath at the Cenotaph, &~~
~~showed & wore vigilant, severe, determined,~~

thoughts

~~"Its a very fine training" thought Peter, beginning to keep
step with them.~~

~~Not that they looked robust.~~

<which made> ~~& an expression so similar on each~~ <their> faces
~~that the letters of a
legend~~ like ~~one~~ <the> ~~leg~~ letters of a common legend ~~such as
is written by~~ such as is engraved on the base of
~~obelisk~~ monuments. ~~Its h say test~~ expressing some great
~~common feeling~~ <emotion>, such as gratitude to the dead, or
pride
in England.

It is, thought Peter, beginning to keep step with them, a very fine training. They did not look robust. They were weedy for the most part—boys of sixteen, who might perhaps serve behind counters They ~~carr~~ wore on them unmixed with sexual pleasures the pale solemnity of this wreath which they had fetched from Finsbury Pavement to the empty tomb. They had taken their vow. The traffic made way for them.

I cant keep up with them, thought Peter Walsh, as they marched up Whitehall, & sure enough, on they marched in their steady way, as if one will worked arms & legs, uniformly, & they had renounced life with its variety, its temptations, had laid them under a pavement of monuments & wreaths & drugged them by ~~marching uniform~~ discipline.

There they go, thought Peter, passing at the edge of the pavement. And all the exalted statues, the black, the spectacular images of great soldiers, stood in ~~Trafalgar Square~~ looking ahead of them as if they too had made the same renunciation, trampled under the same temptations, & secured by means of it an everlasting ~~repose.~~ rest.

They dont know the troubles of the flesh yet, Peter thought as the troop of march~~ing~~<ers> <marching boys>
disappeared towards
Charing Cross. I've been through it. I've been through it, he thought, crossing the road impetuously, & standing under Gordon's ~~stare. stone~~. effigy. Gordon, whom as a ~~boy he had~~ loved ~~& still~~ as a boy, Gordon standing lonely with one foot raised, & his arms crossed.

And just because nobody knew he was in London, except Clarissa, & because he had landed two days before, from a long voyage, & the ~~pe~~ earth still seemed

like an island to him, the strangeness of ~~his situ his situation~~
~~overcame him, & in order to~~ standing, alone, alive, at half past
eleven, in Trafalgar Square overcame him, What ~~is~~ is it?
Where am I? And why does one do it? he thought—(for on he
would go to his solicitor.) ~~ah but the~~ An irrepressible
delight rose up in him. A sense of complete understanding
filled him.
A vast philanthropy expanded his heart. ~~And as~~ each,
~~idea vague, powerful, & for the moment &~~ <a> surprising <a>,
delicious, ~~as~~
~~a traveller looking out of a train window is though~~ uncertain,
~~perfectly vague; as if~~ as if, inside his brain, by an agency
~~which was external to himself;~~ strings were pulled, shutters
moved; & he, having nothing to do with it, yet recognised with
~~amazement, the boundless capacities of his own mind.~~ He was
not old!

~~This morni~~ The endless avenues down which if he chose he
might ~~now~~
wander. He had escaped! He had escaped! as ~~only~~ happens
after some
~~in some~~
~~only very rarely when~~ sometimes, very rarely, ~~in childhood in~~
~~then~~ in <the> sudden downfall of habit, ~~alone, standing alone,~~
~~which leaves~~ <when like> the mind bare, ~~like a flame seems~~
~~capable of~~
~~bl~~ blow from its ~~holding;~~ socket;
like an unguarded flame bows & bends & seems about to
~~stream flat off~~ stream away; ~~& Peter Walsh, thought~~
~~Peter;~~ I haven't felt so young for years, thought Peter; &
~~yet he was no child could have had~~ yet it was not
~~youth~~, young, this feeling of irresponsible adventure;
~~rather it was <not> a childs feeling: but a man's; & it~~
~~& not a normal man's but an a queer man's, Oh no, oh no.~~
~~And For Down the steps of the National Gallery there came~~
~~a young woman; It was a mans,~~ but a man's feeling,
who after ~~being~~ wound himself about with ties &
~~responsib~~ duties, burdens, & privileges, suddenly perceives
their vanity, <&> ~~his~~ <his> freedom, ~~& at I yet knows,~~ as a child
~~cannot know, how~~ but only for a ~~moment~~. <second.>

~~So <he thought> the girl coming down the steps of the~~
~~National Gallery, with her handbag & slowly hesitating &~~
~~looking about her, is the~~ She is ~~amazingly~~ <extraordinarily>
attractive; he thought.

Across the Square, walking in the direction of the Haymarket
came one of those ~~figures of feminine~~ women's figures which
seem ~~almost unbelievable. in their perfection. since~~
~~almost unbelievable, since~~ almost unbelievable, not
that they are ~~of~~ perfect <in> beauty or ~~size but~~ bearing,
but that they confirm a ~~suspicion question~~ ~~<sus~~ suspicion>
which ~~we~~ has
~~have~~ been ~~asking for years perhaps;~~ haunting us for years,
~~perhaps, that such a first in~~ bring into existence some
type which has been haunting us for years, to which we
have given a secret love, & here she is complete; just as
she should be: with her white gloves, her distinguished
shoes, & a face slightly averted, which is ~~yet~~ gay yet
pensive, ~~exquisitely distinguished,~~ & adorably maternal.
all in one, so that, Peter thought, as he turned, straightened
himself & looked after her, it is impossible to imagine
ever speaking to her, & yet one would like, he thought
beginning to follow after her, to do her some
extraordinary service, to

Across the square, ~~walking~~ <walking> in the direction of the
Haymarket
came a woman's ~~figure, which, as walking,~~ who, as
she ~~advanced &~~ passed Gordon's statue, ~~&~~ seemed, ~~so~~
Peter thought, ~~actu~~ to shed ~~a~~ one veil after another
until miraculously ~~she was of~~ as she passed him,
~~She~~ she was the very ~~image embodiment of that~~
~~image~~ woman ~~who had been~~ whom he had always
~~loved~~. . <imagined.> So he ~~started forward;~~ straightened
himself, &
then, ~~putting his fingers nervously to his tie,~~ clasping his
~~knife started~~ half opening the main blade of his
knife started stealthily to follow her ~~at a little~~
~~distance. yet after—~~ to follow an excitement,
~~a~~ which seemed, even with its back turned, to shed

[margin:] the shoes
delightly. then
the gloves. Then
the long black
cloak. Then
the grave, maternal
averted, gay
pensive, y young.

~~on him as he followed & back on him a rosiness, a~~
~~till his which turned him which changed him, changed~~
~~to transform him; to make him~~
a ~~softness,~~ <light> which ~~seemed at once~~ to connect them
together,
~~from all the other people, & to~~ & made him feel
himself singled out, & ~~challenged~~ <&> to ~~some proof of the~~
<pressed to>
be, ~~as he had never been,~~ more exactly & <more> strictly
~~himself,~~
~~true to more adventurously himself: She turned up~~
~~Cockspur Street.~~ challenged, stimulated, as if
~~among all~~ the random chaos & confusion ~~&~~ of traffic had
resolved itself suddenly into one birds voice crying
his name. Peter, the lady called to him, ~~or her~~
by means of her ~~hand~~ white gloves, her shoulders, & her
& thin long cloak; ~~& he~~ which the air stirred
as she walked past Dents shop in Cockspur Street, &
~~& how maternal as she was with an exquisite~~
~~maternally; for there was a mournfulness in the~~
~~flow of the black expressed the mournful tenderness~~
~~of a mother, a young mother, to whom her child comes~~
~~crying, at the end of the day, when an enveloping kindness~~
arms that would open & take the tired—but
she's not married, thought Peter, seeing her reflection,
ah, but she's ~~quite~~ young, thought Peter, & there burnt in
her breast his eyes the pink carnation which he ~~though~~ he had seen on
first as she came towards him across Trafalgar Square.
~~She is not in her first youth, perhaps, but~~
young enough ~~at any rate to look very cool, &~~ he thought, to
be adorable to confide to; for she would not, he thought—
Now she paused, waiting to cross. ~~How~~
There was a dignity ~~in~~ <about> her. She was a woman of the
world. ~~Yet, not,~~ But she was not worldly; nor rich.
Like Clarissa, like Clarissa.

Was she, he wondered, as she moved, quite proper? ~~had she not some~~
Oh yes! She had a beautiful fidelity, to a man who was no
doubt inferior to her; for she could talk, had charm & wit, not a
noisy wit, but a cool, waiting wit, which
flickered ~~out~~ upon the air like the tongue of ~~some~~ a
~~green~~ lizard, & ~~She was slight, yet And~~ She ~~was~~ moved.
She crossed. To embarrass her was the last thing he wished;
but she still said, as she walked up the Haymarket yes, yes,
~~& gave him changed him, very slightly, made him shed~~
~~his~~ & melted him, ~~into~~ & made him feel that he would if she
turned laugh like a boy & ask her ~~in~~ to have an ice, &
there would be no embarrassment, none whatever—
For he had escaped— ~~escaped from~~ Would she turn?
Would he have ~~the coura~~ Again she stopped at a shop window!
~~So he would speak to her!~~ —And then again on she went,
~~to his relief, but still he~~ & now since he had missed his
opportunity, he was ruffled, angry with himself,
& the sense of unity was snapped, & he felt like a
pursuer, who has been checked— So she went on
For, ~~as A~~ <as> other people in the street now got between them,
blotting her out, giving him a ~~most irritating~~ sense of
wilful obstruction, ~~as if they obscured her maliciously,~~
~~he~~ his eagerness increased; she ~~bec~~ changed; ~~she became~~
~~swift and capricious.~~ There was colour in her cheeks,
~~a~~ mockery in her eyes. ~~She walked provokingly,~~
~~conscious of his pursuit. &~~ <And> He ~~too~~ became
~~once more~~ an ~~old~~ adventurer, ~~careless,~~ reckless,
so he thought, ~~&~~ of all these damned proprieties &
restrictions, & Clarissa's evening parties; ~~& the rest of it;~~
what nonsense it was to say that anything mattered except

this! The excitement, the romance!—which connected itself with every dream, every intensity, <&> fusing into ~~one sudden~~ diamond all the ~~jewels of~~ gems of all the hours; all those moments ~~which at~~ which shine out in the day, remained visible in the year, moments ~~of~~ for which it was worth while to throw oneself over precipices, leap gulfs, & go spinning down & down into endless disaster, for which reason he was a fool! Laughed at! ~~Called~~ A failure— Never mind, he encouraged himself, ~~crossing Piccadilly Circus.~~ still following, ~~but~~ gaining a little too closely upon the

280

70 And to ~~plunge~~ <risk>, & to fail; Anything's better than ~~sitting~~

0 ~~still~~ <that>

& growing old, ~~&~~ (~~for the ex~~ comparing himself with the

19.60 ~~pe~~ well dressed people who were ~~speak~~ paying, or stopping, & staring, at fishing rods, & paper & silk dressing gowns,) &

~~And so on & so on,~~

But she disappeared. ~~The door of a great shop opened, & she went in,~~

~~But I have had my adventure thought Peter. I will wait till she comes out again.~~

And suppose the door of one of the great shops opened, & she went in?—& he lost her? or if she took a cab; or went into the Tube?—Some ~~prescience As~~ But he knew ~~more that he as he knew;~~ instinctively, as he knew everything of importance, that ~~she would~~ this would not happen; for he controlled her, as he controlled what happened to himself. And so, on she went, across Piccadilly circus, & up Regent Street; &

He was never very close to her. He saw only her cloak, her ~~little~~ <hand> ~~han~~ bag, her parasol, & a reflection in windows, which combined beautifully with the fine clothes, ~~blouses, skirts~~ hats, ~~stockings,~~ gloves, within; as if she wore the spirit of them escaped. That she was the spirit of everything desirable he could not doubt; so different from other people, so mysterious, for now the bond between them. was renewed, & again from one to the other went this wordless call of you. ~~you,~~ {And now she had crossed Oxford Street. And now she went up Great Portland Street. ~~&~~ Now she had mounted the steps of a little house ~~in a street~~ with a brass plate upon the door,} ~~A~~ But now there was laughter in it. as if this woman knew the merriment of the sport, knew the preposterous ~~absurdity of~~ nature of life, & was ready to enjoy as he was the momentary ~~nature of~~ pleasure without going into details—for instance about he must be at his) solicitors' about this matter of the divorce. Now she had crossed Oxford Street; & crossed Great Portland Street, & turned down one of the little streets, & now & now & now the great moment was approaching—for now, as he had known would happen, she ~~went up to a house,~~ slackened, ~~began to~~ opened her bag, & with one look ~~at~~ in his direction; but not at him had stopped, fitted her key, opened the door & ~~vanished~~ gone. The door shut. Remember my party Clarissa had said. ~~But this~~ The house was one of those flat red houses with hanging flower baskets, of vague impropriety. It was over.

[*blue crayon*]
Ring up Mudie's

[page 20 *verso*]

Well I've had my fun, thought Peter, nervously feeling in his
pocket
for his cigarette case. I've had it, he thought, looking up at the
~~baskets~~ swinging baskets of pale pink flowers. It was
impossible to do anything more. Impossible to calm himself.
He was
all in a twitter. ~~She might come out. No, she wouldn't come
out.~~
~~He would walk from~~ Looking once more at the window he
started off, where? No matter. And his boots on the
pavement struck out 'no matter;' yet, even as they struck
~~the flagstones~~ out no matter, so positively, & by
their regular tattoo brought a sort of calm to him,
the zest & reality of being alive returned to him, ~~& made him
even personally, solid, powerful. in control. independent, &
in control. robust, independent. He~~ It was a splendid
morning. Like the pulse of a perfect heart ~~the life—
cabs omnibuses men & women walking; bicycling; motoring—
flooded the streets, serene~~ life struck straight through the
streets. There was no fumbling, no doubt ~~about it~~ <about it>.
Sweeping ~~to the door,~~ <swerving> there, precisely at the right
instant,
the motor stopped. at the door. ~~Out sprang the girl.
The door opened. A chow barked car barked. Out
a~~ The girl alighted. Admirable butlers & tawny chow dogs
Peter saw & approved, & passed.

it was strange how sentimental he was about his family—

A splendid achievement it ~~see~~ was. Coming as he did of course
of these families which for at least three generations ~~have~~ has
ruled India. There were moments when the solidity
of civilisation seemed to him dear as a personal
possession. There were moments of pride in England,
ridiculous ~~enough~~ considering <everything> that he had been sent
[ ] [ ] <he had> down from ~~England~~; Oxford. ~~That he had failed.
Not a bit of it. Still~~ its very jolly, he thought, to find

~~it all going on,~~ Its all so jolly, he thought. And
the doctors, ~~the~~ & the men of affairs, & the capable women
all going about their business, punctual, alert, robust,
it seemed to him wholly admirable—good fellows to whom
one would wave one's hand, entrust one's life; who would
see one through. And what with one thing & another,
~~really there was nothing to complain of. though~~ really
the show was tolerable. He felt for a cigar. And
now to ~~re~~ sit down in the shade & smoke—He had always
thought Regents Park the worst of the Parks, <a> dull,
symmetrical, park
not a patch on Kensington Gardens, where as a child,—
odd how he was always thinking ~~now~~ of childhood. It was seeing
Clarissa, ~~& having time on one's hands.~~ perhaps—poor
dear Clarissa. Women live much more in the past
than we do, he thought. They attach themselves to places.
Bourton was a nice place, a very nice place, but ~~the old man was~~
I never could get on with the old man, he thought. There was
quite a scene, one night, an argument about something or
other. . . ., ~~But~~ what ~~it had been about~~ he could not
remember.

Yes, he remembered this long ~~straig~~ straight ~~path road,~~
walk, with the little house where one bought airballs on
one side; a straight walk leading to an absurd statue of
some kind. He ~~sat down on an empty seat.~~
looked for an empty seat. ~~He sat down.~~ He did
not want to ~~be talked to. He saw one. He sat down.~~
~~have anybody sitting next him. Old~~ He did not want to be
bothered by the gossip of housemaids.—except that this one,
sewing, looked a quiet pretty girl, & there wasn't an
empty seat anywhere. He sat down ~~in the corner~~.

& smoked.

She's a queer looking girl, he thought, suddenly seeing ~~the~~ Elizabeth Dalloway as she came into the room. Grown lanky; ~~he~~ not exactly pretty. Well, she can't be more than eighteen. Probably she doesn't get on with Clarissa. 'Heres my Elizabeth,' that sort of thing—

The rich & benignant smoke descended into his throat & then ~~he~~ pursing his lips, it ~~came~~ <issued> out in soft quivering rings; which breasted the air bravely for a moment, & then evaporated. wobbled away.

I shall try & get a word with her alone, he thought
May as well go, he thought; And really it delighted him to think that ~~though he had~~ only landed two days ago, already there he was in the thick of things,—invitations—adventures—

Odd shapes they take, he thought, watching one ring ~~& t~~ twist, taper, and disappear.

And then being led on to scientific theories, & so to ideas which were remote from the actual scene,—he was only vaguely worried by the annoyance of the child throwing its toy into the ground.

Dont do that dear. Well if you do, I wont pick it up again.

~~They~~ ~~Only~~ The nurse~~maids voice~~ words confirmed him ~~va~~ in feeling that there is ~~an~~ a tremendous amount of scientific work to be done, & the vague sense of opposition wh. her tone had sound in him, gave way a moment later to comfortable conviction.

And so being led on to make a theory about it, & so passing to ideas
which were remote from the actual scene, he heard the nursemaid
as she ~~rock~~ ~~sayin~~ murmuring no darling, chk, chk, ~~as~~ or something ~~of the~~ of
~~touched~~ <moved> the the kind
perambulator ~~soothing & at the same time encouraging~~ as if she confirmed
with her foot him, ~~in his~~ soothed & encouraged him, in his scientific theories.
in his ~~general~~ sense of sagacity, ~~&~~ prosperity. & well being.
And then ~~the~~ <a> great brush ~~descended,~~ swept smooth across
his mind.
~~running all the thoughts into one. He opened~~ Sweetly he
closed his eyes. With an effort <Raising his hand> he threw
away the
end of his cigar. ~~That done he shut his eyes again.~~
The brush again swept smooth across the whole broad
vista, sweeping ~~together in~~ somehow, the trees & the
light children's voices, & the passing of feet, ~~sweeping~~
~~them~~ with a ~~broad~~ wide current of perception—for
he perceived with extreme clearness some ~~scienti~~ theory about
the nature of aeroplanes, which fact was very moving,
~~full of beauty,~~ very beautiful, & ~~it was all indeed~~
~~perfectly delicious. To rl relinquish, the struggle, was~~
~~perfectly delicious. or rather to soar, above to~~
~~understand.~~ both in itself, & in the light it seemed to
shed ~~on his own engaging~~ upon his own exalted &
spiritual nature, which now somehow, for scrutiny was
~~impossible, seemed to be <too>~~ merging ~~into~~ a general
goodness.
warmth, comfort, . . . He started violently. & opened his eyes.
~~A slight discomfort.~~ He ~~w~~ exerted his will power to keep
awake. ~~Very luxuriously~~ He abandoned his will power.
Again, the great & benignant power took him into its
keeping.

He sank down down into the plumes & feathers of sleep.
snoring, as he went, at first with <an unconscious effort at>
restraint, later with abandonment.
~~Mildred, the nursemaid, thus~~ roused by the noise, <the
nursemaid> looked up from
her crochet: ~~He was a funny old boy, she thought,~~ She looked
at him gently, stupidly, indulgently & ~~returned to her work.~~
then her eyes, as if filled with what they saw, rested ~~up~~
very quietly for a moment upon ~~a~~ the path. ~~Then~~ With a
little start she resumed her work.

In her white dress, moving her hands indefatigably yet
quietly, she ~~might have been~~ seemed like the champion of the
rights of sleepers; like one of those spectral presences which,
rise up in twilight, in woods, made of sky & branches
~~& which yet are endowed with an v a vast personality,~~
~~& tinged with sorrow, with benignity, <a rare streak> yet~~
~~extremely aloof,~~
~~& yet after all seem to reserve in themselves in her~~
~~their capacity yet lure the solitary traveller to their~~
~~arms by some likeness to himself, promise of~~
~~understanding combined with a sense of vast power.~~
~~An outcast, a voyager, to confide h his suffering to them,~~
~~to say, as he advances down the grassy ride, how they~~
~~alone understand the <his> immense weariness, of the~~
~~pilgrimage, & which th ceases to be weariness, on the spot,~~
~~& becomes luminous with the silver light of the sky~~
~~between the branches, & deep, & romantic, & refreshing, as~~
~~all the leaves rustle & shake in the eve twilight wind.~~

~~to~~ <~~seek for wit~~ for in> whom the ~~lonely traveller feels, as as he~~
~~twilight~~
~~haunter~~ lonely traveller, the haunter of lanes, ~~&~~ the
disturber of ferns, ~~brushing through spider webs &~~
~~slash~~ & devastator of great hemlock plants,
~~offers~~ <feels> as he advances an ~~strange~~ extraordinary
~~confidence,~~
intimacy, aloof though it is, this ~~presence~~ <shape> of sky &
branches;
& mysterious too, when, the wind rising,

tosses the branches, & the leaves ~~stir & darken & rustle with murmurs & whispers & She takes me to her, he thinks, & understands my immense weariness.~~
& the pale skirt of the great presence flows this way & that.
<&> ~~It may be~~ It is the soul, he thinks. Yes, though he is by way of
being an atheist, he has ~~this~~ these moments of secret exaltation.
~~He has this is~~ His ~~conscious~~ being seems made ~~of~~ in layers.
One will detach itself & thus float off. ~~Oh what nonsense, Oh what nonsense, he thinks the~~ such experiences are contradicted by science & reason. {As if one cherished endless possibilities, he thinks, & in favourable conditions ~~they are~~ <states of mind> are
liberated.} This figure in the sky is only a state of mind.
She is my embodiment of ~~some~~ <an> instinct. ~~She has no external existence.~~
~~She blesses my extreme weariness, & consents to take me up into her arms. Yet~~ Those are only leaves; Yet,
re which demands that something should solace our
~~extreme~~ weariness. Something should ~~take me into her arms.~~
be conscious of my sufferings. Something august should exist outside these miserable bodies of human beings; ~~&~~ whether it is inside or outside, ~~whether it exists~~ perhaps scarcely matters. For if I can conceive of her, then, in some sense, she exists. Thus guarding himself as well as he can, from ridicule, he is astonished, ~~indeed alarmed,~~ to find ~~how~~ himself ~~as actually endowing the sky & leaves with~~ advancing
[doodles] towards the sky & leaves, ~~the glowing skirts,~~
as if they were the complement of his own person; ~~as if~~
& ~~the some part of him had blo~~ as if they ~~confirmed~~ confirmed an existence otherwise incomplete. ~~And losing touch with~~ Once surrender, & ~~there is no~~
then, like ~~a~~ unreason rushes out, decking these leaves &

280 ~~branches with the qualities of wo~~ to
80 how ~~lav~~ spontaneously <rapidly> he endows these branches
22,000 with womanhood;
how grave they become; how magnificently, as the breeze stirs
them, they disperse ~~from uplifted arms; what is it?~~ <with a
flutter of the hands,>
charity understanding, <&> absolution; & ~~express, as they curtsey
deeply &~~
~~then fling curtseying & recovering express in the breeze~~
~~express something while, each time they & then,~~
& then, flinging themselves suddenly aloft, confound the piety
of their
aspect with a wild carouse.
Such ~~visions~~ are the visions which ~~rise unsought, to to~~
~~supplement a pilgrimage supplementing the graver view,~~
~~snatching flashing their light in the eyes, eagerly~~
~~enticing the solitary traveller to~~ proffering ~~their~~
great cornucopias full of ~~ripe & tempting~~ fruits. to the
solitary traveller; murmuring in his ear, like sirens lolloping
away in the green <sea> waves, ~~how if he tastes of them he is~~
~~rapt aloft in bliss saved~~. inviting him, on & on, to
dashing like embrace them. ~~Like the~~ as he takes his way down
roses in his lanes, or again in the street. Like bunches of roses
face, they are dashed in his face. He sees them rise as the
fisherman sees ~~the pale~~ pale round jelly fish ~~with~~
~~streaming tentacles~~ rise to the top of the water, ~~& then~~
~~& perpetual temptress <ing>, & beckoning, this beauty, this
symbol,~~
~~this presence made of beech leaves & branches, supplements~~
~~the & promises says~~
like the globes of jellyfish which rise to the surface of the green
~~waters~~ <sea>
sea waves & tempt the fishermen to flounder ~~down to embrace
them,~~
~~like like all~~ through the floods to embrace them, for
ever tempted, haunted, & sung to the solitary traveller
takes his way.

[Draft of "The Pastons and Chaucer." (*The Common Reader*, 1925)]

[28]

Rodmell
Aug 2nd 1923

& There at the end of the ride, sees this giant figure displayed.
It is the soul, he thinks. Though he is by way of being an atheist,
he has these moments of secret exaltation. His being seems made in
layers. One will detach itself & thus float off. For the
figure in the sky is only a state of mind, a desire that something
should solace our weariness, be conscious of our suffering, &
dispense relief. Yet, again, surely something must exist outside these
~~besides~~ miserable figures, <these> feeble, ugly, craven men & women?
Anyhow, if I can conceive of her, he thinks, then in some sense
she exists. Thus, advancing down the path, with his eyes upon
sky & branches, he rapidly endows them with womanhood;
sees with amazement how grave they become; how ~~sug~~
majestically as the breeze stirs them they dispense with a
dark flutter of the leaves charity, comprehension, absolution;
& then, flinging themselves suddenly aloft, confound the
piety of their aspect with a wild carouse.

Such are the visions which proffer great cornucopias
full of fruit to the solitary traveller, or murmur in his
ear like sirens lolloping away in the green sea waves,
or are dashed in his face like bunches of roses, or rise to the
surface like pale faces which ~~fis~~ fishermen flounder
through floods to embrace.

Such are the visions which ceaselessly float up, pace beside,
put their faces in front of. ~~the actual se what is before us~~
the actual thing: ~~now seeming to obscure, now to illuminate,~~
often overpowering the solitary traveller, & taking
away from him the ~~wish~~ sense of the earth, the wish to
return, giving him ~~instead a~~ for substitute a ~~greater~~ general
peace; as if (so he thinks advancing down the forest ride)
all this business of living, ~~all this detail, suddenly merged itself~~
~~in an became quite~~ <were> simple <enough,> & myriads of
things merged
~~themselves~~ in one thing: & ~~in this~~ this figure, made of
sky & branches had risen from the sea of life, (he is elderly, he is
~~more than~~ <over> fifty) ~~so~~ as a shape might be sucked up out of
the
~~sea~~ <waves> {~~& Those, with trailing draperies, & stars for eyes,~~
~~might typify innumerable <glowing> waves. She has draperies,~~
~~he~~
~~thinks, raising his eyes once more to the vast great figure;~~
to shower down from her magnificent hands compassion,
to ~~thread~~ <afire> all the little lights into one ~~green~~ glow;
~~And then, or impatiently she tosses; She tosses her~~
~~head impatiently. She is fierce. She is free.~~
So may I never go back, he thinks, to the lamplight, & the
sitting room, never finish my book, knock out my pipe,
& ring for M[rs.] Turner to clear away; rather let me
walk quite straight on towards this ~~magn~~ great vision,
who will with a toss of her head, ~~mount me upon her~~
~~lift me to~~ mount me in her streamers & let me blow
to nothingness ~~on the~~ with the rest.

~~And then, the up go the branches; out fly the~~
~~grey skirts of her robes, & & the green flash of sunset~~
~~flashes in the eyes of the solitary traveller.~~

Such are the visions. ~~& seductive. And if,~~
~~after~~ Nor are they bestowed only by ~~the~~
~~queer su correspondence but which is yet so~~
~~natural sights, which, being so different & cools~~
~~& external safe is have something.~~ The
skies & branches, the flash of the sunset, & the ~~deep~~

~~& the leaves, roughly &~~ which roughly design upon the
evening sky some symbol of our desires. The solitary traveller
is soon beyond the wood, & there coming to the ~~window~~
<door>, with
shaded eyes, possibly to look for his return is ~~the~~ <an> elderly
woman—with hand raised, with shaded eyes, with white
apron blowing aside, she seems (so powerful is this
uniformity) to ~~behold~~ seek ~~for the~~ a lost son, to search
~~a for~~ a sunken ship, to be the figure of the mournful
mother whose hopes have been destroyed in all the
battles of the world. And now, as the solitary
traveller advances, down the village street, where the
the men dig women stand knitting at the doors. <& ~~the~~> this dreadful
in the garden strange flaw in him makes the evening ~~dreadful~~ <ominous>, &
all the
quiet ~~village people~~ figures still, statuesque, ~~like as if~~
~~the witnesses of~~ as if, ~~soon, inevitably,~~ some august
fate, ~~which they~~ is known to them, but not dreaded,
were ~~soon to~~ abuse to ~~flutter, to~~ annihilate them as they
stand.

More strangely still, ~~there comes flows out from behind~~
~~the same~~ indoors, among ordinary things—the cupboard, the
table, the window sill with its ~~gen~~ geraniums,
suddenly ~~there from behind~~ the outline of the landlady, bending
across the table to remove the cloth, becomes soft like light, &
~~in her~~ she too seems ~~to be stooping from a~~ to
~~scrutinise the pigmies at her feet; or, raising herself to be~~
~~quit of some~~ an adorable emblem, ~~& only & the~~
~~recollection of a~~ which only the recollection of cold
human contacts in a previous world ~~pr~~ forbids us to embrace.
She takes the marmalade in her hand & shuts it quietly in the
corner cupboard. There is nothing more tonight Sir?
~~No, thank you.~~ The solitary traveller replies; ~~& adds~~ replies;
but scarcely knows whether his little voice will reach the
so far, or carry any meaning with it; so distant she seems,
so indifferent; & in her

.IV.

13th Aug. 1923 M$^{r.}$ Walsh woke up with extreme suddenness. He had suddenly
remembered something about Clarissa which interested him
very much.
He had a queer tag for it in his mind "The death of ~~a~~ <the> soul."
So magnificent a name certainly promised something startling.
Yet it was nothing; ~~absolutely~~ nothing. <more than this> ~~There~~
~~had been~~
~~a party at Bourton,~~ There were several people staying at
Bourton, probably in September; anyhow fine hot weather;
& they were sitting in the drawing room—that he could
remember perfectly well—with the windows open.
(~~this~~ <it> must have been in the early nineties) There had been
a lot of talk~~; &~~ about some neighbour, ~~who~~ a
rich ~~well known~~ man, a considerable figure in ~~society, who~~
the country. who had married his housemaid. This poor
woman had to go visiting with him; & in order to make out
that she was not a housemaid, she dressed absurdly.
Clarissa described her. 'like a cockatoo',
Chattering too. She never stopped talking. But the point
was that she had had a baby ~~by the Squire~~ before ~~they~~ her
marriage.
The sexes did not married. In those days, ~~it was not usual certainly to discuss~~
discuss things ~~of that sort~~ in public. ~~Poor Sally Ben R.~~ It was
such Sally ~~Silcox~~ Seaton who ~~started the discussion~~
insisted upon it—whether it ~~really~~ made any difference
to one's feelings & so on. "Oh" said Clarissa, quite
suddenly, "~~I didn't know that~~— I'll never
~~let her come her~~ speak to her again. ~~I couldn't~~." <~~& the whole~~
~~party broke up. It was very~~>
~~Nowadays of course, nobody would say that. And really~~
~~she turned pink; & after dinner, when <afterwards> Sally had~~
~~told him~~ [ ]
~~that~~ Clarissa had sat up half the night, ~~saying~~
~~how one couldn't speak of such things—that there were the~~
Poor Sally wanted to know whether he found anything
odious in her, ~~That was what~~ <And> he <had> called it
"the death of the soul", ~~this being in an absurd state~~
~~of mind no doubt.~~ He had felt, not that

He had not blamed her for minding the fact, since in those days,
a girl of twenty-two—was she?—knew nothing; it was her
manner. ~~There was a rigidity in it, something hard in
her exquisite It was very difficult to describe~~ It was if she
drew her skirts round her in a ~~silly timid way which~~ <flutter but
& like flutter. &> but
~~was~~ yet ~~very~~ <very so> arrogantly; ~~rigidly~~; <rigidly.> ~~It was
unimaginative~~. <So unimaginative.>
Its the death of soul he had said to himself, sitting there
smoking a cigarette. His intensity was of course absurd,
but then, being in love with her, one had these sudden, ~~terrible~~,
revelations, of a reality so startling that it was literally
true—they lasted a lifetime. Nothing she could do or say
afterwards ~~glossed it over~~ <made any difference>.~~—even
though he could see the whole
thing from the outside; could see his own~~ It remained, a fact
about her that that he knew. ~~The party~~ <They all> wobbled; yes, that was his
feeling,
everyone~~'s relation~~ seemed to bow ~~before what she had said,~~ &
then to ~~re~~ stand up, ~~but to be~~ different. The sexes, probably
felt themselves separated The men wanted to be alone.
Perhaps the women did too. He could see Sally now,
like a child who has been in mischief, rather flushed,
wanting to ~~justify herself~~ <go on>, ~~yet afraid to say anything
more.~~ <yet afraid>
~~very handsome, but not his style. She was a wild creature in
those days.~~ How she had come to be Clarissa's greatest friend,
he did not know. ~~But she was always at Bourton,
there when he was, & she was always in mischief. &
there a sense of insecurity.~~ She was always at Bourton,
a wild attractive ~~absurd~~ creature with the reputation
in those days of great daring. He uses to give her cigars.
She had either been engaged to somebody, or quarrelled
with somebody—At any rate ~~she had more experience than
Clarissa & the rest & used to lend her books—she talked,
rather well too; discussed questions;~~ She said these
upsetting things at meals. Clarissa went off by
herself. He remembered ~~with a~~ how angry she had made him—
~~by her manner, when she made~~ She had ~~made~~ <given> some
excuse,—

speaking to the servants or seeing someone—& then ~~the door~~ she
had flung herself upon that great woolly dog who ran after
sheep &
kissed it all over, as if to say to him—it was all aimed at him
~~Yes I am~~ See what an extraordinarily ~~affe~~ sensitive
person I am!
~~Yes, They <they> had always had <had> a connection~~
~~of that this power of~~
~~over each other. of affecting each other. of transmitting~~
~~feelings without any words. had this sort of connection~~
always been this ~~odd~~ queer ~~kind of~~ sympathy between them—
~~a power of transmitting feelings quite plainly~~ She knew
directly he criticised her. Then she would ~~make~~ <do> something
quite obvious, ~~in~~ to defend herself; ~~&~~ like this fuss over the dog—
but it never took him in. However, she ~~had gone~~ <went off>.
Then Sally suggested a walk; It was their usual habit.
~~But no.~~ But he was too much out of temper & besides,
Sally would ~~talk. He wanted to be~~ start talking—would
make him ~~side with her against Clarissa~~ <discuss things>—She
~~had no~~
was one ~~of the greatest~~ of those He ~~wanted to be alone.~~
went off therefore, somewhere or other, miserably, to brood;
He remembered looking at a horse ~~in a state of fury.~~
He remembered ~~Andre~~ Sullivan, the old coachman.
Though the Parrys were not by ~~any means rich,~~ <very well off,> ~~this~~
they always seemed to have ~~nice~~ grooms & stable boys & so
on . . & of course there ~~was a~~ <the> cook, or ~~a~~ <her> nurse, what was
her name? old ~~D Light~~ Boody, <old> Moody, some such
name; who was ~~almost one of the family.~~ always
called 'old', & one had to visit her. But that was an
~~terrible~~ <awful> evening! As for the pleasures of love, there
may be <no doubt>
such things, but surely no one has ever described the tortures!
~~anguish—Probably it was Clarissa was And~~ To be in
love with Clarissa was the devil. ~~She was a virgin—a~~
prude—~~no, it was extremely difficult to but it wasn't that,~~
~~no, not a prude;~~ but a woman who ~~simply lacked~~ nothing
attractiveness, in the ordinary sense of the word, but lacked
that particular quality which ~~Mary Molly Seaton for~~
~~instance had, quite obviously, the moment~~ one calls sex ~~in~~ as
passion;— you had only to ~~compare~~ <see> ~~Sal Mary~~ Molly
& her

in a little room
with <lots of>
bird cages

But it was an awful evening! Now it seemed ridiculous; but then
it had been a tragedy, for he condemned her; & she knew it; &
how
could he see her alone, ~~before dinner~~ to explain? ~~Talk of the
delights of
love—<but> has anyone ever described its miseries? he
wondered.
But what he had seen was final;~~ For that was the ~~dev~~
devilish part of being in love with Clarissa—<~~but~~> one saw
~~through her, & yet it mad exactly how limited, how
narrow~~ through her ~~of course~~, & yet ~~she had that~~ it made no
difference. One ~~felt this knew of~~ <saw> that she was cold. She
lacked precisely the quality that Molly Seaton had—
yet there could no comparison between her & any other
woman—
she had, then at least, ~~a charm, a~~ some queer power, of
~~like~~ fiddling on ones nerves—turning one's nerves to fiddle
strings, yes
~~playing the violin, yes. making music, yes.
However,~~ He had gone in to dinner. rather late, from some idiotic
wish to make himself felt. ~~perhaps~~ (~~& of course~~ he could see now
~~that he~~ what a nuisance he must have been) Old Miss Parry,
'Aunt ~~some~~ Helena", M[r] Parry's sister, who was supposed to
superintend, detested ~~that sort of behaviour~~. people being late.
She sat there, in her white Cashmere shawl, ~~with a very high~~
<& with her head>
~~fore head,~~ against the window. ~~It was one of those awful~~
280 ~~dinners when one can't speak.~~ <She> ~~a strange,~~ formidable old
80 lady
22,400 ~~to most people, but he had always liked her, She was a
great botanist,~~ He had won her heart <once> by finding a rare
flower, ~~which~~ <for> ~~for~~ She was a ~~great~~ <great> botanist. It was ~~an~~
awful ~~evening—quite awful!~~ He could not say a word.
Everything seemed to <go> rushing past him. And he could see
But the through it all. ~~It was that evening that he had realised—~~
extraordinary ~~This was the very first time he had even thought it possible that~~
thing was ~~Clarissa would marry Richard Dalloway.~~
That he had ~~had,~~ about halfway through dinner, ~~a sort of~~ an
sort of revelation. 'She will marry that man."
He didn't even know his name! He ~~was a~~ was a

friend of somebodies, had been brought by some one, was
staying in the
neighbourhood. He had been shown round the grounds, ~~& had~~
~~by~~
Sally, ~~who~~ had said that he ~~was a~~ seemed ~~rather fond~~ interested in
dogs or plants or something. ~~He was a politician.~~
~~This~~

he had been called by the wrong name.

~~It was Richard Dalloway.~~
~~Someone had brought him over, that afternoon;~~
~~he might The first distinct impression that Peter had had of~~
~~him was~~

Oh yes he did—~~it was for a ridiculous thing had happened~~—
<he remembered it all now.>
He had been brought over by somebody that afternoon; &
Clarissa had ~~mixed him up.~~ <got his name wrong>. She had
called him "Mr Wickham."
Suddenly he had said "My name is Dalloway."
That was the very first impression ~~Peter~~ he had of him—~~sitting~~
a fair young man, rather awkward, ~~with a little stammer~~,
blurting out 'My name is Dalloway.' Molly made a
joke of it. 'My name is Dalloway' she called him; ~~until~~—
How did one get these sudden impressions? The ~~vulgar~~ ordinary
explanation would have been that Clarissa meant him to
feel ~~that~~ it—~~meant him to see how easily she could charm.~~
But no. There was something ~~absolutely~~ ~~spontaneous~~ <innocent>
about her: ~~spontaneous~~ <something>; ~~She had, then at least,~~
~~something almost boyish about her~~—It was difficult to
find any word for it. ~~And yet this quality~~ Never was
anybody more feminine. Yet one could never call her a
flirt.

~~No, the probability was that she was genuinely interested~~

All through dinner he tried to overhear what they were
saying. Afterwards he could remember standing by ~~old~~ old
Miss Parry's chair in the drawing room,
Clarissa, of course, tried to ‘draw him in’, ~~in the for her social~~
~~instinct surely~~ as a hostess: ~~which seemed to him absolutely~~
<enraged him>
absurd, ~~though~~ yet he couldn't help admiring ~~the strength of~~

her ~~&~~ social instinct. What a gift she had for it—a sense of
people in the mass~~—a gift for making them talk—bringing them
together—a positive genius;~~ She could bring them together,
make
them get on, the most unlikely people. Even at that moment
he had felt rather a brute, for ~~being such a stick.~~ refusing.
So she had left him. And he <had> felt as if they were all
gathered together in a conspiracy behind his back. There he
stood, ~~for hours it s~~ by Miss Parry's chair—as if he
were ~~paralysed.~~ cut out of wood.
He talked about wild flowers. ~~Then with that <some> queer
insight which <instinct wh. all women have>
even old women seem to possess she had made him sit down &
began telling him about her youth,~~ Never, ~~never~~ had he
suffered so infernally. ~~Then there was a stir behind him.~~
At last he ~~saw~~ <woke up &> Miss Parry looking rather
disturbed, rather
indignant, staring with her ~~rather~~ prominent eyes fixed,
& he felt that he ~~was going to break down in & explain~~
must burst out & ~~tell her that how it was~~ <explain> that
<[luckily?]> he couldn't ~~answer~~ <attend>
because he was in hell. People began going out of the
room. Doors opened. They ~~cried out~~ <said> ~~"Have you go~~
It'll be
very cold—& "Wait & I'll fetch my cloak" & so on.
They were going boating in the pond by moonlight, one of
Sally's mad ideas. She thought it so romantic
He could hear her ~~talking about the moon; in emphat~~
talking, emphatically, ~~to~~ about the moon.

"Dont you want to go with them?" said Aunt Helena,
(poor old lady! she had ~~no~~ guessed) And he turned
round, ~~as if~~ with an enormous effort, & there was Clarissa.
"Yes, come along," she ~~had~~ said ~~"in an odd voice. "They're~~
They're
~~waiting" gone on."~~ waiting." ~~Nothing in the whole world
So, possibly, there had never been such happiness as his, as
he walked down. . <with Clarissa> got into the boat. & Then
rowed about
that absurd pond which little pond, in & Dalloway was
in the other boat—&~~ So he went. He knew he
was a fool. . He knew he ~~was right to~~ should have

stopped. However, he had had perhaps twenty minutes of
exquisite
happiness; ~~When they did get on, no two people could have
been better~~
~~suited~~ for when Clarissa chose, ~~of course she had him~~
~~could do anything. There was no one to like her~~—Everything
about her was
exquisite. Her voice, her dress—something floating, crim son—
her adventurousness & insisting that they should all disembark—
explore the island—only a wretched little hung in the middle of her
pond: & ~~then singing~~. startling a hen, or some heavy
bird which flew up—& singing, ~~nothing romantic,—something~~
~~about~~ All the time he knew that that ~~poor~~ <the> young man
~~& then talking & laughing.~~ All the time he knew that the other
young man—"my name is Dalloway"—was falling in love.
But he was in an exalted state of mind. ~~at one moment,~~
~~somehow, he had Sally Seaton in his arms as she tripped over~~
~~something; & & he caught hold of her. But everyone was in~~
~~an exalted state of mind. Everything that Clarissa did~~
~~seemed to him perfectly right~~ Nothing seemed to matter.
And he ~~felt himself~~ felt himself ~~saying~~ becoming more & more
brilliant. In those days he could be brilliant. He was
above himself, as nurses say. He talked a great deal
And ~~this was what she liked in him—that he should <him to>
be <like that:> extravagant,~~
~~she liked him to be vehement; say be a socialist;~~
~~say that everything was be a socialist. She liked laughing~~
~~at him. She liked to to be extravagant, & to say that~~
~~they were all blind fools, & there was sure to be revolution~~.
~~to talk a little socialism, or~~ she liked laughing at him.
~~Oh he <had> talked about~~ Ibsen. ~~His recollection was that
they had~~
~~sat down on this~~ They sat on the ground & talked—he & ~~Sally~~
~~He & Clarissa &~~ <he> & Clarissa argued. Suddenly his own
words came back without any meaning. 'The death of the
soul'. What had he meant? Why had he been so
unhappy. And then, as if they had some power to
act of themselves, these words ~~seemed to~~ shrivelled up what
Clarissa was saying, burst a hole in her. Again he

[Margin: Oh how ~~wonder~~ <amazing> she was]

he felt that he saw through her; ~~that they~~ But he wasn't in the
least angry—only profoundly unhappy. And Dalloway
arranged
everything, got them into the boats, helped them into cloaks—was
extremely adequate in every way.

~~And~~ He had said to himself quite dully "They ~~had better~~ suit
each other." He had said it without any resentment, indeed he
had liked Dalloway. He had liked him from the first. He was a
good specimen of a ~~type of youth who comes with whom he very good kind of young~~ certain type—~~but Clarissa was so much more than that!—a thorough <a> gentleman. a public school man, a gentleman—more than that;~~ a perfect gentleman & all
that, more than that, ~~indeed~~ to be fair. {There was something
very attractive about him ~~at that time~~} ~~his honesty, his~~
~~He was more open-minded than one would have expected.~~

He was going to ride ~~h~~ back ~~that night,~~ twenty miles,
to the house where he was staying. though it was late already.
He had
an appointment, a political appointment, which he would not
break. Sally began rhapsodising about this ride—through the
woods at night. She wrote in those days ~~an~~ extremely florid
~~style,~~ descriptions of things <in> ~~she kept~~ a diary, ~~& if you got to knew~~ which she lent you~~—some of it was great fun too, for, she was a~~ & ~~very amusing bits accounts of people too. (but about people she could be very amusing) And she began about the night & the stars but her description~~
~~She he~~ She said how wonderful ~~this~~ <it> would be; the
glow worms; the stars; the wind; the dawn; & ~~how~~ & so on
~~it was then~~ what thoughts he would have—at least she
would have; for ~~in her~~ she was a tremendous egoist, very
~~vain, very ch~~ And Dalloway ~~sat~~ rowed them in—
& said nothing. But somehow, as they watched him start,
jumping on to his bicycle, & wobbling off down the
drive, waving his hand & disappearing, yes, he had
almost cursed him for having that ride ahead of him. . He
felt infinitely older (they were both 25 or 6) much
more intelligent but Lord. Lord! What <a ride that was going>
torture that night
had been!

~~This was his first attempt~~ He was ~~becoming~~ beginning politics, & he took it all very seriously.)

to be.

~~How~~ He had envied him!
~~Looking back, there~~ His demands upon Clarissa were
absurd. ~~Nobody could have given him all he wanted.~~
Nowadays he would have told a young man in that state of mind
~~not to stand—be a fool—to that~~ <not to> he ~~was~~ a fool. She
would have
accepted ~~married~~ him, he believed. ~~Indeed they might have been very~~
~~happy together.~~ Sally thought so. She used to write to him
all that summer, ~~saying how things giving him~~ news—
long letters, ~~which he used to tear from their envelopes~~ &
how Clarissa had devour—~~for~~ how they had ~~sat up till very late~~ <talked about
talked about him, him>, <&> ~~how~~
how Clarissa had cried— ~~But all the time she was meeting~~
~~Dalloway, & that was going on.~~ How Sally had praised him
~~for being 'unconventional'~~. ~~She had said he was~~
It was an extraordinary summer! all ~~let those letters,~~ agitations,
scenes, telegrams, arriving ~~suddenly~~ early in the morning,
walking
about till the servants were up—.& then appalling tête à têtes
with ~~old~~ Mr. Parry at breakfast Aunt Helena very
formidable, but ~~somehow~~ kind; Sally sweeping him off for
walks in the vegetable garden; & Clarissa in bed with
headaches. ~~She was easily knocked up.~~ Among all this
talk ~~fluff~~ & nonsense (as it now seemed to him)—~~but then it was~~
~~the only possible~~ one or two ~~scenes stood out~~. little scenes
remained
one at luncheon: when Sally (whose life must have been a
burden to her) ~~said, by way of a joke~~ <called Dalloway>, 'My
name is Dalloway'
Clarissa ~~froze up <up> at once—Already she would not have him~~
~~laughed at. instantly changed. showed that she would not have~~
~~him laughed at.~~
The final scene, the terrible scene, which, he believed, had
altered ~~him~~
his life had happened ~~in the~~ at three o'clock in the afternoon on a
hot day. A trifle, ~~one of those~~ led up to it.—Sally at lunch
saying something about 'My name is dalloway'—~~&~~
Clarissa suddenly stiffened, coloured (in a way she had) ~~&~~
~~said something <sharp> about 'feeble jokes".—It was over in a~~
~~moment.~~
~~which made~~ & rapped out very sharply that she thought
they had had enough of that feeble joke." Nobody

it was another moment of [ ] feels like that about him; then I'm off"

noticed it. except perhaps Sally; but for him, after all those weeks of ~~ups &~~
~~downs~~, hoping & not hoping, of quarrelling & misery, this was final.
If she ~~can talk like that of another man in my presence he said,~~
then ~~it is over: then I it is time to end it. I'm off. Then she's got to~~
~~choose between us.'~~ He sent her a note by Sally—Sally tried to
prevent him but he overcame her~~—saying~~ asking her to ~~come to the~~
meet him by the fountain at three, ~~since~~ "something very
important has happened" he ~~put in vaguely~~ <scribbled> at the end.
The fountain was a little broken affair, ~~surrounded by trees,~~
in a small shrubbery, far from the house, ~~a~~ with shrubs & trees
all round it. ~~The fountain merely dribbled.~~ Here she came
even before three, & they stood by the fountain all the time with the
spout dribbling water between them. ~~Queer newts came to the~~
~~top, he remembered.~~ How sights fix themselves in one's mind!
For example
the vivid green moss.

~~She did not cry~~ She did not move. She seemed
like some one contracted, petrified ~~as he bombarded her—oh~~
~~For he had felt as if there were two of everything in front of him—~~
~~his forehead bursting & a rigidity all over him:~~ sometimes she
flinched a <little>
as he charged her. Tell me the truth, he kept on saying. Tell me the
truth. (And then that perfectly ridiculous old man,
Breachhammer, or some such name, had popped his head in,
with the Times under his arm; had looked at them; ~~had gone~~
~~away~~ <gaped>—
They were both in such a state that it made absolutely no
difference; but he could still remember his astonished stare—)
All through his speech he had felt that Clarissa would yield.
It was like vipers flung in his face; it was physically
shocking ~~startling when she said~~ "~~No, I dont care for you. I cant care for~~
~~you.~~ <when she did speak at the end.>
~~This is the last time—This is the end. Go I can't~~
~~She merely said "I dont care~~ . . I'm afraid of no one . . ~~Im very~~
<This must be>
end ~~sorry~~" That was literally all. But it was extraordinarily
~~effective; as if some very unpleasant woman, whom he did not~~
~~know, had spoken for Clarissa~~—It was if she were
determined to kill; to exterminate. Oh Clarissa he had cried. He
cd remember the physical effect <of speaking> as if something
sharp edged had
expanded in his chest & burst assunder. After that the silence
was
complete.

It was awful, he said, looking at the trees—awful, awful. .
He had thought this in a very few minutes. Sleep still hung about
him so that he did not quite know what he was looking at.
The elderly nurse, ~~having~~ who had been ~~looking with a~~
staring vaguely ~~gent vague stare~~ at the path, now resumed her work.
~~And a child who had been~~

"~~Put my~~ There! said little Elsie Mitchel, putting ~~her~~ a
~~peb~~ handful of pebbles on the nurses knee; & she was about
to run off, to find more, when she saw the old gentleman in
the corner of the seat. ~~sitting there,~~ staring.

She ~~was frightened.~~ gazed at him. She stood perfectly
still. His mouth had fallen open. His eyes, the ~~bright~~
~~softly~~ luminous <yet strangely fixed> eyes ~~of an active minded~~
~~man,~~ were
~~fixed quite in an~~ stared straight ahead of him. He
had forgotten himself, his surroundings, so completely that
~~every~~ his face had a kind of exultation; ~~something~~ an
~~expression at once intense &~~ a kind of intensity that
terrified. t the ~~child~~. little girl.

As if ~~to~~ she wanted to get away from him;
she ran down the path, running with her arms stretched & ~~her~~
eyes some such look of terror that Rezia who saw her
coming said to herself,

"Everyone is afraid."

But then this question of falling in love—of women. She always
~~contrasted herself~~ compared herself not with her own sister
~~but with that~~ who was too much like herself in those ways,
but with someone <~~as~~> utterly different~~—with a as~~ <with>
Sally
Seaton ~~had been~~ <in fact>. Their relationship had been really a
very strange one. ~~No one had influenced her more.~~
The ~~influence~~ <friendship> had been so tremendous while it
lasted—it was
like being in love. ~~It began in a way~~ She sat on the floor—that was her
first recollection of Sally— She sat on the floor, with her
hands about her knees, smoking a cigarette. Where could it
have been? at some party, (where she could not remember)
for she had a distinct recollection ~~of being shocked &~~ saying
to the man she was with Who is that? ~~girl? The next~~
~~thing was very~~ She was rather shocked, but ~~still~~ could not
take her eyes off her. It was an extraordinary beauty.
~~In every way they were completely the opposite. Sally~~
the kind she <of> ~~was the kind of person that she often wanted to be—She was~~
most ~~the type most unlike her own—the one she most admired~~.
admired. dark, In every way they were completely opposite. ~~Yet she had~~
large eyed; & ~~never envied her for a single instant. & she had~~
~~exactly that quality which~~ with that quality, which, as she hadnt
got it, she ~~most admired~~, <always ~~would~~> ~~then at any rate—~~
~~something~~
~~a power of a kind of~~ admired—a quality that made it
possible for ~~Sally~~ to say & ~~do things which in any~~
asking to do anything—It was commoner in foreigners than in
Englishwomen. Sally said that she was descended
from somebody in the French Revolution. So then she
came to stay at Bourton. Was that the time when she
arrived without a penny in her pocket, quite
unexpectedly, walking in upon them after dinner, ~~saying~~
~~bursting into tears, &~~ & upsetting poor Aunt
Helena to such an extent that she never forgave her.

~~her own account was that her home was intolerable. And how~~
She had had a quarrel. ~~All~~ That was so strange—to
quarrel with one's parents ~~seemed then to Clarissa quite~~
that ~~one's parent~~ <they> should quarrel. ~~They sat up all night~~
~~things that seemed to her so awful, so~~ All that side of life—
~~the shady side~~ <quarrels>—money difficulties, Sally was the
first
person to reveal. They sat up that night, very very late . . .
~~But~~ "~~Aunt~~ Its society thats got to be changed"—she could
hear Sally say~~ing~~<ing> ~~that <a> for the intoxicating~~
(sitting on the floor as usual) Really she hadn't the ghost of an
idea what Sally meant. (They lived an extraordinarily
secluded life in some ways—she knew nothing about
sexual life, or social problems; ~~or poverty:~~ except what
she saw with her own eyes in the village, & Aunt Helena
always hurried her away—~~still~~ she had seen an old man
dead. She ~~did know~~ had seen a cow just after a calf was
born—~~)~~ it was the talking about such things that seemed so
strange)

There had been some awful ~~family~~ quarrel. To quarrel with ones
parents—that one's parents should quarrel—was inconceivable, ~~to her.~~
~~to talk about it, even worse.~~ The horror of it. Then Sally was
always short of money. But she was much too proud ever to take
money—insisted upon paying ~~even~~ <her share even> for cabs & buses.
~~She tried to make money by writing.~~ She literally hadn't a penny
that night when she came to them—she'd pawned a brooch
to ~~pay~~ <come down> the fare~~—she'd come off there'd been a scene at~~
~~There had been a scene at lunch, & she had come left the house~~
~~straight away.~~ They had sat up till all hours of the night
~~how extraordinarily~~ happy talking. Sally made her feel, for the first time, how secluded,
how ~~sheltered,~~ <happy> the life at Bourton was. She knew nothing
about sex or social problems. She had seen an old man who
had dropped dead in a field—she had seen a cow just
after its calf was born. But Aunt Helena ~~always~~
~~hurried her away. was extremely shy.~~ never liked any discussions
~~(It was Sally who first talked about 'social problems'. lent gave her~~
~~William Morris.) Sally was a socialist in those days.~~
~~It was Sally who lent her William Morris—she was a socialist~~
~~in those days. She must have~~ been, making all allowances,
an ~~extremely brilliant~~ creature. There they sat hour after
hour ~~talk~~ talking—about the difficulties of life, & also its
~~po~~ duties, its ~~possibilities, its~~ responsibilities—for ~~they~~ both
had ~~at that time at that time~~ an ~~extraordinary ambition~~
were both at that time extremely ambitious.
~~For example~~ They ~~wanted to found~~ <meant to found> a society.
~~It seemed quite easy then—to~~ They meant to abolish
~~poverty.~~ private property. That was Sallys idea.
But her charm was inconceivable! There was her
gift with flowers for instance. At Bourton they
always had stiff little roses all the way down the table—
Sally went out & picked hollyhocks ~~& cut their~~ & all sorts
of flowers that couldn't possibly go together & made
them swim on the top of the water. She cut off their petals.

The effect was quite extraordinary—coming in to dinner, ~~in the sunset,~~ &
seeing ~~all those bowls of flowers~~ that blaze of colour.
(~~Of course~~ Aunt Helena thought it was ~~perfectly dreadful to~~
quite wicked to treat flowers like that) Then she forgot her
sponge & ran along the ~~corridor~~ <passage> naked. That grim old fogey
Ellen Atkins ~~went &~~ <went about> grumbled<ing> ~~<about> to Aunt Helena~~ "Suppose any
of the gentlemen had seen her" & so on. ~~And dear Papa,~~
She ~~said she~~ & ~~said~~ <threatened to> ~~she would~~ tell the Master, ~~as if~~
~~dear that old darling, who Sally All that <P> he would ever say~~
~~about Sally was that she was Papa never much admired her.~~
untidy, Papa said. ~~He thought her untidy.~~ Indeed, she did shock people. She was
the strange thing ~~on was~~, in looking back, ~~how entirely~~ was the
~~uncritical,~~ the absolute nature of her affection for Sally; ~~It~~
~~made her angry if people criticised her. People it was entirely~~
~~without jealousy; it had a kind of purity, disinterestness & purity,~~
it was not like one's feeling for a man; It was disinterested <completely without jealousy>; &
besides, it had a quality which ~~other never existed in~~
could only exist between women, between young women ~~who,~~—
~~She used to think of Sally <a> feeling~~ & it was odd that she, ~~Clarissa,~~
who was the younger, should have it so strongly for Sally,
~~since~~ <for> it seemed to spring from a ~~desire~~ <wish> to protect her, ~~an~~ a
~~an~~ a ~~sense of danger, as if~~ That was one of the things
they talked about; how ~~they were bound to marry,~~
marriage was bound to be ruin.

---

very strong sense ~~that she was running risks in~~ of something
threatening, menacing, ~~in life—not, as nothing~~ <which was felt> definite,
(~~though of course~~ they always ~~said <talked~~ or> ~~that marriage~~ <as> was ruin)
a catastrophe ~~that must happen~~—but this danger
was nothing so definite as that—it merely seemed
to her that Sally was bound to be injured.
She had an absurd, a schoolgirlish vision, of Sally ~~being too good~~
~~for the world~~—going out to be slaughtered. And it
was this feeling between them that made her so resent
~~the~~ what seemed to her liberties—not that they were
anything of the kind; only Sally would do extravagant things—

~~And it seemed to her that~~ so angry, ~~so unhappy,~~ when Sally did
or said the sort of thing that made ~~her seem fast. Then quite nice~~
~~people say of her—as they did~~—seem fast. ~~When people~~
~~criticised Sally <her> it put her into a frenzy. she minded it~~
~~infinitely more than Sally did—when for instance she~~
~~She~~ Girls, perhaps very young men ~~too~~ (no, it was
scarcely likely) had ~~this what a kind of~~ at that age a sense
of being in league; an ~~presentiment that entirely loyalty~~
~~to each other;~~ a presentiment of something ~~coming that~~
~~would to come~~ that was bound to ~~part them. come between~~ part
them. ~~Her own devotion to Sally seemed to her now~~
~~half foolish, half Her devotion to Sally was~~ (& indeed
they had been parted, completely) ~~But what she~~
~~And then for~~ girls, ~~perhaps~~, There was always this
obscure dread, ~~which was exciting but so very~~ <which> ~~strong~~
~~in Sally's~~
~~case, of marriage. had so strongly, of marriage. She~~
~~certainly never felt it for herself, but Sally used to talk~~
~~as though But besides that, also one felt that~~
~~at any rate she could not endure it when it was an extraordinary~~
~~thing—one girls devotion to another; It There was nothing~~
~~sickly about it It was rather severe. But~~
~~her devotion to Sally; &~~ Beyond that, ~~the~~ a
sense of hostility. {And then one always protected the
other. It was natural to protect Sally, because she did
such foolish things—smoking a cigar for instance
~~to win a bet, or~~} She had an absurd, schoolgirlish
vision of Sally going out to be slaughtered. ~~It was~~
~~partly Sallys because Sally did abr was reckless in~~
~~those days~~—She was reckless in those days. She
rode a bicycle round a parapet: ~~three feet from the~~
~~ground.~~ She smoked. cigars. And ~~when~~ <then> ~~Peter Walsh~~
~~she behaved~~ when ~~Peter Walsh~~ <some young man> was rude to
her—or
Sally at least said he was rude to her—she sobbed

a sort of devotion
to each other,
more on her side
than on Sallys

(Sally felt it more
strongly than
she did)
of marriage as a
sort of doom.

~~all night <of course> Looking back, it was clear that there was & she had~~
~~complete misunderstanding <stood>, because Peter Walsh, was much too~~
~~had meant nothing of the kind. He was much too timid,~~ too
~~very~~ ~~But~~ And she had
she was in a desperate state—~~sobbed all night~~ <talked all night>, said she could never
respect herself ~~again~~ <again>; & wrote him a letter, which she, Clarissa, had
had the sense to tear up ~~in pages & pages of self analysis,~~
~~how about analysing her~~ explaining <defending> her ~~character~~ <~~motives~~ character>—~~as~~ &
~~quoting dragging in Shelley, of course, as she always did,~~
& ~~saying how~~ demanding an ~~explan~~ apology. There was
of course something absurd about her. ~~But then the~~
charm, the beauty, ~~was so~~ <were> overpowering. ~~that~~ literally ~~she~~
Clarissa could remember standing in her ~~old attic~~
bedroom at the top of the house, & taking up the ~~wat hot~~
hot water can ~~to pour out water~~, & saying aloud "She is
beneath this roof". ~~It was as She had~~ Why did she
~~remember taking up the water can?~~ It was as if she
wanted to ~~to~~ do something, ~~so~~ to hold to something, to ~~grasp~~ grasp.
~~mark~~ that amazing moment. ~~And now it was~~ <She had seen> only a
~~kind of shell!~~ "She is beneath this roof. She is
beneath this roof." The words meant absolutely nothing now.
~~But~~ She could not get even an shiver <echo> of her old emotion—but
she could remember being quite cold with excitement, & doing
her hair in a kind of ecstasy (& now it began to come back to her & why)
with the rooks floating up & down as usual, ~~&~~ <in> the pink <evening> light &
the trees; & going down to dinner & realising—yet <it> that was the
queer thing. how no <that such an> happiness wh. is ~~so~~ intense can possibly
last. "If it were now to die—to come down to dinner in a
white frock & <to> meet Sally Seton!

That was her feeling, Othello's feeling—

It was almost impossible now to understand what any of it meant.
Sally herself had become so different—~~There was, of course, this sense of its being~~
~~illumination. a moment— Her only wish then had been that Sally~~
There was of course this sense of her presence in the room, which made all
the ~~ordinary things old~~ <usual> things ~~like glass & silver~~ look different—
And one wanted her to ~~let~~ admire them so immensely. One looked anxiously
even at papa—~~even~~ at Aunt Helena in her white shawl—to
see what impression they would make—whether ~~he~~ Papa had
changed or come in ~~in his~~ <to dinner> as he was. It was so odd that they seemed
to feel no difference. Aunt Helena ~~said, just as usual to~~ <asked> the servant
just as usual to bring her a cloak, as she felt the draught. ~~A~~ &
That dreadful old cloak, with mouldy <brown> fur, was brought in; ~~&~~
~~What sort of impression were they making, she longed to know?~~
~~It was so amazing to go on eating one's dinner, talking, without~~
~~making any difference Clarissa could see them all, as Sally saw~~
~~them. She could~~ she could see it now—she could see them all
as they must strike Sally & ~~As for Sally, what did she look <was she> like?~~
But as for Sally herself, ~~&~~ one only felt her as a kind of radiance—
~~something so dazzling that she could not look at. it~~ She ~~had only a~~
~~memory of~~ <She> wore pink gauze—Was that possible? She seemed
anyhow, all light, glowing; ~~& very~~ like some bird, or air ball~~oon~~—
something that has flown in, ~~& got~~ or just ~~fastened itself~~ attached
itself for a moment to a bramble. But nothing is so strange
when one is in love—for it was after all being in love—as the

[Margin: & then her voice was so beautiful.]

extraordinary indifference of other people. Instead of treasuring every
moment of Sally's company, Aunt Helena just wandered off after
dinner, & Papa read the paper—Who else was there staying in
the house? Peter Walsh might have been there—& old Miss Cummings.
M[r.] Breitkopf certainly was, for he was a fixture, coming
every summer, poor old man. for weeks & weeks, ~~because~~
~~scarcely speaking; &~~ & pretending to read German with her,
but ~~liking best to~~ <doing nothing but> strum on the piano, ~~which he did by the hour,~~
~~& to sing & only it was more like~~ which he did by the hour. ~~Some one~~
~~always had to ask him. Once started, he was happily~~ (He had been

kind to her father when he was at college, & ~~as papa~~ had ~~made~~ <lost all his> a ~~mess <failure mess>~~ of ~~his~~
~~his~~ life, ~~so that papa, who never~~ Her father never forgot anyone
who had been kind to him—) ~~At any rate,~~ But ~~all~~
all this existed only as a background for Sally She could not
remember a single thing that ~~Sally~~ <she> said, ~~though:~~ only a general
impression ~~of this~~ <a> ~~beautiful emphatic voice; someone much older; than~~
~~herself; more self-possessed~~, of her standing by the fire place,
talking in that beautiful emphatic voice, which made everything
she said sound strange & romantic, to papa~~—asking him~~
~~questions about the house~~ who, ~~now that he had dined,~~ <began to look at her> began to
~~notice her;~~ to be charmed, rather against his will, (~~he had come~~
& indeed to be very fond of her, ~~& though they were never quite~~
~~at their ease. <but> she was untidy, he said). Everyone had to notice~~
~~her, whether they liked her or not. She he thought it all~~
~~a great pity. to feel her, as everyone did, a wonderful crea~~
(she was not at all his sort~~)~~ He lent her one of his ~~beautiful~~ precious
books & she left it out in the rain.) Peter Walsh was there,
because he had started an argument. ~~But~~ And then suddenly
Sally said "What a shame to ~~stand~~ <stay> ~~arguing~~ indoors talking—&
moved to the window, ~~& there she stood against the in the moonlight,~~
~~& they all went out onto the terrace; & made them~~ they all
~~go~~ <went> out of doors to look at the moonlight. They were alone together.
Sally took her arm.) Then the most exquisite moment of her life
arrived simply that Sally picked a flower & as she gave it
her. ~~she~~ put ~~her arm round her~~ <shoulder> & kissed her. Peter Walsh &
M^r. Breitkopf walked up & down arguing. ~~about~~ She & Sally
strolled behind them. ~~up It was the most wonderful, the~~
But really it ~~might have been a different world—It seemed~~
~~as if she had been wafted away~~ by that kiss.
The others went miles away. Nothing else existed.

& she had known only that ~~there was she~~ possessed ~~something so~~
~~exquisite that merely to hold it without looking at it was enough to~~
~~change the whole world.~~ what changed the world. The body must be a
finer instrument than people know. ~~For~~ The physical change was so
extraordinary. From being exalted, hot, cold, all spasms & starts,
she became ~~now~~ instantly ~~soothed very~~ soothed ~~into a~~ & yet stimulated, as if
myriads of bells ~~had begun to~~ chimed. all through her. ~~Indeed,~~ its
~~&~~ strange <in> how ~~many~~ <many> ~~much~~ <ways> one can feel in ~~the mo~~ the same
moment; ~~She had a sense~~ too of those heavy white flowers &—what
~~are they~~? tobacco plants probably; ~~she had a sense of~~ the pale blue,
sky, ~~pale, starry~~; & ~~<she> walking<ed> very lightly~~ & the sky, she saw there,
~~pale~~ blue, but pale with stars; & then much more profoundly, at the riot
~~She felt as she walked on There was this sense of yet a part too~~
~~of the whole sensation,~~ was ~~a~~ the <this> sense of entire & absolute trust,
~~delight, in another human being. Nothing could have been purer,~~
~~than her at the same time more penetrating, than her feeling~~
~~that she knew Sally to the depths, & It was the~~ so moving, so
strangely exciting, & yet—to use an odd word religious—~~as~~ of being
able to care, with out ~~any~~ <any> reservation, ~~but without blindness~~ <a properly [ ]>, for
another person. ~~That, after all, had been the source of <all> the happiness, of her~~
~~as well as all the sorrow, of her life—the power to realise out of her~~
~~own family. Sally was the first person she had felt this for, &~~ it was
~~to her~~ of her life, & she realised it first ~~on the terrace~~ that night
~~How absorbing, how~~ The power to care—naturally it was a revelation.
And then, at one of these times, Peter Walsh & <old Joseph> ~~M^r^~~ Breitkopf faced them
"Star gazing?" said Peter sarcastically.
~~He & old Joseph slipped old~~ It was like a slap in the face.
It was his tone more than what he said. It was like running against a ~~granite~~ wall of granite.

She was immune.

which <as they walked> she began to uncover: no, ~~the~~ it was more or ~~if, as she walked,~~ the
radiance that was inside it began to ~~glow~~ <burn> through; ~~w~~ <as she herself glowed out,> filling her with
an extraordinary satisfaction; ~~letting her whole being It was as if~~
For the first time she cared, without any reservation, for another person, not
one of her family. It was a religious feeling, to use an odd word; it was a revelation. And then, turning, Peter Walsh & old Joseph Breitkopf faced them, & stopped.

"Well, said Peter satirically, star-gazing?"

It was like running one's face against a granite wall in the dark. shocking—horrible.

But she had no feeling ~~of any kind~~ about herself; she felt for <~~that~~ only> Sally
how ~~she was going to be thrown~~ was being ~~thrown~~ marked already, maltreated; she felt ~~a~~ the hostility in Peter Walsh's voice;
~~or~~ his jealousy; his covetousness; his determination to break into their companionship ~~& impose his own wishes~~—all this she saw as one sees a landscape in a flash of lightning; & bend as it but ~~felt herself outside yet, & almost,~~ <quite> ~~secure—like a~~ She felt Sally's surprise of [ ] to be excited
& yet stood apart from it herself.

Sally was ~~not only amused;~~ <only amused.> ~~&~~ <She>began laughing at him.

She made <old> Joseph tell her the names of the stars, or the points of the compass—the sort of thing old Joseph took with that delicious simplicity which made one love him. But Peter was ~~very~~ angry; ~~even then, she knew him well enough she knew him~~ <to know that he was angry>
~~very slightly then—he was a even then, she knew him well enough to know that how when either because his vanity was injured, or his He was a strange young man.~~
What right had he to be angry? No doubt she was in an exalted state of mind herself, ~~but~~ the state in which one sees in flashes, has revelations—thinks one knows, ~~as~~ at 20, the whole ~~truth about~~ of life—~~&~~ <but> it then seemed to her ~~certain that for a woman~~ ~~to~~ life ~~live was to descend~~ <oneself> ~~into an embroilment of strife, unavoidable,~~ perfectly <horribly> terrible—this <to give one> vision of ~~perpetual~~ strife. ~~No doub~~
~~The blow is always dealt by the other sex. This vision, which each sex presumably gives the other, or the~~ to detract forever from the goodness of life—It is a shock which comes

~~meaning something perhaps, that~~ as if she had known all along
~~that~~
that something would ~~spoil~~, interrupt, & embitter her moment
of happiness.
something implicit in the nature ~~of the world. of things~~.
~~of the world~~. things.
Yet after all, how much she had owed to Peter later—
what a friendship theirs had been. Indeed, she sometimes felt
that ~~it was~~
when she & Peter ~~were alone together, some & at their ease~~,
~~they~~
~~could share everything—there was & & knew each other,~~
~~as no one & as no one else knew them. had an intimacy, an~~
~~understanding which that they had~~ there was no one
who knew her as he did ~~or to whom~~ or who roused in her
more curiously a ~~desire that~~ even now, at the age of
fifty, ~~such as~~ <such a> a <clear> wish ~~that he should respect her,~~
~~think her clever~~,
~~pretty even, & more than that what in their you~~
for his good opinion. P ~~There was no one left who~~
~~He~~ <Then> They had had so many jokes together—had ~~almost~~
<almost>
a language of their own; & then, as she was beginning
to feel~~, the people to whom one can say "D'you remember old~~
~~Goody? & & be sure they would know what one meant~~ were
the ~~people who knew~~ old Goody, ~~for example,~~ who had known
Bourton, had known old Goody, had known her father
~~before his illness,~~ were now becoming, since her illness
perhaps, more ~~necessary to her than ever.~~ sentimentally
dear to her. ~~Peter would say it~~ was 'sentimentally' ~~dear to her.~~
that was one of his <~~or Peters words one of his~~> favourite
words. ~~But~~ And though her
heart ~~was only~~ He ~~would~~ used it ~~or~~ practically of ~~any~~
everyone. A book was sentimental, a person was sentimental;
~~to think of the past was sentimental; & when, as sometimes~~
~~happened now, since <she knew that her> her heart had b was~~
~~damaged,~~
she ~~often caught herself It w~~ He ~~wa~~ would ~~say it as~~
He would call it sentimental to think as she had
been thinking. Indeed it was!
So

Oct 1st 1923 "It is wicked!" she cried. ~~No~~ I wont stand it! she said. No I wont!
&, kneeling by the railing she caught the child, kissed it, & ~~said~~
~~She was It is wicked From~~ Every tree, with its curled & malicious
leaves, sneered at her; shook, & ~~so~~ rocked her heart. Yet why? ~~Why~~
why should ~~t~~ she be exposed, ~~tortured~~? Why not left ~~to~~ in Milan? ~~safe?~~
Why tortured? Why?
~~Some great cross <brooch> she wore sprinkled with white green stones;~~
~~caught the little girls eyes; & gravely observing the she gravely observed it;~~
~~touched it:~~
What are you afraid of? she asked.
~~Fear~~ To cower there holding a strange little girl in her arms, ~~to feel~~
while above towered the enormous trees, vast clouds, of this
indifferent world, gave her such ~~calm security~~ safety as a
bird's, sheltered under the hollow of a leaf: ~~sh The leaf rai~~
~~As the leaf moves, the birds heart leaps. Bewildering~~
as a birds ~~be~~ bewildered by sun as the leaf moves, ~~be~~ cowering
as the twig cracks, as if ~~this~~ <the> dry little noise were thunder.
As for herself, she had ~~done nothing;~~ been ~~perfectly~~ happy;
she had done nothing; she loved ~~pleasure~~ life. She had had a beautiful
home, & there her sister lived still, making hats. Why then, ~~then~~
~~because she loved, should she had married~~ should ~~she be unhappy?~~
~~it have happened?~~ she suffer? ~~Why had she left with~~ She had
~~gone. She had left them. She had~~
And now, as a leaf ~~fl~~ lifts over

So, ~~when~~ the leaf lifts, <&> the bird <is> ~~exposed to the sun, & if the eyelids shut~~
looks up at the sun & blinks.

Elsie Mitchell fumbled in the lace at Rezias throat.
~~She wore a looking~~ attracted by the white & green brooch she wore—

~~I could be happy, said Rezia thought.~~ What is this suffering, Rezia
thought. Why do you blaze at me, the Hercule seems to ask
with the same petulance; ~~the same for the same~~

Rezia ~~now~~ got up. She saw the ~~grey nurse,~~ & ~~Peter Walsh,~~ <elderly man,>
& the perambulator; & the ~~grey nurse, &~~ how the nurse, in grey,
was rolling up her ball of wool, & looking about, jerking her
head, Oh yes, that was the childs nurse. {There was a baby in
the perambulator: ~~for~~ There was no need for her to go.
Suddenly Elsie Mitchell, ~~cried out &~~ ran away.—to what doom? to
what suffering?

Slightly glazed by tears, ~~why that~~ & shaken by the
discomfort of her own heart, the broad path lifted itself before her
eyes; & ~~again the perambulator, the seat & the~~ again an
& to fall & to tumble & to be rocked by the malignant torturer—
~~who has everyone at his mercy, & never pities, & removededly
takes the unoffending & grinds out of them every pleasure
for no fault . . . this again yes yet I have done nothing
to deserve it—this~~ all this enraged her. ~~Her~~ She
stamped her foot; she frowned. She was in a passion of anger.
There ~~Robert was~~ Septimus sat, in his overcoat, staring at the sky.
His lips were moving. He was talking to himself, or talking to
Evans, a dead man. She had never even known him. He was a
nice quiet ~~boy~~ <man>,—~~who had Sl~~ not handsome, not big, not
clever like Septimus who had been killed. Such
things happen to everyone. Everyone gives up <something> when they
marry. She had given up her home. She had come to live

39 no education
58 on the side of the North
64 no [forms?] in the books.
65 greatly object to <u>all</u> novels
70 [read?] Liberty

[page 55 *verso*, *pencil*]

here, in this awful city. But Septimus had grown stranger—
stranger. He had let himself think about horrible things. So
could anyone.
He had begun to forget things. He frightened her. ~~Sometimes~~
He said people were talking behind the wall of the bedroom.
Mrs Filmer thought it odd. He had seen an old woman in the
leaves of a plant. And then he was as happy as could be for
hours together.
floating, he said, They went to Hampton Court, where all the ~~crocuses~~ flowers
like little lamps, were out
Suddenly he had said "Now we will both kill ourselves."
~~And now she could always see him~~ And there was the lake;
He had looked at it with an expression which ~~terrified her.~~
She ~~now knew when he saw anything that~~ had seen when ~~he~~
a train went by them, or an omnibus, <or,> they walked by the
river.—a terrible look because it made her feel that ~~he was a~~
~~stranger. She was absolutely alone, as if he had~~ already died.
He ~~squinted too.~~ as if he were already dead, & she walked
with him holding his arm. He squinted too, & ~~His eyes~~
It was his eyes that were terrible. He wished to die.
He would not burden her, he said. He ~~could not love her.~~
could feel nothing, ~~anymore, &~~ And then ~~suddenly trembling, or~~
~~with tears running down his~~ quite quietly, like a clever man,
he would begin to argue. He would tell her that he knew
what people thought before they said it. They were bad, he said.
He could see to the bottom of their souls, he said. And
Then suddenly trembling, he would begin to talk about
religion. He would put up his hand & say I can't hear'
as if somebody were telling him extraordinary things—~~about~~
~~his~~ Yes, yes! he cried. Theyre alive. And then he
would tell her to write down something about trees, or flowers;

~~and as they~~ He ~~tremble tried not to look at them in the st~~
as they passed in the street.
~~as if he were trying to escape. As they,~~ He pointed at
people in the street. <He laughed.> They ~~too~~ stared at him. He
said he was an
outcast. And then <as> they went back
~~He became~~ so tired that he dragged his feet; & he lay on the
sofa, & she
fed him like a child, & ~~then~~, he made her ~~sit quite close~~ &
hold his hand tight, to prevent him from slipping & from falling
down & down—~~He made her feel that they were falling.~~
He cried out that he was falling. Down down! he cried.
And yet there they were, in their sitting room. ~~"I'll clear away"~~
to clear away. Annie came in—she must have noticed. Suddenly he began to
talk, & to laugh, as if ~~somebody were there; pull~~ as if
he ~~could be~~ were talking to somebody. He became very
excited. ~~He sat up. He said They're alive! Oh theyre alive.~~
~~& told her to write it down. And then he waved his hand, &~~
~~talked &~~ ~~Theyre alive~~ he cried!
He told her to write down what he said—Theyre alive!
~~Oh~~ There he sat, beneath the tree, muttering. Laughing,
She cd not show it looking at the sky.} She would leave him! She would go
~~home. She could endure no more.~~ back! But it
must be almost time. ~~They must be at the Doctors at twelve.~~
almost twelve. They must be at the doctors at twelve.
She saw him sitting beneath the tree, ~~muttering, laug~~
looking at the sky.

She sat down beside him.

"Where is your wedding ring?" he asked.
"I slipped it off. I put it in my purse. I ~~am~~
have got so thin" she said. I am so
unhappy. You make me so unhappy.
~~Sitting~~ as He saw ~~the~~ her small bare hand.

So our marriage is over, he thought with extreme ~~relief~~. relief.
I am now free. ~~This wretched world~~ No longer would he have to
move tables, or lift boxes, or catch ~~the~~ trains ~~because Rezia was~~
~~frightened if he was~~ late. It had all slipped from him; &
he was left alone now to ~~scale,~~ explore, on behalf of humanity.
~~The misery that~~ The rope was cut, & the ~~o~~ world fell ~~from~~
leaving him free ~~him, leaving <letting> him~~ <to> mount higher & higher, yes,
higher, & higher,
into ~~these~~ that region ~~of voices~~ where the voices ~~kept~~
kept breaking ~~against the clouds~~ like little glasses against the
clouds. Now that he was free, ~~he do nothin could~~
~~do nothing but listen, (& undoubtedly~~ as it was intended that
he should be free, he could ~~go among these~~ live solely to
~~among the voices,~~ could ~~understand those voices,~~ & accept his
mission, as the interpreter, ~~e~~ called forth ~~to~~ in advance of the
mass of men to hear the truth, the meaning: which ~~had~~
now was to be given whole to . . ~~to~~ To whom? he said
aloud. "Mr Asquith" the voice whispered. Of course,
to Mr. Asquith. ~~Theres no crime.~~ Trees are alive.
Everything is alive. There is no crime. ~~Yes,~~ (And ~~then~~
this all can be proved: Darwin; said the voice. A
skye terrier trotted pass. Septimus ~~shuddered~~ <trembled>. ~~It~~
~~has a <the> man's face~~
~~is coming through the hair, he said.~~ Its turning into a man! he
cried. The head seemed to him to be wrinkling up like a man's
~~Of course~~ <of course> ~~his face,~~ he ~~said~~ thought, shutting his
eyes, with a
sense of divine relief, ~~that~~ I can now see ~~through~~ the truth of
everything.

~~& he thought~~ he could see ~~pink~~ cheeks beneath the hair; & was
[margin: & beginning to laugh!] terrified lest the dog should begin to speak. I can't watch it
happen, he cried. The dog trotted away. Septimus sank
~~back with a sense of relief,~~ & thought what has now
happened is that I can see the truth of everything
What could the scientific explanation be? ~~for~~ The sun, which
was very hot, seemed to him to be melting the flesh off
the world; seemed to be macerating his body till & the nerve fibre
alone was left. ~~Having reached~~ <At> ~~a certain pitch of evolution~~,
~~He was spread like a veil upon a rock And so he had only to open his eyes to see through, to the depths. So wonderful a gift had been bestowed on him.~~ And so the
wonderful gift had been bestowed upon him, of seeing through
~~every~~ to the truth:
~~Like a person~~ He ~~held the~~ possessed the power; he was
[margin: Carried on her back] exhausted; he was resting. Nature waited for him to awake.
~~Cradled in her arms~~ he lay resting, waiting, ~~carried on her back.~~
[margin: He lay] High up ~~am~~ on the slopes of the clouds ~~he lay, where,~~
where the ~~gentians spr grew~~ red flowers grew through his flesh, by his
head; where the dead mounted past him, But nobody
had any wish to hurt him: ~~when Everything was <had> now done~~
~~for his pleasure; to on purpose to a~~ only to convey to him
this truth; which, lying here in the sun, at his ease, he could
accept, ~~he~~ <is in> ~~could let flew past him, or merely bathe himself in exquisite~~ He could merely lie there. They would
sing to him. ~~And the~~ <The music here.> An ~~old~~ motor horn, thats all it
it is" he said aloud; but ~~it~~ But then heard like this,
cannoning from rock to rock, among the trees, it was
lovely melody; <&> ~~like~~ a shepherds boys pipe; (some old man
has joined in on a penny whistle by the public house he
thought)

twined round now by the tendril of a shepherd boys piping (an
<really> old
man playing the penny whistle by the public house, he said)
~~but now~~ which, as the boy ~~climbed,~~ stood still came bubbling
out of his
p pipe, & then as he climbed higher, ~~came~~ made its distant ~~so~~
plaint, ~~where the roses hung. Roses growing in the snow,~~
while ~~beneath the traffic passed,~~ omnibuses, vans, taxicabs
~~streamed,~~ the traffic passed beneath. He's in the High Street,
~~said~~ & that, ~~then was~~ of course was one of the remarkable
truths; how this <~~piping~~> penny whistle piping is beautiful; takes
place daily; (for I'm quite aware that this is Regents Park he
said)
among the traffic. This boys elegy is heard among the traffic.
28,000 ~~Charming in its~~ gaiety, in its exquisite fun, rippling & bubbling,
now, ~~said~~
thought, he withdraws; he vanishes into the snow; the roses
hang about him; the roses (I have roses on my bedroom wall
paper) ~~they~~ cluster, ~~thick~~ & ~~those~~ the thick musk roses, the
~~his~~ & if I ~~sleep now,~~ let you go now, said Septimus, I shall
~~I am absolutely safe now. This music;~~ I can have you
again. ~~I~~

To trust, ~~to yield, to fight no more,~~ no more bothering
even to remember; {now, couched there on the back of nature,
upheld ~~in her arms,~~ by her, let me} that's ~~is my next stage~~
~~he thought.~~ now the discovery, he thought. He let himself
lean back on his chair; that is, on the mountain turf, he
thought, &, though he was ~~afraid of falling,~~ terrified, afraid of
falling ~~down~~, the mountain, or cloud, upheld him, ~~&~~ in its warm
~~slightly~~ trembling ~~living~~ back, And ~~There~~ so ~~it~~ this is the fact, he
oddly quivering. thought; one ~~his down, relinquishes,~~ his back, so—&
Then they (the world that is) ~~come about one;~~ bear up the
~~whole~~ weight, & ~~really~~ come ~~all~~ about one, carrying; oh yes,
~~showing themselves purely good. That is it. perfectly~~
<wholly> good. Thats
the meaning of it. ~~Such a discovery~~ seemed ~~to flood~~ to
~~smooth,~~ to ~~as~~ his back, & the world is good. Strange music
came breaking through the stalks of the flowers; the mud

5/ a week ~~then not to tire or to distract, but to please merely, the hoa~~
~~rougher~~
55. 500 ~~breeze which came through reeds rustled; & the sun spots~~
~~kissed~~
~~rested here & there:~~ No words, yet, said Septimus.
only sound, ~~only~~ sensations, signs like those ~~of goodness.~~ ~~There~~
~~is a~~
~~happiness, he thought, For~~ of the world's desire to caress.
Each nerve ~~throughout~~ <in> his body thickened itself, as if ~~wax~~
a line
of frayed silk were drawn ~~along~~ <[through?] wax> ~~a line of frayed silk~~; &
thus stilled,
smoothed, composed, he lay in the ~~back of~~ heart ~~of goodness~~,
sealed up ~~secure, enchanted; secure his eyes shut, but~~ sealed up ~~in~~
in the heart of treasure, which, ~~if he wished,~~ he was his ~~forever.~~ without
stirring,
~~given,~~ if he chose to look, if he chose to sleep, given ~~to~~
yes ~~<he was> the first man to cross from life to death was~~
given, with ~~a~~ smile, ~~g~~ to the first man who had
crossed from life to death. ~~The drowned, have been washed up~~
~~here, he thought, but who have passed through green waters~~—
men who have leant over boats & fallen, have woken, when
the drumming in their ears has ceased, on this cliff; but I
go & come through those waters. ~~I am the inter~~
~~without drowning & And It is no~~ only a green mist.
~~at last, our~~ because of Darwin, evolution, (A.D. stands for
Anno Darwini in future he ~~th~~ ~~said~~ muttered)
And now . . . he gently beat his hand, & very cautiously opened his
eyes

~~Now I will wake, he~~ said. ~~Now I have passed through~~ death.
~~he said.~~ I ~~am dead~~ have passed through death, he said.
~~But~~ I still hear the old man playing by the public house.
So I am the first to ~~conquer~~ cross.
~~Now I will wake, he said.~~
He lay, like a drowned sailor, tossed on to the shore; & ~~for the first~~
~~time in the whole world, the dead were alive; He could~~
~~hear the shepherd boy piping. through the mist.~~
~~He could~~ I have passed through death, he said. I am the first to
cross. ~~And I can~~ He could hear the shepherd boy piping
~~through~~ in Regents Park; as before waking. The birds, the
milk carts, sound through a veil, sound ~~frail. plaintive.~~
~~joyful, let~~ joined in a melody ~~which in~~ the ~~can~~
& then, still ~~in~~ asleep, the sleeper ~~thinks~~ feels himself
drawing towards ~~the~~ life, hearing more & more truly,
recognising, & yet ~~still~~ everything still sounds
~~louder,~~ a little stronger, a little ~~more~~ richer, ~~& a~~
~~queer excitement begins as if it concealed something.~~
than usual, as if each cry & chirp were the prelude
~~the opening.~~ & draws nearer & nearer to the shore,
& ~~sees~~ feels stir in him the extraordinary excitement of
landing, & is yet half afraid, so now, Septimus
drew towards life, & felt himself about to ~~awaken in~~
open his eyes.

He had only to open his eyes. Some ~~apprehension was in them.~~
weight was in them. A ~~little~~ door was ~~between~~ shut.
a freed murderer He pushed through; ~~awoke; & was accepted~~. <he woke; he ~~rose~~
~~with~~ fawned ~~like~~ rose into life.> Long streamers
~~joyful~~ at his of the sun caressed him, the trees ~~turned their branches~~
kill. <waved>
~~proudly welcome.~~ welcome. Everything was alive,
was conscious of his coming. was} ~~Such beauty.~~
Each movement was timed. ~~And First the trees, then the~~
~~grass & the sun; & to look was only to — A~~ Gladness,

~~happiness.~~ ~~Septimus fancied a Really,~~ <We welcome> the
world seemed to say,
we accept; we laugh. ~~And everything~~ <Its> is beautiful, said
Nicholas Septimus. ~~Absolutely~~ Nothing was ugly. ~~Movement~~
Wherein As his eyes fell, beauty sprang ~~under them~~ <up>—a movement, a
colour, a Merely to watch a leaf quivering filled him with
rippling this way exquisite joy. And then the birds, swooping & soaring &
& that in the flinging themselves across the sky & yet always in
wake of the air perfect control—dancing, it seemed. And the
as if elastics sun, rising & falling in compassion. ~~And the all the~~
[unruled?] them, as if ~~poison which has silted up in the creases of the soul~~
they were dancing ~~And above all the sun,~~ And the sun
laughing, mocking, & saying Now here, now there, as,
like some
dazzling it with soft ~~ruffled~~ gold; & a murmur of sound
breaking through the grass stalks, ~~which were resounded,~~
chiming on their wires, ~~all~~ this is ~~the truth,~~
~~thought Septimus.~~ all true, thought Septimus. I have
now been admitted. ~~to the~~ I am now being instructed. Listen.
~~I will tell it to Mr Asquith.~~
like Mr Dyall. I must ~~now~~ get the plan perfectly clear (for I cant stand & I will
the pressure of this experience much longer he thought.)
~~The They go climbing The dead climb are climbing, higher;~~
~~how~~ the great men climb highest, ~~& we follow~~
after death; can <[then] be> ~~still~~ be met; Shakespeare is actually
now
up there; & ~~now, owing to evolution, a few~~ of the living
~~have access to this world;~~ can stay here for a few moments
(he ~~felt too muc~~ must now rest) I ~~will~~ <shall> come back
whenever
~~I like.~~ come back whenever you like. But

a general voice replied, bringing at the same time a vision of a
~~man~~ high ~~pea~~ mountain side, & a man climbing, ~~yes,~~
they climb higher, ~~& hig~~ the voice said, I shall hear
Shakespeare talking, said Septimus; ~~I shall sing to~~
In time, said the voice. Time, <~~said~~> Septimus, <said> ~~& either~~
impelled by
some force, his tongue shaped the words of an ode, of a poem,
which as he spoke ~~them~~ <it>, was replied to, with laughter, with
showers of words, falling into perfect shape. ~~I am one of the~~
~~great poets~~
~~thought Septimus.~~ Whether he spoke them, or whether he heard
~~them, he did was sure; & but this is one of the greatest poems in~~
~~the world, he said; Whether the words were Greek or English he~~
~~did not know. only they fell like <thick> shavings from a plane,~~
& ~~that~~ back again transformed & fitted into its place, carve
the words 'like <thick> shavings from a plane' ~~infinitely~~
~~beautiful.~~
~~lovely words;~~ <hard,> new, white, lovely. I am ~~in the centre of~~
making poetry
now, he muttered. ~~Every thought that came He had only to~~
~~think;~~ &
Whatever he thought was swept out of his mind by the
<u>breeze</u>, & shaped, & let fall ~~into its lines. In~~ This
~~words An Never It was a poem of extreme sadness &~~
~~beauty; a <now> lament; now extraordinary beauty. As each~~
~~word was taken from him; Septimus~~ & as each word
was taken from him, ~~Septimus~~ it ~~wore a~~ hardened,
it spun, it flew to ~~pos~~ its place, & Septimus. ~~thought~~
~~This ode to Time will lives, forever.~~ saw it join
the rest of the ode ~~to Time~~ this, immortal, ode to Time.
This poem which was ~~faultless~~ <flawless> from its birth, &

{From behind some hedge (he kept his eyes shut)}
An ode grave, ~~impersonal,~~ majestic, flawless

From behind some hedge (he kept his eyes shut) a ~~bird sang~~ a bird chorus now sang, one voice separating off from the rest, ~~&~~ singing by itself, ~~addressing~~ singing to Septimus, the voice of Evans, undoubtedly, ~~the voice of Evans,~~ who hid himself behind the leaves, so that he might not frighten Septimus by the sight of his mud & wounds. His mud & wounds, the birds voice sang, making the words into <spin fly into> a chant about death;
& adding, without pausing ~~stanzas, of~~ stanza after stanza, of such ~~perfection that they brought with them consolation calm; laughter.~~ of such perfection that Septimus thought this is Greek poetry. Then all the birds laughed. Then the leaves rustled, & Septimus saw something grey & moving— ~~No No! Not yet! he cried; for~~ Evans, it must be Evans, coming ~~out~~ towards him. ~~Sta~~ Evans came towards him in a grey check suit.

~~The~~ <a> Greek nightingale
which ~~Evans sung, about death;~~ sang; Evans was a Greek
nightingale; Evans, when he died, went back to Greece,
& now sang this ode, about death; hiding behind the hedge; ~~He~~
'After I left you that night' (he had been killed at two in the
morning)
I went to see old Fuller". ~~He had been shot, & his~~ The ode
began therefore, ~~quite gently;~~ very gently, in the hush of ~~dar~~
~~midnigh~~
dawn, when the dark was on the fields, & the dead went out of his
room.

~~But~~ "Fuller ~~was asleep,~~ <will tell you that he> saw me, & I
went on to Brindisi"
through the fields of Italy. the plains of Italy. ~~Here the bird~~
~~chorus sang with him imitated the rustling of leaves, & the~~
~~flowing of a river.~~ "And so I reached Greece"; where,
~~of course~~ he joined the poets, in Thessaly, ~~where they~~
~~have never died.~~ "~~I assure you they come there day after~~
~~day, & all this lamentation about the war is frightful rot.~~
"That is where we go, to Thessaly, <to> the plains of Thessaly."
"all right, all right, I'll remember," said Septimus. They go to
Thessaly. "There we wait till the war is over." Then we
come pouring back. I'm in Edinburgh now. ~~I'm coming~~
~~back.~~" ~~Septimus saw~~ Something grey mov~~ing~~<ed> behind
the hedge. "Evans! Evans!" Septimus cried out.
in terror. "Dont come! Evans laughed behind the
hedge, laughter which fell in a shower of words beautifully
to earth. ~~"I'm coming." he said again.~~
~~Septimus saw the hedge move.~~ Now I have got to face the dead,
said Septimus, sitting perfectly upright & staring ahead of him,
staring at a man in a grey check suit who walked
straight towards him.

where they ~~people the~~ stand up in the ~~grey~~ fields like orchids,
"~~There~~ after all these years—Septimus cried.
He was not changed. There was no sign of death. no mud, no wounds. ~~And~~ The loneliness~~;~~ was over.
{"I am so unhappy, so fearfully unhappy" ~~he he~~
the voices of the} The dead were pouring back.
~~The awful dream was over.~~
I am so unhappy, said Rezia.
I will ~~go to~~ <tell> the Cabinet & tell them said Septimus, that Evans Evans has—
~~I am so fearfully unhappy,~~ said Rezia.
~~He is~~ <Of course> I knew <you> you werent dead <never died> really, said Septimus.
as Evans approached, smoking, ~~ordinary,~~ & ~~lifting off~~
relieving Septimus ~~in~~ each second of ~~such a <his> load & of anguish that in <such> lonely days, the tears in solitude, which, since here was Evans safe & sound, standing towards him, seemed <seem> like the panic of a child lost in a dark room while, across the next door, the nurses sat happy eating their supper in the lamplight. He is coming he said, They will all come back now. Behind him,~~ driving away the floods of darkness that had closed him round, pushing straight through the waters with a ~~shaft~~ & ~~blazing~~ lighting up the heart wh with such relief that it might have been flame & every vein yellow fire.

I am so fearfully unhappy said Rezia.

~~One, two, three, four.~~

This is my gift to the world, Septimus muttered.

of astonishing ~~relief & joy & certainty & as if from the whole world at last this terrible cloud was lifted.~~ since the
~~whole~~ of death was over.

Hullo, he said.

~~The leader who has~~ It was a moment of such extreme relief,
as ~~could~~ come ~~only to~~ only to ~~the~~ <some> colossal figure, ~~in~~
who ~~has~~
after lamenting the fate of man, for ages, in the desert, dark,
alone, with hands pressed to his forehead, & down his cheeks
furrows of despair, ~~saw~~ perceives on the horizon first a
thin line of light, which broadens steadily, mounts over the
sky, & soon strikes this same crow-black figure into
gold; Behind him press million on million, legion on legion
of little men; to whom after wards he will give the light; ~~B~~ but
for one moment he, this colossal figure of man, risen, with
hand raised above his eyes, receives the whole glow. Septimus
raised his hand, ~~such joy, such triumph was his.~~
& gazed.
Evans, he ~~said~~ muttered.
I am so unhappy, so fearfully unhappy" said Rezia.
~~All~~ <~~So~~> the ~~black legions~~ <the millions> ~~behind murmured;~~
lamented;
for ages they had sorrowed. He would turn round, after a few
moments,
only a few moments more, of this relief, of this intense joy . . .
What is the time, Septimus? said Rezia.
She put her hand on his knee to rouse him from his stupor: to
make him sit up for that gentleman was staring at him
Please, please, he murmured, as a sleeper begs not to be roused,
~~We must go she said,~~
Let me see I will tell you in a minute he said.
your watch. ~~Why, The man was staring at them, & in order to~~
Time, he said, in the strange way he had lately, of stressing

saying things, ~~as if he were~~ rather languidly, mysteriously,
sometimes
smiling as he said them.

1 As he sat there smiling, ~~there struck~~ the quarters struck.

5

There was nothing, ~~very~~ as a matter of fact, very strange in the sight of two young people sitting under a tree in Regents Park on a fine June morning.

Indeed, Peter Walsh thought as he passed them, there was something ~~jolly~~ oddly moving, exhilarating, about London,
coming
~~when on landing after being away~~ <back to it after> for five
years in India.
seeing it with fresh eyes.

This susceptibility to impressions had of course, been his undoing. Still, at his age, ~~everything~~ he ~~woke up feeling~~ had, like a boy, or even a girl, these alternations of mood, good days, bad days, happiness from <a pretty face,>
dazzling
green, depression from some lugubrious barrel organ playing in ~~a drizzle~~ in a back street. After India, ~~the after the very~~ one fell in love with every woman~~, with~~ one met. There was a freshness about them: & to him ~~at least~~ the fashion had never been so enchanting, so becoming—~~these~~ <the> long black cloaks; ~~E~~ the ~~elegance, the~~ point, the slimness, the elegance; & then this delicious & apparently universal habit of paint. Every woman—even of the most highly respectable classes,—~~had a face like a mask,~~ the rose ~~of the cheek~~ bloom~~ing~~ed sedately; ~~the lips sharpened~~—lips had their outlines & focus. There could be no doubt that a change had taken place of the very greatest importance ~~during his absence~~—probably in everything.

This susceptibility had of course been his undoing,

He had never sold his soul.
~~Such at least would have been his~~ But even as he ~~spoke,~~
thought this, & felt that clutch at the throat which ~~is the tribute~~
~~paid by men of fifty to men of fifty~~ showed how much he
had endured, how nobly he had conquered, how ~~strangely~~
<~~much~~>, ~~nevertheless~~
strangely been ~~the world~~ had ignored, him, he ~~recovered his equanimity~~, ~~&~~ was
~~thought of Dalloway,~~ <propelled> ~~glided~~ back into that stream
of thought, which
28,000 ~~today~~ for some reason or other was all about him today—the
100 thought of the dalloways, of ~~that long, rather~~ of the past—
30 ~~which was pressing~~ Not that it seemed very far away.
60 Certainly it was not over. No, he would be in the thick of it
80 ~~all~~ tonight. Yet ~~time, who delights~~ the effect of breaks in life,
like going away, coming back, is to ~~complete to~~ give one a
complete view ~~queer~~ detached~~;~~ view—Dalloway, for example—that jaunty
young man who jumped on to a bicycle & wobbled off down
the drive at Bourton almost thirty years ago—what about
Dalloway? Now he had ridden off; he had gone through ~~that~~
those
woods that Sally was always romancing about.
They were famous for something or other—squirrels, or
fireflies.

one ~~can~~ <could> never be ~~intima~~ intimate with him. <of
course>partly ~~of course~~
because he had married Clarissa. Yet now, that too ~~now~~
seemed ~~to be~~ rather distant not a matter of great importance—
~~The fact~~ that they had talked about him, pitied him ~~perhaps,~~
decided against him, as of course they had done.

Riding off through the woods—playing golf, shooting—
~~at~~ that ~~of course was really very~~ <the> jolly <thing> about him.
~~Undoubtedly~~
~~some men require support to be at their best.~~ Clarissa
liked that side of him. too. He brought her a <young> squirrel
once
which he had caught in the woods. Clarissa was not
~~naturally~~ fond of animals. She was not instinctive, ~~in~~
~~the~~ not maternal, as some women are. There was something
detached about her—She had an extraordinary sense of the
ridiculous, too. Dalloway had ~~been at his best with that~~
~~wretched squirrel.~~ made her bind up the poor little beasts paw.
Even then, though, he was pretty pompous. One saw ~~then~~
what he would be like in middle age—grown a little
heavier, more dictatorial, ~~a little~~ more obtuse—
excellent ~~in every way but not~~ but not presumably making
~~an a brilliant success. <of his career.> What had been his~~
~~career?~~
~~secretary ships. Some small job in the government.~~
~~But he wasn't any longer in the running for any of the~~
~~much in the public eye.~~
He had not had what is called a brilliant career. He had
been on Commissions. He had held unimportant posts. ~~in~~
~~One heard people say that he~~ He was talked ~~about~~ of with
respect. ~~Nobody could help liking him.~~ He was, as
they ~~one~~ says, generally liked. A very good fellow, thought
Peter Walsh, But what was <could be> his relations with
Clarissa?
~~In the old days~~ <Why had she> ~~Clarissa had, without a doubt,~~
married him? Were they happy? What did

they have in common? <such [as?] roses?> Politics? ~~Drink~~
bills, tariff reform,
trade. There was some Balkan state which Dalloway
had ~~made~~ taken up. Did Clarissa really ~~like that sort of~~
thing? Did she ~~sit on the platform, &~~ write his speeches for
him. Did she go to meetings & ~~really believe take an~~
~~interest in oppressed nations;~~ get on a platform. No doubt
she made herself <look> very charming.

But in the old days she had had a mind, of a sort.
~~Pictures, & music, & books—she had had some feeling for~~
~~them all.~~ He had kept all her letters. When he first
went to India she wrote to him quite often—long after she was
married, she kept it up. ~~She was~~ And certainly then she
was full of ~~ideas.~~ ~~She was really musical.~~ interest in
things. She would go to a concert & tell him ~~all~~ <all> about ~~a~~<it>
~~piece of new music.~~ <&> the same with books: ~~She read in~~
~~those days; she~~ Dalloway was quite unable to follow
her there. His attitude ~~to all that~~ was simply <that of> a
schoolboy.
There was that extraordinary conversation about Shakespeares
sonnets. Late at night, in the ~~smoking~~ <drawing> room, when old
Aunt Helena had gone to bed, & Dalloways ~~point was that it~~
~~they were indecent, not for the obvious reasons, but because~~
~~said it was indecent to talk <write> about one's feelings.~~ Some
how it
came out that he had never read the sonnets. He wouldn't read
them because he thought it indecent to talk about one's feelings.
Another argument was about the Deceased Wife's Sister Bill.
~~This led almost to an open row between them.~~ It was
really violent. Dalloway said that he would not allow his
sister, or his wife ~~if he had a wife, to~~ or his mother or
any woman he respected to visit a lady who in the eyes of his
law living in sin. One owed respect to the law, he said;
to any law however bad. One was a citizen. One had the
protection
of the state.

'<I would <not> allow> ~~No~~ <any> woman that I respect,
~~Dalloway~~ said. ~~to visit Mrs~~ Dalloway in
to go there" (there being the Hughes' home) ~~where the~~
He ~~had a very~~ announced this sort of thing very pompously. ~~It was~~
~~an irritating manner He went on with the usual argument~~
~~about obeying the law; "I consider myself a citizen"~~
~~However bad the laws were according to Dalloway, one had to~~
~~obey them.~~ Dalloway <He was> was ~~just~~ about twenty two at the
time. He already ~~took himself very seriously though as a~~
~~citizen thought a great deal about his duty to the state.~~
And so they went on ~~abusing~~ <arguing> ~~each other~~ with
Clarissa sitting
there, ~~&~~ making it all more ~~bitter~~ <heated> than it need have
been ~~by her~~
~~presence~~ But women really are unaccountable. She saw
the absurdity of Dalloway & the sonnets; she saw ~~through him~~
<through him>—
~~She must have seen what an extraordinarily limited,~~
~~a blockhead he was, with his she could even laugh at him;~~
but there was something in him which
~~& yet she simply allowed him to do what he liked with her.~~
~~The Hughes question cropped up after they were married.~~
~~Dalloway wouldnt 'allow' Clarissa to go there. And she~~
~~obeyed. Terrible! Terrible! a woman of her courage, of her~~
but yet it seemed to fascinate her— She respected people
who had principles she said. ~~Richard Dalloway~~ <He> would
always do what he thought right. "And make other people do it
too",—that was <just> the way they used to quarrel,
he & Clarissa, for ~~she'd shut up,~~ he couldn't resist
these little digs; & then Clarissa stiffened—Her way of being
angry was to ~~bristle~~ sit extremely upright & turn pink.
She hardly ever said anything. In all their quarrels it
was he who had been the aggressor. She was
always very self controlled.

that was the sort of little dig he used to give—

~~one felt that she bristled all over.~~

Dalloway called out the maternal element in her—
so Sally used to say ~~Dalloway gave her~~ <was> She married
him because she wanted a religion—that was another theory—
Sally being fond of analysing. She was ~~very~~ hard on Dalloway.
She was a great tease; cruel like most clever girls;
She couldn't see what a good sort he was at bottom. how ~~if peo
went to him, this blessed day for instance, & said you could
always count on him.~~ He was better with men than with
women probably ~~An awful bore!—Yet any woman
could~~ He had no facility. never knew how to turn things
off somehow, went floundering in; lectured; laid down the
law. ~~And yet Clarissa had married him.~~ But with
men that didn't so much matter. Besides, he did know a
certain number of facts—one could always get him onto
[Bimetallism?], ~~the~~ Tariff Reform or whatever it was,
~~But even there of course he was a bit of a bore—~~

The trouble was that he had a second rate mind But it was unfair to call him a mere

He knew quite a lot—of course the quality of his mind was
tenth rate, third rate, ~~quite~~ negligible. ~~If he hadn't had a
He had done what he had done by sheer industry—
He never had an idea of any kind of his own;~~ could put up any
ideas of his own. ~~Any But then that was~~ <had its uses> ~~useful
in politics,—~~
But he was courageous; he kept his end up. Compared
with most of these politicians he was presumably,
respectable. And he was a gentleman.

~~That sort of thing does count Sally didn't care a
was a strange creature—She had in With all her
absurdity the she was a had that quality
None of this made any difference to Sally of course. She
naturally~~

Oh yes, he had all the marks of that queer breed—~~their~~
His greatest friend was Hugh Whitbread. ~~That Well,~~ That
~~explained~~
explained a good deal; of course Dalloway was the
better specimen by far. But he could ~~spend associate~~
~~say all the right~~ live with those people; he could talk like
them, dress like them, do all the right things—he
belonged to that herd, ~~the Whitbreads, the~~ <wh.> Sally, ~~it was~~
~~one~~
~~of her used to was always gibing~~<hated>~~ at them~~, the
~~beautiful young men, who went to Eton & Winchester, Eton &~~
~~Christchurch—"You always knew them by~~
perfect gentlemen she called them, ~~who~~ & swore they were
~~always~~
~~the most ill bred~~ & one knew them by their "horrid
detestable slang" & their "perfect perfect clothes";
& then "a stable boy had more real sympathy than they had."
~~For The unfortunate Hugh Whitbread was not her type~~—
This referred to some row with Hugh—some argument
~~about Women's Rights, perhaps~~—at Bourton,—in the
dining room? after dinner?—when Aunt ~~Hel~~ Helena had
gone off, vaguely disapproving it ~~always~~ seemed, & yet
rather glad to be quit of them, to go & sit in her own room,
cutting up flowers with her glass stuck in her eye—
Sally was hopeless in argument—She really was a
most ridiculous creature—But she was extraordinarily
alive. Among all those intolerably respectable
people & the Parrys ~~had a~~ knew a perfect
menageries of dullards, Sally was the brightest
specimen by far. To hear her pitching into Hugh
Whitbread was

[margin: rather gave him away of course]

Sally would argue—she was hopeless at argument, but she
would argue, & lose her temper, & even, yes—surely ~~once~~
once there was some terrible scene when she accused Hugh
the admirable Hugh of all people—of insulting her. of
kissing her? Incredible. Yet it did happen, in the smoking
room, ~~when~~ after ~~the argument about~~ after one of those
extraordinary arguments which people had in those days
about ~~womens rights. People used to get very~~ men & women.
~~It might have been even votes. <for women> We were there for~~
~~a~~
~~weekend, thought Peter, & the argument went on more or less~~
~~the whole of Sunday—Sally & he against Hugh & Dalloway,~~
~~And Sally of course dragged in what she called "women in~~
~~Piccadilly" & Hugh was shocked, & Hugh insisted upon~~
~~Poor~~ Hugh ~~was a got thoroughly upset.~~ Prostitutes
of course came in; & "~~the~~ <poor> women in Piccadilly" she
called them; & Hugh flushed, & ~~put~~ hitched his trousers up—
he always had such nice socks, & really he was
home life was the intolerable. "Miss Sally" he kept calling her.
greatest influence He became quite emotional. He said nobody could
for good that a tell what his mother had meant to him: he said
young man knows; ~~his home was the most greatest influence for good;~~
& Sally was down right rude & echoed "your mother
of course your mother—your nice respectable
middle class home . . ." Hugh, ~~vagu~~ who was
middle class to the backbone, of course ~~detested~~ all
loathed that . . . And then oh yes—~~Sally~~ the
big dog upset the lamp. There was a general
scrimmage. Sally shrieked. Hugh was
~~manly~~ intolerably efficient—helped the ladies.
he could see him now holding the door open for
Sally to go out—& saying "something about

mere men having their uses." overdoing his chivalry ~~to the~~ of course; after wh. Sally came into the smoking room to give him a book & was—so she said—kissed ~~by Hugh!~~ on the nose!

It was reprehensible. It had made him in the eyes of some very
good & respectable men, appear not serious, ~~. . .~~ That is,
after all one of the most fruitful sources of dissension
between elderly people. What is serious? At the age of
fifty, it struck him, thinking with that ~~lightness —~~
~~which is good temper which is going to let off~~
abandonment which is the result of alighting in the
midst of ~~life of~~ a society which for the past five years
has gone on its way without any help from you,
at the age of fifty ~~these matters are~~ the lists are posted:
~~there's no help for it one way or the other. There came~~
~~before him the His whim was~~ He saw lists ~~hanging in the~~
nailed on the door of some Senate house. The people who had
passed were on one side. The people who had failed on the
other. He had failed, of course; ~~only then, his as~~ he
but ~~against~~ his name ~~somehow was glowed~~—& he was
looking at it quite dispassionately—~~with the virtue~~
~~yes, he had liked the right things—that was it;~~ with
~~the~~ really he had very little interest in the matter—
his name was ~~entirely different from anyone elses~~—
~~merely for this~~ reason—this obvious, incontrovertible
~~reason~~—stood out from the rest simply for that reason—
he had made the right choice. ~~such decisions at the age~~
~~of fifty seem to~~ He knew which things were serious,—
~~which weren't.~~ Any other decision would have been to him
impossible:

[Margin, beside lines 6–10:] ~~which~~ has proved its capacity to live without you.

[Margin, beside lines 16–17:] saw it quite apart

Incredible! incredible! But then the whole thing seem<ed> now
incredible. Sally of course was far the ~~most~~ best of them.
Anyhow she was never taken in by the admirable Hugh.
"The Whitbreads. The Whitbreads? Who are the Whitbreads?"
he could hear her saying ~~now. Respectable wine merchants.~~
<Respectable wine merchants>
~~Nobody thinks the worse of them for that. Now my great~~
~~grandmother—" & then she went off on her mother's~~ family
who had been ~~French aristocrats~~ ~~"A thoroughly~~
~~commonplace dull young man" she said of him~~.
~~But after the incident in the smoking room~~ she
"~~But the lon~~ Stable boys are so much more interesting <have
more to say for themselves>" she
said. Hugh thinks of nothing but ~~his socks. Hugh is in~~
~~love with~~ his own appearance. ~~& his uncles property in~~
~~Wales~~.
~~He has a property in Wales.~~ He has an uncle who has a
~~grouse moor in Scotland married some an earls daughter.~~
~~a property in Wales. He's a snob—he's a bore—he's~~
~~a perfect specimen of the English public schoolboy!~~
~~I've known heaps of them. They're always the same.~~
He'll marry one of the Royal Princesses. ~~To have a~~
~~butler & a And Theyre always the same—these~~
~~beautiful young men who go to Eton & Oxford.~~
He ought to have been a duke". And of course ~~h~~ Hugh had
the most extraordinary, the most natural respect
for the British aristocracy of any human being he'd ever come
across.

To be a snob on such a scale was almost sublime. ~~He wasn't~~
~~like Dalloway,~~ who ~~But~~ After that scene in the smoking room—
nobody ever knew what happened~~—it was considered too~~
~~awful—~~
~~whether he kissed her or not, merely brushed against her, or~~
~~after that scene Sally~~ it had to be hushed up~~—Sally was~~
Clarissa murmured something mysterious—but ~~nobody could~~
~~believe a word against the admirable Hugh, was always a~~
~~perfect gentleman—~~ after that 'encounter' as she called it,
Sally ~~was outrageously unfair of course~~ never had a good

word for the poor man again. He was the essence of the most
detested in <the> British middle classes ~~life~~. "No country
except
England could produce Hugh Whitbread" she used to say.
"You've only to be in the room with him for five minutes to
~~discover~~ <see> that he cares for nothing—nothing except his
own ~~fame~~
importance, his own appearance, ~~his own dignity,~~ his own
family. "And who are the Whitbreads? Respectable wine
merchants.
He hasn't read <well>, he hasn't thought <well>, he hasn't felt
<well>. A stable boy
(Sally <was> always talking about stable boys,)—has more
~~to say~~
~~for himself than Hugh.~~ <experience> life in him than Hugh.
~~Anyhow~~
~~what he feels is real. But with Hugh its nothing but~~
~~Hugh is nothing except what other The first old dowager~~
Oh no, he wouldn't demean himself by marrying Clarissa!
(there ~~had~~ been some ~~idea~~ <talk ~~of~~> ~~that he was~~ of it) A
dowager—
a lady of title~~—somebody of position~~—thats what he's
<Hugh's> after—"
And she'd been right there. He had married some~~body— some~~
~~highly respectable. of the sort~~ honourable, ~~in~~ some lady of
title, some lady with connections about the Court. Hugh
had some comfortable little post <there>~~—likes of the~~
went about in
knee breeches & lace ruffles. Life ~~was~~ <really> ~~absolutely~~
is ~~astonishingly~~ just, <[ ]!> thought Peter. ~~An absolute~~ A
[people?] ~~perfect artist. People always got~~ <Always does the right thing
for> Who could have cast Hugh
better? A little ~~pos~~ job at Court!
As for Sally herself, that romantic, that brilliant ~~creature,~~
~~figure,~~ creature—for so she had been,—she had married a man
~~called Haig in~~ from the North. called Haig—a rich man,
a cotton spinner; ~~or a most unlikely marriage~~. In that
case life seemed a little off the mark. ~~unless indeed~~
~~there had always been something~~ What had become
of her he scarcely knew. They had all drifted apart.
~~Sally~~ She had ~~never~~ written to him quite suddenly six or

seven years ago for no reason—had been reminded of him by
seeing ~~&~~ 'one of those blue hydrangeas which ~~th~~ they both
loved'
She was very sentimental, & yet great fun. She told him she
had six children—anyhow some very large number. ~~And~~ she
said he must come & stay with them. That was after the
catastrophe. ~~after~~ the breach with Rose. It was nice of
Sally to write but, of course, ~~quite~~ impossible to answer her.
{impossible to begin again. Yet he would like to meet her.
He would like to ~~get her off on Hugh Whitbread again~~.}
~~Writing had been one of her passions~~.
impossible to explain to anybody ~~why, why one behaves as one
does behave~~.
the reasons for ones actions. Moreover it was all so painful—
~~There were things in him that were~~ He had behaved badly,
but one can't go on all one's life thinking about it—
~~No, no, no, one makes the best of a bad job,~~
There are ~~horrible things in oneself.~~ These horrors? No doubt
they're
true— That's the truth too—the rest is illusion—Pleasure is
illusion. All this is illusion—
He stood on the edge of the road ~~by the little shop
where one buys
airballs.~~ outside Regents Park, <with> ~~holding~~ his pen knife
half open in
his hand;
~~Its a marvellous affair all the same, he said to himself~~;
So people say, he thought. But why? ~~an illusion? Is the
sun <shine> an
an illusion? warmth, health, comfort?—I'm hot. I'm
well. Warmth? Health?~~
Given warmth, he thought, & health,~~—not much money,
[ ] a four hundred a year:~~ & a little money, &
~~given~~ my ~~kind~~ <sort> of ~~interest in things, my —still last
my time, he thought, I shan't life is
given all that, then~~ Oh it was intolerable that it should
ever end—ever

Its all I want, he thought, ~~wa~~ as the omnibuses went by, & the
vans; as the people ~~went p~~ passed him;
Its absolute bliss, he said to himself. ~~To be back in London. to be in~~
~~the thick of things again.~~ To lunch out, to dine out, to hear a little
music; to be ~~among people again who~~ could talk;
to sit in a room & have the door opening & people coming in,
& the hostess getting up, & saying "d'you know so-& so"—
& then ~~starting something quite fresh, & meeting new people~~.
plunging into ~~& making finding someone body~~ <something> quite new, ~~making~~
plunges into talk ~~to friends—well any how getting hold hold of new ideas,~~
saying of her ~~to of~~ talking & talking ~~talking~~—talking about ~~reasonable~~
~~things~~, unleashing things, rummaging in ~~this tremendous~~
~~interminable and~~ bran pie—(a phrase of Sallys)
And to meet her, & Dalloway, & Hugh Whitbread even—
~~all good fellows, all old cronies, after all—yes, yes,~~
~~other how do adorable—how adorable—to meet~~
~~quantities of people &~~

[blank]

[Draft of "On Not Knowing Greek." (*The Common Reader*, 1925)]

Thursday
Dec. ~~2~~ 13th
1923. These five years—from 1918 to 1923—had been somehow very important. People looked different. Newspapers seemed different.

Now for instance there was a man writing quite openly in one of the respectable papers about water closets. That was a
1918 thing you couldn't have done ten years ago—couldn't possibly
5 have ~~done~~. mentioned water closets in mixed company. But on board
ships coming home there had been lots of young men & girls; ~~& they seemed,~~ you come upon them; & they weren't a bit upset. There was ~~young Miss Patty~~ that young ~~woman Betty~~ couple Betty & Bertie—The very names they ~~gave themselves~~ reminded one of ~~bears bears~~ <[polar?] ~~pet~~ bears> at the zoo!—carrying on quite openly—the old mother sitting & watching them with her knitting—~~not a bit upset. <calm curl~~ on a couch
The girl would let him ~~powder paint her eyebrow~~—powder her nose.
~~They weren't upper class of course, but still they were quite respectable,~~
there on the deck, in ~~the~~ front of everyone. And they weren't engaged;
just having a good time; As hard as nails, she was.
~~And~~ <But> she'd make a very good wife. ~~by the~~ at thirty. The sort of woman who ~~in~~ lived in the suburbs,—~~lived near~~ married a rich man & lived near Manchester.

Who was it who did that now?—lived & lived near Manchester? Somebody who had written him a long gushing letter—~~Sally Seton of course. Of all the odd &~~ quite lately,—~~saying something~~ about "blue hydrangeas"—~~Oh Sally Seton—Sally Seton of course!~~ She had seen
thought of the
old days! "blue hydrangeas" & had thought of him. ~~& the old days~~ Oh Sally Seton Sally Seton of course—the last person in the world one would have expected to marry a rich man & live near Manchester. ~~A strange creature.~~ <A strange attractive creature> ~~One would have expected anything else—Dis Disaster, tragedy, a wandering Bohemian existence,~~ of all that ancient lot, Sally was

probably the best. Considering ~~how tongue-tied the~~ what girls
~~were then one had to give her credit~~ were ~~like then—~~
~~one must give her the credit of being trying to~~ she tried
~~anyhow~~ to get hold of things by the right end~~—she was~~
She saw through ~~that~~ the admirable Hugh <Whitbread>
anyhow—
~~that "perfect gentleman" (Sally's phrase) who was such~~
~~that awful whom~~ <whom> ~~everybody took adored~~ Clarissa &
~~the rest were at his feet.~~ whom everybody else adored—
She was quite spiteful about him. "The Whitbreads! The
Whitbreads! Who are the Whitbreads?" he could hear
her saying— "Respectable wine merchants. Hugh
thinks of nothing but his own appearance. ~~He has an~~
~~uncle who has a property.~~ He'll marry one of the
Royal Princesses. He ought to have been a Duke."
~~And then there was~~ And of course Hugh had the most
extraordinary, the most natural respect for the
British aristocracy of any human being he'd ever
come across. ~~<it was noticeable> To be a snob on such a scale~~
~~was~~
~~almost sublime.~~ Even Clarissa had to own that.
<Oh but> ~~But then his manners were supposed to be perfect: he~~
he was such a dear—he was so unselfish—he
~~loved his mother~~ gave up ~~everythi~~ shooting because it
frightened his old widowed mother. <& so on> ~~He was a tame~~
~~cat about the place Clarissa meant him to marry~~
~~somebody or other—And~~ his ~~beauty~~ <beauty & his manners—
& his> was really
~~almost excessive. He was the kindest of creatures.~~

Sally saw through all that. One of the <his> most
vivid <of> memories was of an argument on a Sunday
morning at Bourton ~~about votes for women—incredible~~
~~though it seemed. Sally was hopeless at argument. But~~
~~he could see her, very flushed, telling Hugh that~~
when she told Hugh that he represented all that was
most detestable in the British middle classes. She
considered him reponsible for the state of those poor girls

He had a way of hitching <at> his socks which got on ~~his~~
<one's> nerves.
He was just what Sally said—a perfect specimen of the
public school man—No country but England could produce him.
~~And~~ <But> she was really spiteful~~—& of course there had been
some~~
for some reason, seriously Disliked ~~d~~ him; it wasn't mere
~~sport~~ fun—something had happened in the smoking room?
He had insulted her? kissed her? ~~Heaven only knows what.~~
Nobody believed a word against Hugh of course—
Indeed, it was incredible—that he <kissing Sally> should have
kissed Sally in the
smoking room,—If it had been some lady of title <now>—
For of all ~~the~~ people he'd ever met, Hugh was undoubtedly
even at that age, ~~the greatest snob. the most tame
most naturally impressed, being a simple duffer, a
m himself almost devoid of intellect, by anything
other surfaces—by—this sort of thing.~~
obsequious. No—he didn't cringe exactly. He was
too ineradicably stupid <too bovine> ~~& placid ever to to exhibit
the~~ for that kind of exhibition—He was respectful, ~~rather~~
A first rate valet was the obvious comparison: ~~discreet~~;
~~reverential.~~ somebody who walked behind carrying a
suit case. could be trusted to send ~~wires~~ telegrams.
And he'd found his place—married ~~some~~ <some> Honourable
Eleanor, got a comfortable job, ~~& w~~
& went about in knee breeches & lace ruffles—
How remorseless life is! A little job at Court!

280 looking after the kings ~~e~~ cellars, or horses, or something.
100 He had married this lady—whoever she might be—&
they lived ~~in~~ hereabouts—so he thought,—for he had ~~gone the~~
28,000 lunched there once, ~~in~~ in a house ~~with linen cupboards.~~
which had, like all Hugh's possessions, something no
other house had—linen cupboards perhaps. You had to
go & look at them; ~~It was a dark stuffy place.~~
~~They gave probably were giving but & listen to that~~
~~There was always~~ you had to ~~say~~ spend a great deal of time
always admiring whatever it ~~was~~ <is> was—pillow cases, wine,
pictures, old oak ~~chairs~~—furniture which Hugh, ~~or~~ of course
~~Lady Eleanor~~, had ~~bought for an~~ <picked up for> old song.—
~~But~~ <But> M$^{rs.}$
Hugh ~~was so~~ sometimes gave the show away.
She was one of those obscure, mouse-like <little> women, who
admire ~~these big~~ big men. She was almost negligible.
Then suddenly she would say something quite unexpected—
something sharp
~~She would put him in his place~~— She had the relics
~~of that~~ of the grand manner perhaps. The steam coal was
a little too ~~strong~~ <strong> much for her ~~some <at> times~~.
~~perhaps.~~
~~After all, Hugh's manners were a little too~~
~~the solidity. the prosperity, the the house seemed~~
it made the atmosphere thick. ~~There was an air of~~
~~solid comfort & You could never~~ And so there they
lived, at the rate of five thousand a year, ~~presumably,~~
with men servants & motor cars, ~~going to court, going to~~
~~Scotland,~~ & ~~rea~~ & never
while he was cadging a job.

who was <~~3~~ 2 years senior to> a ~~year or two older than~~
<Hugh'~~s senior~~> Hugh, cadged for a job.
At fifty ~~one~~ <three> he had to come & ask them to ~~find him~~
put him into some secretary's office, to find him some
usher's job, teaching little boys, running about in a
white waistcoat perhaps.—something that
brought in five hundred a year. ~~& left one with which would~~
& left him time to ~~do a little~~ hear a little music.
Dalloway could do it presumably; or Whitbread.
~~of the two he would rather be beholden to Dalloway,~~
~~Dalloway—He was~~
He didn't mind what he asked <old> Dalloway ~~to do for him—~~
~~You could trust him to~~ He was a thorough good sort—
honest, yes; a bit thick in the head, yes; ~~but not a bit of a snob;~~
~~a disinterested in his own way; He took things up &~~
~~quite disinterested in his way—a He had an extraordinary~~
~~capacity for talking but utterly disinterested in his own way.~~
~~He was always taking things up—even as a boy he had~~
~~not a bit of a snob. He~~ Whatever he <did> ~~took up he~~
he did in the ~~same thorough~~ <thorough> ~~going capable way,~~
~~without~~
a touch of imagination, ~~without a or humour~~ But
he had ~~that~~ <the> inexplicable niceness of that sort of ~~young~~
~~man~~—
class. He ought to have have been a country squire of course.
~~He was the sort of man who~~ He was his best with ~~animals.~~
~~There was that scene at Bourton with the squirrel,~~
with horses, with animals, with dogs, ~~who~~ for
instance that big shaggy dog of Clarissa's, when it
got caught in the trap. & had its paw half torn off.
Clarissa couldn't bear the sight of blood.
Dalloway did it all, on the hearthrug, with basins &
bandages & so on.. Perhaps that was why she married
him: There was so little of the instinctive in her—
She was <insincere> so unmaternal; & yet. ~~so feminine. so~~
in some profound way, so exquisitely feminine.

[*blue pencil*] ~~He bandaged it~~;
Hugh & Dalloway did the whole thing; bandaged, made splints, told
[*red pencil*] Clarissa not to be a fool. That was what she liked him for
Clarissa presumably~~—or what was their relationship?~~
that was what she needed, ~~somebody who would say to her, kindly &~~
~~firmly~~ . . . "Now ~~Clarissa~~, <my dear;> don't be a fool"; ~~And then~~,
~~about the same time there was~~ Hold this—fetch
that." all the time talking to the dog as if it were a
[*blue pencil*] human being~~—at his very best, Then there was~~
Human But how could she swallow all that stuff about poetry?
How could she let him hold forth about Shakespeare? ~~&~~
~~let h say that no decent person could read the Sonnets~~
~~because it was listening at key holes?~~
Seriously & solemnly, Richard Dalloway ~~sat stood up~~ <got up on his hind legs>
~~before them all in the drawing room~~ & said that no ~~one~~
decent man ought to read ~~Shakespeares Sonnets~~ (or let
No doubt ~~his wife visit at the home of a man who) married~~
~~his deceased wife's sister;— Actually that was what he~~
said. ~~And the~~ It was <because> listening at key holes he ~~said.~~
~~It was a case~~ of being a ~~citizen; & respecting~~ all laws ~~good or~~
~~And the other thing was breaking your country's laws.~~
~~Clarissa~~ No decent man ought to let his wife visit
at ~~of~~ <the> home ~~where the~~ <where the man ~~&~~> ~~of a man who'd married~~ <visit> his
a deceased wife's sister. ~~It was~~ intolerable!
incredible! The only thing to do was to pelt him with
silver paper. with ~~silver paper~~. walnuts. And Clarissa sucked it all
in—thought it so honest of him, so independent of him—
Heaven knows if she didn't think <say> ~~him~~ him the most
original mind she'd ever met!

That was one of the bonds between Sally & himself. There was a
garden where they used to walk, a walled in place, ~~with~~
paths; ~~cabbages, & rose trees, just wide enough for two—~~
~~half kitchen garden,~~ with rose bushes & giant cauliflowers—
he could remember Sally ~~stopping to~~ <tearing off a flower>
snuffing up the roses,
exclaiming at the ~~moonlight on~~ <beauty of> the cabbages—she
was certainly ~~an~~ extraordinarily vivid ~~for~~ in ~~all she did~~ <her
ways>—

They came back—he could hear her voice—

& imploring him, ~~in half~~ <half> laughing of course, to
carry off Clarissa, to save her from the Hughs & the
Dalloways & all the other "perfect ~~you~~ gentlemen."
~~who would bring out the conventional side of her,~~
~~when there was so much else—when she had a soul—~~
~~& a spirit—when she~~
'stifle the soul' in her, make ~~her~~ a mere hostess of her.
~~somebody to stand at the head <top> of a staircase,~~
~~a British~~ wanted her to stand on ~~their~~ staircases, to
pour out tea; know the right people.

But

One must do Clarissa justice; she wasn't going to
marry Hugh anyhow: ~~even if he asked her.~~
She had ~~a narrow, but in her own rather very limited~~,
~~very~~ why a perfectly clear idea ~~of the thing~~ <of life> she
wanted. ~~She wasn't emo~~ <Her> emotion~~al~~<s> ~~beneath the~~
~~surface.~~
were all on the surface. Beneath she was very
shrewd—a much better judge of character than
Sally for instance—& with it all—~~that was the~~
~~she had~~ possessing that woman's gift, that

She made her own atmosphere

essential one: ~~<of>~~ making life wherever she ~~happened to be.~~
<happened to be>
~~stood. She had only to come into a room,~~
She came into a room. Everything was changed. ~~She~~
She got into an omnibus. It was just the same
this morning—there she sat with her scissors &
her silk & her dress over her knee &

& ~~somehow it was a complete little~~ <it was like coming into
another> world ~~of its own~~: a
It was unconscious. There was no ~~triumph of personality~~;
<thing flamboyant about her;> ~~she~~
you didn't ~~&~~ notice her, as you noticed Sally; ~~but of the~~
~~She had nothing flamboyant. She was But~~
but of the two it was Clarissa wh~~om one remembered~~ stood out—
a very queer gift, ~~essentially feminine, a~~ <essentially femme.>
~~no man has it; &~~
~~for that reason women must always dominate.~~
their great power;
~~you couldn't she made something~~ but it was Clarissa one
remembered. ~~It was extremely difficult to explain.~~
Not that she ~~dressed~~ was striking; ~~she was~~ There was
nothing picturesque ~~or flamboyant~~ about her as there was
about Sally; she never seemed to assert herself, or to say
anything ~~that~~ specially clever.[22]

No, no, no! he was not in love with her any more!
It was only the emotion of coming back & seeing her. again.
~~feeling It was only the romance of it all.~~
~~The sort of feeling he couldn't help having of how different~~
~~things might have been. But happily she had refused~~
~~him And then the sight of her there with among her~~
~~things~~ <with her> scissors. & silks—as usual~~;~~ getting ready for a
party—~~Her What She was a great~~ She had a
~~passion~~ <genius> for parties. ~~She made other people talk—~~
~~that was~~ People said of course that she was ~~a~~
worldly—~~But she never dropped her old friends.~~
~~But it was more She had a liking, certainly, for—~~
~~What was her phrase?~~ She cared too much for
rank & money & getting on in the world—which
was true in a sense; she had admitted it. She
couldn't bear frumps—that was her excuse; she

weakness & cowardice ~~couldn't had some~~ <She would say> ~~would say she hated~~
& women who ~~cowardice more than~~
didn't anything; ~~& this worldliness of hers was largely a her~~
do their hair— ~~desire to People ought to~~
the power of ~~She couldn't see the why people~~ Her parties, her great
ladies, ~~her~~ her politeness & the rest were ~~a form of~~
~~adventure~~ her adventure; her form of self expression,
by way of something she did ~~gallantly—as <indeed> one never found her~~
showing off— ~~in a dressing gown; moping never~~
like an artist—just as, so far as he could remember, he
had never found her, in all these years, ~~in the dumps,~~
other than dressed & upright—Why, if she was ill,—
you went to see her. She was bright as a new pin.
~~She had a~~ You could ~~speak~~ always get her to ~~speak~~
20 own up, ~~if if to that sort of thing~~ if you took the trouble.
20 What she would say was, that she hated frumps,
fogeys, (failures like himself; <presumably)> thought people had no
right to exist merely—must do something. ~~must~~ be
something; & these ~~great peop grand~~ great swells—
these Duchesses, ~~prime Ministers wives,~~ &
hoary old countesses one met in her drawing room—
unspeakably remote as he felt them to be from any
thing that mattered a straw—~~were <really> to anybody~~—
~~were~~ stood for something ~~to her.~~ real to her.
She said they held themselves ~~straight~~ <upright>; (so did Clarissa
~~a~~ herself. She never lounged in any sense of the
word—). She said they were ~~far more far more~~
~~open-minded—~~ courageous— In all this there was
a great deal of Dalloway; ~~one could see his~~ of
course; a great deal of ~~pe the~~ <the> public spirited,
~~imperial~~ British Empire, tariff reform, governing
~~classes~~, <spirit> element; which had grown on her, ~~&~~ as

it has ~~a way~~ <tends to do> of doing ~~when you're past fifty & have a comfortable~~
~~settled income A~~ With twice his wits she had to see things
through his eyes: (one of the tragedies of ~~married married couples~~) <married life)>
~~The~~ With a mind of her own, ~~m~~ she must be always
talking of Richard—"~~My husband~~ <Richard> thinks this ~~or that...of~~
as if, ~~Richard would say~~ <Richard feels that> "—as if anybody ~~cared~~ wanted <couldn't know all>
all to ~~hear~~ know what ~~that~~ Richard thought, ~~what Richard~~ <or> felt—
~~Richards views.~~ After all, one had only got to read the Morning Post <to know> ~~if one wanted~~
~~from~~
~~reading the leaders~~ ~~to know Richards opinions! But Even so,~~
~~in~~ ~~And the worst of it was that Clarissa wasn't like that by nature—~~
But ~~in herself~~ she was ~~different~~ <~~in a~~ real>—these parties, for
example—this social business—really whatever one might
say, ~~it was a she had the gift; she had the <she had the socia> of being bringing~~
~~people together, of making her world, as~~ she had the social art—
whatever it might be—{over & over again he'd seen her}
take some} ~~she was an artist there—expressed herself—~~
made her ~~own~~ drawing room a sort of ~~world~~, meeting place.
~~She took~~ over & over again he'd seen her take some
raw youth ~~in tow, & bring him out & smooth him down—~~
& make him shine: Infinite numbers of old women
conglomerated round her of course. ~~She had a~~
~~She had a foot in a great many worlds. And~~
~~she still knew some of the~~ And odd, unexpected
people turned up, an artist sometimes; <sometimes a> writers; though
she made no ~~pretence of~~ <attempt at> a salon. ~~The whole~~
~~thing depended on her.~~ Behind it was all that network
of ~~calling~~. ~~kindnesses, keeping up with~~ <of visiting> being kind
to people; <of> running about with bunches of flowers, &
little presents; so-&-so was going to cross the Channel—
must have an air cushion—all that
interminable traffic that women of her sort kept up—
but she really did it genuinely, from a sort of goodness.

Or take this view of Clarissa. It was Sallys

[drawing of floor plan, *pencil*]

V's Study	L's Study	Bedroom
Kitchen	drawing room	Bedroom
[ ]s [ ]	[ ]s [ ]	Press Office

[page 94 *verso*]

(Jan 3rd 1924) There was an age when the pavement was grass; another
when it was swamp; an age of tusk & mammoth; an
age of silent sunrise; & through them all the battered
woman—for she wore a skirt—with her right
100 hand exposed, her left clutching at her knees stood
80 singing of love; ~~which love unconquerable in battle;~~ <fight>
180 ~~which, she sang, after lasting for millions of years,~~
~~after a It <Which> had lasted a million years; yes, a million years ago~~
~~so she sang, her lover, &~~ which she sang was immortal,
~~though her lover,~~ & millions of years ago ~~her lover,~~
in May, her lover, who had been dead these centuries,
had walked, she crooned, with her in May; but
in the course of ages, ~~when~~ long as summer days, &
~~hung~~ flaming, so she remembered with nothing but
red ~~flowers~~ <asters>, he had gone; death's enormous sickle had
swept over those tremendous hills; & ~~now~~, when,
at last ~~she laid her hoary & immensely~~ she laid her
hoary & immensely aged head on the earth
now become a mere cinder of ice, for it would have
outlived everything—her memory of happiness even—then
she implored ~~that~~ "lay by my side a bunch of
purple heather "; There ~~where~~ in that high burial
place which the last rays of the last sun
caressed. a bunch of purple heather; for then
the pageant of the universe would be over.

~~Lay by my side a bunch of purple heather,~~
~~she sang,~~
But, as the ancient song ~~kept bubbling up, no~~
~~though tusks, through coal & tusks & mammoths,~~
thick rich
through the rich roots of infinite ages, through the ~~bones & the~~
~~skeletons, & the through the~~ & the treasure, ~~any its old~~
~~merriment seemed eternal,~~ it ~~seemed to~~ sucked in
~~some all~~ the salts of the earth; ~~& to~~ it bubbled up, opposite
Regents Park Tube Station, for ever & ever, a merry
perennial it seemed perennial; it
it ~~seemed to come~~ <came> through the roots of infinite ages,
through the skeletons & the treasure, suck~~ed~~ing in all the
salts of the earth, & ~~getting a~~ was positively
sweet ~~with~~ to ~~hear, sweet & rough & wild, &~~
taste; & ~~filled~~ though it issued from so small a mouth—
a mere hole in the ground, muddy too, with root~~s~~ fibres, &
tangled grasses: So ~~it would pour pour forever &~~
~~spreading over the cut, it would soak & soak;~~
~~soaking & soaking soaked the earth through. &~~
~~She was~~—The old singing ~~fountain~~ woman, ~~the~~ was
Lay by my side a bunch of purple heather,
came burbling out. ~~of her mouth~~.
But not yet. ~~awhile.~~
She me

still though it issued from so small a mouth; a mere
hole in the ground, muddy too, matted with
root fibres & tangled grasses, still the old bubbling
burbling song, soaking through the roots of
infinite ages, through skeletons & treasure,

Lay by my side a bunch of purple
heather
The last red aster of a

~~still it came pouring out soaked & soak,~~ streamed away in
rivulets, ~~all over &~~ all along the Marylebone Road & down
towards Euston.

~~She did not intend~~ This ~~battered &~~ rusty old
pump, ~~or~~ this battered old woman, ~~had no intention of
ceasing her~~ would be there <in> ten millions years ~~to come~~ <of
time>
~~with the same song sing remember still remembering~~
& ~~still, through her red lips, would come the regret for
her lover, this paean would come pouring,~~ the praises of
remembering ~~love would~~ stream: how once in May on some flowering
~~coast~~ headland, she, ~~then it seemed~~ had walked with—
~~some youth, whose features were all dim, &
well, it was not important to remember~~ <did not matter> with
whom.
~~& so~~ so that everybody who passed could supply for
themselves a hero or a heroine; & then, as her strain
~~rapture~~ passed from rapture to regret, could
survey a world blanched, moon cold, its flowers
silver frosted, & then ~~again could~~ from that
~~could go on~~. to bathe in the perennial stream,
~~which could gather as they went on their way~~
some profound humorous contentment,: ~~some~~ a
savour like that which rises from an enormous
cauldron, ~~in which herds of animals have been stewed,~~
in that.

to hear it one would have thought that the pageant of the
universe
~~was~~ far from being over, was ~~now so soundly established~~
only now in mid career. ~~This old rusty pump.~~ This battered
<old> woman
was indomitable; no gale would beat her down; no rust ~~would~~
destroy her. ~~eat into her bones; It was true that~~ the eyes had
somewhat blurred ~~the features of memory~~ <the> clarity of that
& the bright-petaled distant May day; she no longer saw the face of her lover,
~~shape~~ flower ~~wh though still~~ <when> she implored him Look in my eyes with
a large looming thy sweet eyes intently; ~~Something very general had taken~~
shadow; She saw only a general shape; ~~&~~ but then, when she
~~said~~ twittered, ~~fresh as a bird &~~ with that birdlike
freshness which comes into very old voices, Give me your
hand & let me press it gently, & if some one should see
what matter they?—~~when; then again, so There was
a time an august indifference to time, a sublime
unconsciousness, something~~ all trifles, all silliness,
all peering inquisitive grazing eyes seemed annihilated;
& the passing generation—the ~~crowd~~ pavement was crowded~~.~~—
~~the road~~ vanished like leaves; to be trodden under. When
they were gone, she would exist.

There is nothing to be afraid of, said Rezia or to
give her her full name, Lucretzia Warren-Smith, as she
paused on the edge of the pavement.

her point of view about Septimus She had an extraordinary, a southern, susceptibility to
sound.

Jan. ~~23rd~~ <28th> 1923

And then when one has been foolish, been unhappy, then theres
such a
pleasure in real things—omnibuses, ~~fine~~ <dappled> horses, with
little bristles of straw in their tails. This ~~poor~~ old <woman
singing.> thing.

poor old thing

except that she looked quite cheerful. But it must be
dreadful to stand in a street, suppose it was wet? &
then suppose one had been respectable, & one's father or
somebody like that, happened to pass ~~& saw one~~—<Perhaps
she had a son, who> had deserted.
~~how dreadful it would be for them.~~ & then ~~did~~
~~she have a room~~—going back ~~at night~~ to one's room.
at night. ~~She was singing though.~~

Ee um fah um so
Foo swee too eem oo

~~The <It was a cheerful> sound which~~
~~Come~~
~~The sound eddied up,~~ Cheerfully & gaily
the sound wound up into the air, like the smoke
from a cottage chimney twining up ~~tree trunks~~—
~~grey~~ clean beech trees, on whose higher branches
~~little tasse~~ the little green leaves trembled perhaps, as
~~the sound went lost~~ were dimmed by the mist.

And then there ~~were~~ <was> Messrs. Whitbreads brewer's
van; & an omnibus; & a covey of small children; & that
summer morning sound,—what was it made of?
motor horns & trumpets & wheels: & all rushing ~~ever so~~
triumphantly, like the legions of ~~some~~ the army of life,
trampling, neighing, tossing their heads up, like the
sea, when it comes racing in with every wave
white; & buffets the ~~old black~~ rocks.

Mr. and Mrs. Septimus Warren Smith crossed

road, by Regents Park Station, & except for the overcoat which
Septimus wore, there was nothing to draw ~~the~~ attention
~~of other people~~ to them. Perhaps they walked a little slowly,
and ~~or, especially in the~~ <in the way the> man ~~&~~ walked there
was something
uncertain—but how usual that is, after all, on a fine
summer morning when people who don't usually
walk ~~at that hour~~ find themselves out of doors, &
keep looking at the sky, ~~find everything odd, as if~~
~~London on a~~ & at this that & the other,—as if
~~they~~ London were a room which one has come into by
mistake at the wrong hour, when the chandeliers
are in holland bags; & the caretaker, summoned
from the basement, lifts one corner of the long
blinds & lets in dusty light upon the deserted
arm chairs.

The young man looked, in short, like a clerk of
the better sort. Education had no doubt a little
spoilt him, or shall we say raised him? ~~above his~~
~~sphere. Th~~ Yes, that explained her attitude—the little
wife's—for ~~one could not doubt that~~ <no doubt> the birdlike
sparrow like little creature who <held his arm with a flesh>
tugged him along,
~~was <must be> the wife, the simple one of the two; innocent,~~
~~rather engaging, married to a with childlike views—~~
~~who found herself a little or~~ <& no doubt> indeed that she
found
~~thought~~ this raising oneself above one's sphere rather
painful. He would ~~take do~~ open his book of an
evening. ~~no doubt~~ attended meetings; & wrote those
long laborious letters which well-known men
receive, asking advice; ~~how~~ what to read, how to
~~raise~~ <educate> himself; They were both on the verge of
the gentle classes.

35 They were both on the verge of the gentle classes. ~~There was~~
For example, ~~his trousers,~~ or his shoes—the working classes do
not
wear brown shoes; & his hands, & his high cheek bones, &
his expression. with that ~~shado~~ shade of absent mindedness
which generally means ~~education,~~ reading, leisure;
And yet it was a rough face—the mother might have been a
mill hand, & the father in orders. And ~~this~~ this boy
being put into works of some kind, ran away. ~~Naturally~~
Then of course he meets a girl somewhere—they think, like
all their sort. ~~first~~ that they won't marry; ~~& then <but>~~ they do.
~~But this ready made clothing fits Yet they're not~~
~~ordinary, either of them; They are happy too, only~~ Then
they live on twopence half penny, somewhere, in two rooms,
suppose;
he won't let his father know~~;~~ because he's proud, ~~he's~~ like
most young men, conceited; must succeed first.
There's the outline ~~at least~~ of an ordinary case; {a ~~suit of~~
~~ready made clothing to clap <fit> on the first couple one meets.~~
~~most cop couples one meets in the street~~ But there
But it ~~leaves out everything~~ encloses ~~a strange case.~~
something strange, this time,} but look once more; & the
cheap handful of observations ~~which anyone <everyone> out of~~
~~their~~
~~teens~~ has by them, ~~to fit~~ is blown ~~aside~~ <wide> like chaff ~~fro~~
when some contemptuous brute snorts ~~at it~~ through his nostrils.
~~When~~ There are certain experiences which human beings
go through, in complete solitude. {Nobody has any
conception what they are.} This ~~young~~ man ~~would feel~~ wake &
hear drumming in his ears ~~when he woke~~ a wild sort of
clamour; the birds tossing in the air, the peach blossoms
trembling, ~~& he caught, cramped. <an> And~~ then a <any>
broken
milk jug, a greasy thumb mark on the bread plate.
But ~~h~~ what does one say?—to one's father or mother
nothing: to one's sister nothing. And what can one say to oneself?

~~For instance, waking <it is> on a spring day; aged sixteen, with the~~
~~birds tumbling & the boughs tossing; waking to Heaven knows~~
~~what confusion of rhapsody, but at breakfast the milk jug is~~
~~broken. the plate smeared; papa is disturbed grumpy, mama talks;~~
~~& the rhapsody congeals & & in & in, & there is nobody to~~
~~Misery, profound & uncomfortable, like a physical sickness,~~
~~invades the which cannot be explained, or shared,~~
~~pervades one; misery at something <something> the strength organised~~
~~against one, at something mean dismal oppressive, this nature~~
~~pervades one; at the dismal but~~
To one's father, to one's ~~sister~~ <mother>, to one's sister, one says nothing.
Its only ~~this dismal~~ <the being together—> breakfast; its only ~~their humbug,~~
~~this~~ <no> sort of that talk goes on; ~~always saying~~
~~what they want one to do; & being different; wanting something;~~
~~but Nobody, in a world where silence is so~~
~~after all it is necessary to share one <the same> sitting room, can~~
~~take stock of these moods; now & when~~ It is ~~a~~ one's
~~desperate matter thought~~ mother mostly—~~has~~ She ~~talks~~
~~such~~ tells such lies; ~~she's Everything must be~~
~~One is expected to be ni polite to chattering old women.~~
~~She is a liar; she is exacting; she tells~~
It's ones mother chiefly. ~~There is a mild weak chatter that goes on,~~
There is an insincerity in it all; ~~a pretence about it,~~
~~There is~~ a perpetual pretence. ~~This is~~ And so,
upstaires, in a little bedroom, or ~~out of doors~~, at the office,
~~life~~ something unsaid accumulates. Observant ~~of~~ elderly
women, without children of their own inviting this
boy Smith to tea, (for he seems <interesting> ~~rather unlike the rest of~~
~~his family~~) try to find out, what it is, ~~m~~ but ~~finding that~~

his chief interest <appears> is scientific, or at least impersonal,
    ~~regretfully~~
~~realise that~~ & he sits twiddling his thumbs for hours at a
time, regretfully cease to invite him. Then he writes a poem,
He is extremely rude; ~~to his~~ & there is a really painful
scene at home about washing. Some small sister no
doubt believes in him. But its all no good. He can
help neither her nor himself, & one windy night,
being ~~very ill balanced~~ <top heavy> with all this unsaid in him,
off he goes to London, leaving an absurd note behind,
such as great men have written, & the world reads later,
when the story of their struggles has been written.

London has swallowed up in her time many armies
of young men called Smith, has thought nothing of
fantastic Christian names like Septimus, with which ~~at birth~~
their parents have sought to distinguish them.
~~But~~ Lodging in Islington or off the Euston Road,
~~in~~ The great experience ~~which~~ which ~~is known~~ changes a
face in two years from <a> pink perfectly innocent oval to
~~a one of those~~ a face contracted; horrible, suspicious, suffering,
took place, day by day, night by night. without record.
The most observant of friends could only say what a
gardener says when he finds ~~a new that a flower has~~ <a new
    blossom on his plant>
~~flowered in the night~~—it has flowered. ~~Septimus,~~
~~was~~ Sensitive, vain, callous, aspiring; a nervous man;
mastered by impulses, <&> fears; proud of his temperament,
affectionate; conscious of low birth & of gentle birth;
at once a snob & a socialist; uneasy in ~~every way,~~
~~quieted by~~ manner; ~~self-conscious~~; at ~~bottom~~
~~such~~ with more surface than usual exposed naked to
the heats & colds of life—such were the seeds~~, &~~
in him, which, all muddled up, ~~in one came, as come~~ the
lived, as live they might, in a lodging off the Euston
Road. There is a graveyard where lovers saunter;

there is a ~~fried~~ fried fish shop; with trays of pale sausages
turning slowly brown; a soup kitchen; & back streets
innumerable, where, flock upon flock, crowded, dense, drab
like sparrows roosting, the poor perch when the days work is
over. Septimus, ~~however he may have~~ employed in
some motor car business, ~~quite <grudging>~~ successfully ~~too,~~
<menially at first, later> ~~succ~~
met Miss Isabel Pole, ~~who~~ lectur~~ing~~<ed> at <a> ~~the working men's~~
~~college~~ in the Waterloo Road upon Shakespeare. ~~&~~
She was about his own age, but cultivated, <&> ~~noble~~, generous;
& when, among her patient class, ~~&~~ she saw this boy,
looking for all the world like Keats, & reflected how she
might give him a taste of Anthony & Cleopatra & the rest,
emotions, ~~not in the l~~ only vaguely sexual, & ~~much to the~~
~~credit of the both, had~~ their way with her, & she lent him
books, wrote him scraps of letters, & lit in him ~~such~~ a fire
123 ~~fire as flame~~ such as burns only once in a life time.
220 There is ~~little~~ <no> heat in it; it is all ~~colour & flame: bri~~ <thin flame~~s,~~ red gold & blue green.>
246 Through it, he saw her—~~she was only twenty,~~ <aethereal,>
246 ~~unspeakably~~ beautiful~~ly~~, impeccably wise, dreamed
of her, wrote poems to her, which, ignoring the
27,06 subject, she corrected in red ink. He watched her,
in a coloured dress, hail a cab; he saw her once
in the summer evening, ~~exercising~~ walking ~~in one~~
~~of the squares She was joined by another woman; &~~
~~then a man~~ ~~r~~ in a square.

This falling in love is also incommunicable,
~~except in some~~ for the pages of Shakespeare, to which
young Smith, or as he called himself <now> Warren-Smith,
turned, only exalt & inflame, & ~~create~~ create the
impression of ~~innumerable~~ <other> tortured souls.
Shakespeare~~,~~ ~~only churns up &~~ instead of lulling; ~~soothing,~~
or putting to sleep raises spirits, ~~which~~ powerful,
~~urgent~~ spirits who are forever breaking one's walk into

a swinging stride, down Portland Road; more than that,
making surge up visions, rhapsodies; quickening life
intolerably, for to whom can one express it, explain it?
What answer is there, what relief?—And the
& the race & disparity between this & that—what one says & does, <these
volume & anger iron railings ~~w~~ & ~~what>~~ what
too ~~one is capable of doing.~~ becomes, when Anthony & Cleopatra
~~is in one's~~ head, ends, more terrific. ~~No one could ever know~~
Yet for all the loneliness that reading Shakespeare
brings, ~~for all the he~~ <it> gives ~~also~~ odd companionships;
~~& in his case led~~ &, ~~strange though the connection~~
a religious ~~appears~~, led in his ~~case to~~ one ~~of those violent~~ <a ~~religion~~> ~~&~~
awaking the gods, in his
~~temporary religious outburst; to~~ visits to shrines,
incense, services, self examinations, & ~~pro~~
prostrations, exaltations,~~—which fell away one~~
~~May morning. some intense~~ but nothing said to anyone.
'It has flowered' the gardener ~~mig~~ <might> would
have said
had he opened the door, & seen ~~how~~ his face ~~had changed~~.
He was now very pale; he was clean; there was a
solemnity about him, & when he rose, with a pad in his
hand to take down a message from Mr. Brewer the
head clerk, he pursed his lips, & stood in an angular
attitude way ~~at~~ by his desk, . . His eyes were neither one
thing nor the other—neither settled steadily, ~~nor~~ on ~~a~~ a
distant object, nor ~~observant~~ attentive to ~~a near~~.
the near. When Mr. Brewer laid his pen, ~~an~~
interrogatively on the letter, Septimus started like a
hare, who has the hounds on her.

M[r.] Brewer, who was paternal with his young men, advised him
to join a football ~~cu~~ club. There was a natural gentleness
about Septimus, especially now that he ~~went to~~ <attended>
Holy Communion,
~~which~~ attractive to his superiors. & ~~the his abilities,~~
he ~~now~~ began, too, to show ability; He would manage;
he would control; he would succeed to the leather arm
chair in the inner room under the skylight with the
in ten or deed boxes round him. "If he keeps his health,"—~~a~~ M[r.]
fifteen years, Brewer summed up the horoscope which it was his
wont to cast with the utmost gravity for ~~the~~ his young men.
~~For~~ <Smith> He looked pale; ~~his interests were bookish.~~ he
should
play football.

Then came an event which threw out many of M[r.]
Brewer's calculations, ~~for how could the most experienced~~ of
~~managers have foretold the European War? dis~~
which completely dislocated his identity, ruined his
horoscopes, took away the ablest young fellows, &
eventually—~~such~~ so prying & insidious were ~~f its~~
~~fingers,—ruined.~~ the ~~open effects~~ <fingers> of the European
war—
~~utterly destroyed life at~~ smashed ~~a garden seat,~~
a plaster statue of Ceres, ploughed a hole in the flower beds,
& wholly ruined the cooks nerves at ~~Miss~~ M[r.]
Brewer's establishment in Muswell Hill.

Septimus ~~was one of the first to~~ volunteered But he was no
patriot. In the dark soil, which no gardener turns
with his trowel, ~~the religious seed had~~ there was

He went ~~out~~ to France to save an England which consisted
almost entirely of Shakespeares ~~roses~~ & Miss Isabel Pole.
And there, in the trenches, blasphemy possessed him.
He became, ~~in every sense,~~ a man; with a marked, but in
the circumstances natural, exaggeration of manliness which
drew the attention of a quiet red-haired ~~man,~~ <sergeant,> older
by
five years, Evans by name. So on the hearthrug one
has seen two dogs at play; one ~~tumbling; biting, no~~
worrying, ~~picking up~~ a bale of paper & snarling over it, &
lifting a paw. the other blinking at the fire. ~~They~~ The ~~old dog~~
~~wags lifts his paw;~~ Apparently paying each other little
attention, ~~yet a yet~~ some very profound interest unites them,
wrangle; must ~~for~~ they must ~~be~~ together even in their quarrels: must
argue; When Evans was killed, Septimus far from showing any
emotion, or ~~showing any~~ recogni~~tion~~sing of the fact
that here was ~~an~~ <the> end ~~of one of those~~ of a friendship
~~which on the classic model, behaved in felt nothing.~~
~~& indeed~~ congratulated himself upon feeling ~~so very~~
~~reasonably that~~ <felt> very little; <& congratulated &> very
reasonably. Indeed
it was sublime. He had seen through the whole show.
Friendship, love, <&> death—~~&~~ was still under thirty & was
bound to survive. He was right ~~in this~~. The
~~guns~~ shells missed him. When peace came, he was
in Milan, billeted in the house of a<n> ~~tradesman, wine~~
~~merchant~~ <innkeeper>
~~whose daughters made hats. with~~ a courtyard, flowers in
tubs little tables in the open air, daughters, making hats—
& to Lucrezia he became engaged, ~~from fear.~~ in a
moment of fear.

when the panic was on him. For now that it was all over,
~~peace~~ <truce> signed & the dead buried, he had ~~these awful~~
~~sensations,~~
~~terrible moments, of~~ especially in the evening ~~of n~~ <sudden>
thunder-claps of
fear. That he might be taken back ~~again into~~ <into> life &
reassured ~~was by~~ of ~~the~~ safety ~~by the living, made part of~~
~~brought to believe in assured that~~ it ~~was baseless—~~ ~~his terror~~
was ~~baseless~~ ~~terrible sensation—was what he longed~~ was all right was
that was what he demanded, ~~almost in stand~~ <opens the door or>
coming into the
room, where the Italian girls ~~made their~~ <sat making> hats.
~~He~~ They were rubbing wires ~~in<to> saucers full of~~ <among>
coloured ~~be~~ beads.
in saucers. They were cutting buckram shapes with large
scissors.
The ~~sci~~ scissors rapped on the table. Snippets fell; ~~& the fear~~
~~was soothed.~~ But he could not sit there all night. ~~He~~
~~could not sleep.~~ There were moments of waking in ~~the nig~~
in the early morning, The bed was falling; he was falling.
Oh for the scissors & the lamplight, & the falling <buckram>
~~sci sci~~
snippets! He asked her to marry him; ~~the~~ Lucrezia, the
younger of the two, the gay, the frivolous; with
those t little artists fingers, which she would hold up & say
that it was all in them, ~~her being light fingered, knowing how to~~
~~they were so light.~~ They could twist up a piece of silk, make a
bow, a rosette; one has to feel ~~for the~~ it, she would say,
as ~~if those hats of hers were~~ Hats were alive to her.
Clothes & hats were what she saw when they walked. It is
the hat that matters most, for it comes next the face, she would say.
~~Sitting in the gardens She would~~ Every hat that passed she
would examine; & the cloak & the dress, & the way the woman
held herself; Ill dressing, not caring, over-dressing, she
stigmatised, ~~all these~~ not ~~savagely, <unkindly>~~ savagely, rather
with a
little ~~impatient irritable laughter,~~ humorous movement of the
hands, like that of a painter who puts from him some
obvious well meant importance, ~~of a picture,~~ & then
generously, but always critically, she would welcome some
a shop girl who had turned her little bit of stuff ~~artistically~~
<gallantly>, or

praise, wholly, with understanding <enthusiastic, [ ]>; a
French lady, descending
from her carriage, ~~walking~~ in her chinchilla, feather, & toque,
<imperiously> moving
all right; ~~all~~ perfectly right,
"Beautiful, isn't she?" she would ~~c~~ cry to
Septimus.

But for him, beauty—~~of~~ was already ~~moving~~
behind a pane of glass. The edge was off it: the vibration
was dull. Even taste, & Rezia liked ices & sweet cakes, had no
relish for him.

He put down his cup on the little marble table—~~the insipid~~
~~sweet stuff. He would sit collapsed.~~ He looked at
people passing: happy they seemed, ~~laughing, talking,~~
collecting as Italians do, in the middle of the street; &
as for this feeling that he could not taste, or feel
or care for things, it was strange; ~~it was alarming~~
a failure ~~it seemed~~ of some sort, ~~in either~~ in him, or in
life. The things that <Rezia was lacking or> Rezia liked so
much, her fun, these
clothes, <[ ]> her mountains,—(she loved them) ~~they~~ were all
insipid. Fear came suddenly <noticeably> ~~by day~~, in the
tea shop, among the marble tables & red plush seats;
sitting there with Rezia talking. ~~She must go on & on.~~
~~But~~ She must not stop. He must pay! Oh yes, he must
~~get up~~ & move & count ~~the change.~~
~~He dissipated his fear in long walks,~~ kept his
~~nor must she~~ <or> guess, ~~that~~ what he had come to suspect
it is a complete damnable humbug.—<this> Beauty,
& the goodness of people. ~~Really it is~~ There is nothing

that he could not ~~live~~ <feel> any more. There was a ~~chasm between~~
~~an empty space between himself <& the rest> & the a beautiful woman,~~
~~a sunset, a glass of wine.~~ Only Rezia must go on talking
on Rezia he depended. She connected ~~them~~ things. If he
could see along her eye to the beautiful woman! But no.
~~All~~ His senses were perfect. The fault ~~therefore~~ must be in
life ~~itself.~~ There is nothing. ~~He paid the bill.~~
~~He counted the change. His brain worked as usual.~~

"It is the English way~~" said~~ to be ~~very~~ silent.~~"~~
~~I like it~~" Rezia said; ~~&~~ She liked it, ~~&~~ <she> respected these
Englishmen, & wanted to see London, & the houses &
the beautiful ~~clothes~~ suits, & could remember
hearing about Manchester from an aunt, who ~~had~~ <had married>
~~lived there. <there> was very~~ <a> rich. man. & lived there.

To ~~change,~~ To break up the outer show as much as
possible, ~~& so~~ by change ~~was~~ might help, Septimus thought,
to ~~press the renew~~ <to mend the [skies?].> what ~~ever it~~ might be; for it was impossible
that they had palmed off this fraud upon him—
~~had palmed off~~ a tasteless world—~~than~~ a world of
~~empty appearances. show,~~ without meaning. They
made him something highly respectable at the office.
His marriage to an Italian girl was unwise, but,
~~the war had operated~~ M^r. Brewer condoned it, as indeed
the war had taught him to ~~tolerate~~ condone ~~many~~ things,
~~such irregularities.~~ "You have fought for us . . .
Its up to the old fellows now." ~~& so on, & so on—~~
~~he was~~ <his> fatherly~~;~~ ~~they were all~~ way,. ~~which~~ And
they were all like that ~~now~~ to Septimus. He was
promoted. They were proud of him. ~~He had~~
And so they took rooms in M^rs. Filmer's house off the
Tottenham Court Road
Here he opened Shakespeare once more

[Margin: The English villages looked ~~mean. lifeless~~ dull.]

[Margin: ~~he sp~~ ~~so he spoke,~~ <he said in>]

2/6 ~~But~~ All that boy's business ~~of words,~~ of the intoxication of
words,
~~all that tumult, <&> hurry, confusion, was over,~~ had shrivelled
utterly.
~~What a loathing~~ <How> Shakespeare had <loathed> ~~for~~
humanity! ~~It~~
~~burnt in~~ & the ~~unutterable shame of life—~~ the putting on of
clothes, the getting of children, ~~the weak~~ the sordidity of the
mouth & the belly!, ~~the unutterable shame of life the life!~~
~~human process!~~ It was now revealed to Septimus;
the message was handed on, hidden, ~~as was proper, by~~
in the ~~the words & their beauty, <in> which, as Septimus read,~~
beauty of ~~shrivelled.~~
words, ~~all shrivelled now, a boy~~ might be entangled, but not a man.
There was Swift too. The ~~final message~~ the secret
signal which ~~the~~ one generation passes to the next
is, loathing ~~of humanity~~; hatred; despair. Dante, the same.
Aeschylus (translated) the same. And there Rezia would
sit trimming hats! She ~~had~~ trimmed hats for
M[rs.] Filmer's friends. She tried them on at the
looking glass; engrossed, like a wax woman, he ~~sometimes~~
~~thought, or~~ a phantom woman, so pale, & intent she was, &
soulless. But let her alone. It was ~~awful~~ <worse.> when she
stuck the hat on his head & laughed.

~~She liked the silent Englishmen~~. She put down her hat,
& kissed him.

"You are all so serious" she would say,
~~There~~ Love between man & woman was repulsive
to Shakespeare. The business of copulation was ~~all~~
filth to him before the end. But then, of course, Rezia
must have children.

They went to the Tower together, to the Victoria & Albert
Museum, ~~he~~ stood in the crowd to see the King pass.
And there were the shops,—hat shops, ~~cl~~ dress shops, shops
with only bags & charms in the window; ~~<but> still they~~
~~fascinated~~
~~her~~ <still,> She would stand staring. There was nothing
like them in Milan.

~~But it always came back to children—~~<She must have>
~~She wanted~~

children. <she said> She wanted a boy like Septimus,
<exactly like Septimus;> for he was
~~remarkable;~~ he was ~~handsome;~~ he was different from any
man she had ever known; ~~at all.~~ so gentle, so good to her,
so clever; ~~& very~~ <so> serious, ~~always reading~~ poetry.
~~Shakespeare.~~
~~Should~~ <Could> she not read Shakespeare too? ~~Was it~~ very
difficult
~~hard~~ to understand?

~~They say because they are that Shakespeare's women are happier than his men.~~

But one cannot bring children into a world ~~like this~~.
<like his>
~~where things are radically wrong~~. To have children is to
perpetuate
suffering; ~~for the sake of a few years of trivial childish joy.~~
to ensure ~~that there shall always be some living perso~~
~~forever~~ <life> ~~something living~~ for the brute to feast ~~upon~~ on.
~~The truth is there that these miserable animals have no~~
~~capacity for affection.~~ And then, ~~boys & girls—children,~~
more men & women; more copulation: more
One cannot increase the breed of these leering, lustful,
cruel, capricious ~~creatures.~~ animals. who have no
lasting emotions. but only surface ~~kinds~~ whims & vanities,
~~eddying them this way that way,~~ making them <leading them
now towards>
pirouette before glasses; ~~But~~ his only hope lay in
Rezia. ~~She would~~ It was like watching a bird,
when one lies on the grass. She hopped, she flitted; she
put her head from side to side. <but> One must ~~not~~ <neither>
move nor
speak. ~~though~~. or move for fear of frightening her.

[margin: each other / now away / ~~[ast?]~~]

Otherwise; the truth is this—in human beings
~~there is nothing that lasts~~; no kindness, no faith, no
charity beyond what serves to increase the pleasure of the
moment. They ~~swarm~~ <hunt, they k> in packs, ~~because they~~
~~dread loneliness~~ they desert the fallen; ~~they This~~ is <their faces
are>
plastered over with a grimace, ~~which~~ <there was> Brewers
<with his> little
waxed moustache, & his coral tiepin; & his white slip.
~~made~~ of him, it was all coldness & ~~The~~ coldness & clamminess

[margin: their backs scour the desert & vanish screaming into the wilderness.]

H.E. of the vaults. Or Amelia Whats her name in the office,
L.Z. handing round cups of tea punctually at five, like an
R.V. obscene little harpy with green fur. And the Tom's &
N.T. Berties, ~~starched &~~ in their clean shirt fronts, oozing ~~a~~ thick
C.O. ~~drop~~ of vice. ~~However, Hatred of the However, he was~~
drop ~~very highly thought of; & trusted with special missions,~~
~~which he carried out with admirable tact, & a so on & so~~
~~on; by these exemplary characters.~~ They never saw him
drawing pictures of them, naked, in his notebook.
The repulsiveness of human nature ~~was~~ poured out of every
corner, like the stream of rancid fat, up from ~~the grill of an~~ <the
grating> of an
fried fish shop. ~~eating house.~~ restaurant. It was exhibited <~~to a~~ [blared?] at
passerbys> on posters, <&> in [bread?] &
[ ] in rubber good shops, ~~in & at all~~ these ~~corners where the~~
<At the street corners> ~~where the~~ wretched
fluttered their gaudy rags; There were hags crippled with cold
on the pavement. ~~Terrible bands~~ of pock marked or
idiotic faces ~~paraded the pressed close, in & leered up from~~
~~blood red eyelids,~~ pressed against one in ~~the~~ omnibuses & in
tubes.
And once ~~the~~ <a> maimed file of lunatics, being exercised, or
~~rather~~ displayed for the diversion of the populace, stumbling,
leering, half apologising, & yet triumphantly insisting
upon the right to inflict their woe, ~~one~~ ambled & nodded &
grinned past him, ~~in the each inflicting his own~~
~~hideous scar. & sapped~~ each ~~his inflicting his~~ <inflicting a>
hopeless sorrow.

Even Rezia, at last, began to perceive the truth.
~~She began to~~ He found her ~~in~~ <Rezia in> tears ~~once~~. She
wanted
a child. She must have a child. M^rs. Filmer's sister had
had a baby. But ~~she they~~ <she> would grow old without
~~children. She was so lonely, she was so unhappy.~~

~~For She too had then had seen this~~
She was lonely, she was unhappy. Now if Rezia too
were going to preserve the truth about life, if she too lost this
connection—he drew a long straight line in his note book
between Amelia What's her name & ~~a triangular body <screwed
up>~~
~~what was~~ himself. to represent the ~~yards & yards of~~
distance, ~~between~~ <&> the break, ~~the emptiness~~ & the
thing seen truly, as now he saw truly, ~~then~~ without illusion,
probably ~~if she joined him, <in their> Then what should they do?~~
it would be best ~~undoubtedly to~~ <for them both ~~to~~> to die.
Sitting on top of an omnibus going, on business, to the
city, that seemed to him best perhaps. ~~Once the connection
breaks~~, There is no sense in ~~remaining, a spectator, a spy,~~
sitting on, a spy; X{Suddenly, where the omnibuses stopped,
by St Pauls Cathedral,}X ~~his He had saved Rezia's life
anyhow. He had sunk. The flood was closing over. He was
being tumbled in the~~ And <his> ~~Physically~~ strain on the body is
And then the And he could not stand the ~~strain much longer;
for to~~ of being blown on by ~~this~~ <the> cold incessant wind,
~~always against him. having~~ to standing ~~up quite~~ alone,
desolate.
~~against the whole~~ world. Rezia was against him now.
~~He had made her unhappy. He~~ One is blown down &
the wind ~~crosses the marsh.~~ goes on. One is blown into the

Here & now ~~happened~~ at the corner of St Pauls
Churchyard
where the buses stop ~~happened~~ the miracle happened.
Two pigeons, that is to say, settled on an old man's head.
This was natural enough. He came there at three every
afternoon to give them crumbs.

~~if Rezia agreed with him~~
~~Then, yes then surely it would be better, if they both merely agreed;~~
~~like reasonable people, to make an end.~~
Far away he heard her sobbing; ~~he could hear it~~ he heard it accurately & distinctly as one might hear a machine ~~work creaking.~~ working.

He felt nothing <whatever> for her. But, as he noted with accuracy,
each time she sobbed, in this profound & ~~noiseless~~ very subdued way, as if she were sobbing to herself, with her hand before her face, ~~he sank down.~~ he ~~himself~~ felt went down another step, into the ~~dark,~~ into the ~~well.~~ pit.

At last, with a melodramatic gesture which he assumed mechanically, ~~& with an~~ & with complete consciousness of his absurdity, he dropped his head on his hands. on the green baize tablecloth. ~~He had~~ reached ~~the bottom of the pit; but that experience had nothing whatever to do with his gesture which was a formal most foolish~~, foolish expression <sign> of the truth that he had reached the bottom of the pit.
Nothing could rouse him. She took his hand She hugged his face. She stroked his hair. At last alarmed she said she would send for the doctor.

implored him to ~~for~~ forget her silliness.

That there was nothing the matter, ~~nothing~~ <nothing organically wrong> was the doctor's
verdict. He ~~himself always~~ went to the music hall when he felt depressed. Milk (warm of course) ~~often helped~~ just before bed often helped people to sleep. ~~But on the whole the best treatment a weekend at Brighton was the~~
These old houses, said Dr. Holmes, are full of very pretty bits of moulding, which the occupants often haven't the taste to appreciate. For example the other day he had found—

But is my husband ill.?

~~He's not a very robust man But~~

Why not go down to Brighton for the week end?

"No, no, ~~no~~ <no>, said D[r.] Holmes,—for she was a pretty
young woman—
now resting his eyes ~~upon~~ not without ~~a~~ covert disapproval
upon his
patient.
~~We all have our ups & downs. The remedy his~~ a great
deal
~~with ourselves.~~ Fresh air, & ~~exercise; & not too much~~ <exercise
not not too much> reading poetry
& he'll do alright" he said, giving Septimus a little pat
as he passed him, ~~& so making off, with the promise to~~
~~look in again towards the end of the week.~~
~~Never would he see another doctor, said Septimus.~~
Since there was nothing the matter, Septimus would
~~work.~~
of course ~~go on~~ work, & walk if Rezia insisted, drink hot milk,
if she
liked, take two tabloids of bromide dissolved in water ~~every~~
at bedtime ~~night,~~ & avoid reading ~~after nine~~ poetry after nine o'clock.
at night.
But now ~~this~~ <the idea> killing ~~one~~<him>self ~~su~~ began
to ~~assume~~
to stalk in ~~come back, & to come back, <stand above one> especially~~
eyeless. about four o'clock in the
morning. ~~It was a frightful thing to see, at~~ one's bedside, the
~~so contemptuous of one too;~~ like a <u>jailer</u> who comes to fetch
one to be
executed; ~~the <He> for one has failed~~; the verdict has gone
against ~~one~~ <him>;
~~But he must rise & follow;~~ He had been condemned to death
by his fellows. ~~by~~ ~~But for what sin~~? He had not minded when
Evans was killed. That was his ~~great~~ sin. Added to that,
he ~~did not~~ had married his wife without loving her
And the rest was all pretty obvious. ~~They hated him at the~~
~~office~~; He was a liar, unchaste, ~~&~~ had ~~stolen; was~~ every vice.
He could see now how everyone at the office hated him.

& repulsive to look at. People shuddered as they passed him in the street, or laughed.

D^r. Holmes came again. He said that ~~he never allowed himself to fall below a certain point of physical fitness; & that there were several golf glu clubs within which he illustrated by,~~ & if he found himself even half a pound beneath eleven stone six, which was his proper weight, he ordered another plate of porridge for ~~his~~ breakfast.

D^r. Holmes came again.

So Septimus had porridge for breakfast. X Then this sleeplessness, ~~which is~~ <wh ~~it~~> often largely imagination—
~~peop~~
people <are> asleep when they think they're not asleep. ~~But~~
~~try—~~
~~well chloral in moderation is However~~ <but> ~~take one~~ there's no harm in five grains of veronal. Don't get into the habit of course—~~Headaches are often caused by eye strain;~~ As for this palpitation of the heart, ~~There's~~ nothing in that
except <That's nerves—his heart is sound enough>
nerves.—One of ~~his patients the heart is~~ all right. & ~~as for this headache, the headaches~~, <the sensation> pressure ~~&~~
on the top
of the head, pain at the back of the neck & so on—~~f~~ why not go to see an oculist? ~~The eyes are~~ So often ~~headaches are caused by eye strain. on the eyes.~~ health is matter of <But> The point of it is, said D^r. Holmes, that we
could
all have these aches & pains if we thought about it. Think as little about yourself as possible. Don't of course ~~overwork, but throw yourself into~~ throw yourself into outside interests. A hobby. M^rs. Smith, your husband should have a hobby." For ~~the truth was that~~ <didn't> D^r. Holmes owed his health largely to the fact that he could always switch off on to old furniture. "While I've been talking to you I've been admiring, if I may say so, that very charming comb you wear!

That is a very common new symptom wh. means nothing

(~~on~~ this being the 6th visit) largely a

health is largely a

matter of <is> our own entire attitudes of life.

~~So that if~~ <When> That damned fool ~~chose~~ to come
again,
Septimus refused to see him. D^r. Holmes, then

~~remarked that if Smi her husband really was 'in a funk',~~
~~quite unnecessarily—for he had 40 years experience of every~~
~~sort of~~
~~that sort of case—They had & they didn't mind paying three~~
~~guineas~~
~~for the wh was what the great men of Harley Street payed~~
~~for the same advice—They might go to see Dr.~~ Bradshaw—
~~Oh anybody—Hughes, Simpson, Bradshaw—All much of a~~
~~muchness—They'll put it into Latin for him, that's all—~~

That Dr. Holmes thought serious. Was he in bed? Yes,
she had
made him stay in bed . . . ~~His head was so bad. he was so tired.~~
And he refused to see a doctor? He does not believe that
anybody
can help him, <she> said ~~Rezia~~. Dr. Holmes really had to
give her a little friendly paternal push before he could
get past her into the bedroom. And he must really ask her to
wait <outside> ~~for~~ three minutes—while he spoke to her
husband, alone,. He shut
said shutting the door.
~~So, Smith you don't want to see~~ me.
So there is no privacy, no escape: ~~they~~ <the brutes> always find
one out <break in>. ~~these~~
~~brutes.~~ They burst in ~~on one with their they bully,~~ at
any hour of day or night; ~~There is no~~ tyrants, bullies; obscene
~~monsters, with their~~ creatures.
And so you ~~don't want to see me, said~~
~~that was taking up, wasn't it, rather an extreme line?—~~
~~have taken to your bed, said Dr Holmes, &~~ you're in a funk
about
yourself said Dr. Holmes; a Well I'm ~~only~~ a doctor with
forty years experience of this kind of thing: Theres
absolutely nothing ~~wah~~ whatever the matter with you.
~~You're as well as I am.~~ But if you lie here, thinking
about your own symptoms, you'll only be fit for a
lunatic asylum. ~~Next time~~ <Now> of course I hope to find you
up & about next time I come; & not making that
charming little lady your wife wait on you".

So Dr. Holmes, who never weighed less than eleven stone six,
& took such an interest in old furniture, became,
one of the allies of death. ~~At any moment, No one could~~
135 ~~keep him out; & the keys of all the lunatic asylums were~~
280 ~~in his pocket: He stood early in the morning at the~~
1080 ~~bedside~~
270
37,800 Here was human nature <(Dr. Holmes)> standing by one's
bedside at three o'clock
in the morning & saying ~~coward & liar;~~ We punish
coward<s>~~ice~~;
by shutting it <~~them~~> up in <a> lunatic asylum. Human nature
(Dr. Holmes) is moreover such a sleek brute: ~~cruel~~, such a
bully; such a contemptible ~~swindler~~ <humbug>, ~~with his talk of~~
~~furniture &~~ probing gold furniture when he has a
face like a bloodhound, ~~or~~ coarse hands, smells of
old tobacco— ~~Anyhow, as Septimus would agree, it~~
~~would be better not to exist than to be like that man,~~
~~whose uttermost thoughts he could read now,~~
But then one has ~~fallen into their power.~~ <is at his mercy.>

But then one ~~has~~ <has ~~put oneself~~> <has fallen into the hands.>
is at the mercy of human nature.
One stumble, whatever it may be, & human ~~nature has its~~
~~muzzle in your face, its claws at your throat.~~
They must escape, to Italy, <or> to France. any where away
from this appalling brute.
But ~~surely this in~~ Septimus,' said Rezia—
Really. ~~she could not understand him.~~ We can
get another doctor."
~~He will be the same" said Septimus. The even~~
~~But you~~ (~~In fact~~ she did <in fact> get the address of Dr.
Bradshaw in
Harley Street)
~~That day Septimus made some mistake in his work,~~
But one could not dispute the brute's right to
exterminate cowards. "I can do what I like; ~~but~~ <or> I can
refrain from doing what I like", so Dr. Holmes had
said, extending his arm, & ~~let it f~~ letting it fall

fall flat at his side. Human nature is omnipotent. ~~Only~~
<Perhaps there is> freedom
only in the middle of a wood, or <on> some very high cliff,. ~~where~~
~~We might try the country~~, <Or we might go ~~away~~ into
the country>, Septimus ~~s~~ suggested.
~~Then he made a mistake in his work;~~ & he said something very
queer to Mr. Brewer. ~~about~~ "When I'm not here"—or something
like that; It was his manner. ~~That was queer.~~
~~"Are you~~ And he seemed put out, quite ~~irritable~~ <upset>, when Mr.
Brewer suggested that he should take his holiday now. gave an
~~It was really~~ You couldn't put your finger on it, but it left an
~~unpleasant impression <sensation>—very. You got the feeling~~
~~somehow—~~
~~not from what he said—that things weren't right. Yet there~~
~~was nothing wrong with his work.~~ He said he couldn't finish
his work one day.

~~About this time~~ <And then> he said something very queer to Mr.
Brewer.
about 'When I'm not here"—It was his way of saying it
~~his look;~~ you couldn't put your finger on it but it left an
unpleasant impression—very. And Miss Edwards
took him his cup of tea & found him in a trance. He didn't
seem to <see> her. ~~He was talking to himself. And~~ He seemed
to be
talking to himself. It made her feel quite funny—he
~~For~~ looked so ~~strange~~. <~~odd~~.> strange
~~It was~~ Either it was Evans laughing or the voice of
his father. Suddenly to hear the dead talking, <from behind a
box> ~~is~~ & yet be in
a normal state <of thought & mind> at the office, or now again
sitting with
Rezia, was ~~quit~~ <to> ~~very upsetting.~~ odd. But there could
~~be no doubt of it.~~ Evans undoubtedly was trying to
~~get~~ at him from ~~a distance.~~ behind that screen, was
very queer. Speak up you wanted to say to them.
~~One wanted to laugh.~~ Evans seemed in the highest spirits—
used the ~~very same <old> slang. orders;~~ all the old slang was
~~exactly the same. wherever he might be.~~ made his jokes.
& Rezia sat there, trimming hats, & never heard them.

~~Evans said that And then Evans began m making signals
with sunbeams, & gently moving the curtains, & there—
on the wall, was a face.~~

Now Rezia had gone <~~went~~ left him> for a little turn—just half an hour, to get a
breath of air. It was clear to him, as he heard the door shut,
that she had given him this opportunity to kill himself: begged of him,
pale & sad as she looked, to ~~take~~ relieve her of the ~~appalling~~ burden.
~~Yet~~ How did one kill oneself? With a ~~paper~~ <table> knife, or by sucking up a
gas tube. It was a difficult business—needed too much effort.
Besides now that he was quite alone, as those that are
about to die are alone, there was a ~~luxury in the~~ it <luxury in it>; a
~~sublimity;~~ which it was hard to ~~forego~~; a desolation that
brought him a <unknown> relief ~~unknown since the horror of~~ <for minutes>
~~had fallen on him.~~ an isolation full of ~~egotistical~~ egotistical
sublimity, & & freedom which the <well liked &> uncondemned can never
know. Holmes had won; ~~but in everything,~~ but Holmes
himself could not touch this last relic, ~~this phantom~~ straying in
the edge of the world ~~quite~~ apart from the rest. And
~~that <it> was~~ surprising—to find this creature ~~alive in one~~ <passerby>, when
the last ~~all of the others had~~ been exposed, ~~an A~~ malicious ~~creature~~ it
man was, the last man of all, ~~with a~~ very anxious to see other people <peering back at them,>
~~suffer. & on the whole~~ determined to live as long as it
could— ~~And then it began M^rs.^~~ Agnes, who did for
the Smiths, thought Mr. Smith was asleep, when she came
in with the ~~coals~~ tray. She put it down rather gently. & ~~& went.
There was somebody whispering in the room.~~
She ~~heard~~ Mr. Smith <suddenly> say "Speak up won't you?" ~~in a~~
& looked ever so queer. ~~That was~~ <The> a voice <whispering> ~~in the~~ ceiling. ~~some where.~~
that was the first of those mysterious voices.

~~Deliv~~ This last man ~~who~~ <was an outcast, an exile. He> had no obligations. He ~~peered~~ <gazed> back
from his ~~pale margin farthest strip at limit at the~~
inhabited region; ~~as~~ an outcast, an exile, a pariah.

That was the first of the mysterious voices, whispering from the
ceiling: how from behind the screen. ~~won't Somebody~~
was trying ~~to get at~~ him: <trying> to say something of the greatest
The door ~~importance. Somebody was laughing Rezia found him~~
opened. ~~trem~~ And now laughing, & now stopping. Rezia
came in. She <crossed the room> was carrying a bunch of flowers, which
she put ~~down on the table. on~~ in a vase on the mantlepiece; &
the sun striking straight upon them, signalled. ~~the presence~~
~~that <this> they were with him~~ <them>. Next, there was a
on the wall; sunbeam
in the corner; then on the ceiling. ~~signals too, &~~ signalling.
"~~That That poor wom~~ "~~A poor woman~~
"There was ~~such~~ <such> a wretched looking man in the street"
said Rezia. "I had to buy them.~~"~~—
~~The man. A~~ <This> man was standing in the street &
trying to communicate with him. Communication
is health, communication is happiness. ~~Thats the~~ <somebody whispered.>
~~way it begins.~~
"What are you ~~saying <whispering> <thinking>~~?" ~~ask~~ Rezia asked, ~~with~~ <her>
~~She looked~~ her eyes ~~almost starting~~ wide with
terror.
She sent for Dr. Holmes. Her husband she said was
going mad; did not <he was> talking ~~nonsense.~~ <to himself ~~&~~ All the time.>
She did not dare to say that Dr. Holmes was coming
He was to come in suddenly, unannounced.
The Brute The brute! <[holmes?] he's come here> Septimus cried out.
And. ~~Now tell me all about it~~ <What is this terrible affair>" said Dr. Holmes.
taking his seat, in the most amiable way in the world.

You damned brute. said Septimus
He doesn't know what he's saying, Rezia said.
~~you must~~ "We will give him a nice sound sleep" said
Dr Holmes, ~~produ~~ & one drop of the precious liquid
which was contained in his little syringe drew all the thick
curtains, made the bed like down, & the water soft & sweet,
& the very water as it closed ~~upo~~ above him linger, a caress.

52 Tavistock Sqre. The large motor car halfway down Harley Street, was, as it
happened, standing outside Dr. Bradshaw's house.
waiting for Dr. Bradshaw, who would be late very
probably; for he was one of the busiest, one of the most
successful, ~~&~~ of specialists, famed not only for ~~h~~ the insight
~~swiftness~~ of his diagnosis, but also,—what is
of almost equal importance in dealing with nerve cases—
for the sympathy & tact of his manner.

His motor car was distinguished but plain. It was new.
For often nowadays he would travel ~~to~~ sixty miles
to visit a patient, taking his wife with him through the
country lanes, & leaving her outside in the car, while
he visited ~~that~~ the rich or desperate, who could afford the
fee, which, very properly, he charged per mile outside ~~an~~ the
town ~~certain~~ radius. The motor car was grey also.
And Mrs. Bradshaw ~~as~~ was tinged, too, with silvery
colours, grey furs, grey hairs, a carriage rug in which
that discreet colour predominated, over ~~k~~ her ~~k~~ knees,
to keep her warm while she waited; an hour or more,
~~under~~ thinking sometimes of the patient perhaps, sometimes
excusably too, of the solid wall of gold which was
as the ~~miles~~ minutes passed mounting up between ~~her~~ them ~~& poverty~~, & all shifts &
~~cares, anx~~ anxieties, until she felt wedged on a calm
ocean, where only spice winds blew; & ~~at the top of the
tree~~; respected, admired, envied, with scarcely any
honour still left to wish for; ~~with her husband at the top of
his~~ tree; large dinner parties every Friday ~~night~~ <night>;
an occasional bazaar ~~now~~ to be opened; Royalty;
~~in short,~~ too little time alone with her husband; ~~but
interests~~; a ~~little~~ boy at ~~school~~ <Rugby>; wished she had more
children; interests she had, however, in photography &
architecture, & ~~often~~ <always> when there was a church or
building of interest in the neighbourhood she
~~visited it, snapped it, & took a photograph,~~ made a
point of visiting it or ~~securing a photograph.~~
while she waited.

Sir William had ~~won~~ won a knighthood, honourably, by the
most excessive hard work all through ~~his youth~~,
the years of youth; & now, at fifty five, dealt opinions, day in
day out, upon the most intricate ~~matters~~ questions, without
respite, save on Saturdays, when religiously ~~he~~ for his
heart's sake, he played golf. He had not lost his interest
in the problems of ~~his profession;~~ <~~his work~~. medicine.> &
found time to dismiss
a little scornfully, the more extreme theories of the modern
school; ~~for~~ <but> the stream of patients, ~~the~~ of correspondence, of
dinners—he made a fine figurehead at ceremonies,—&
more insidiously, the wall of gold mounting irresistibly, &
dulling the sounds of life, though it brought with it,
so they said ~~to each other~~ quite sincerely, other responsibilities
& privileges,—all this had, by the time he was ~~fifty five~~
<knighted>,
given him a ~~tired lo kindly~~, tired look; a heavy look;
the look of one who has seen such a lot of this sort
of thing ~~that~~—has <had> to balance ~~this against that,~~
one thing with another—to ~~cause~~ take long views, to
~~put his patients affairs out of his head, & strike an~~
~~average—~~ realise what importance people attach to ~~one's~~ his
words, ~~&~~ to be tactful, ~~to be discreet~~, to stand on ~~his~~ <his>
~~one's~~
dignity, ~~to be in short <who is> a big man. quite properly~~
~~conscious~~ the look of one who knows, & knows rightly
that he is a man of considerable importance in his
profession.

[margin: ~~& had a gift for after dinner speaking—& spoke well,~~]

[margin: to make allowances,]

~~So that when~~ M^r & Mrs Warren Smith were
announced ~~at twelve o'clock~~ as the clock struck
twelve.

The patient was a young man who ~~had~~ complained
of insomnia, & ~~here these~~ had ~~threatened suicide~~ <threatened>,
but
D^r. Holmes did not ~~think that much weight~~
attach much weight to this ~~to commit sui suicidal~~
~~impulses~~. to commit suicide.

~~But~~ Sir William, <however> looking first at the patient
then at the patients wife, ~~formed~~ took a most ~~ser~~

serious view of the case.
For example, the patient was unable to answer questions in a composed & rational manner. His replies were furtive; his manner suggested ~~that~~ delusions
his appearance, weight, pulse, blood pressure, <were> all
<were> symptomatic
~~intimated an acute stage of~~ <of events a> highly unsatisfactory.

how long had Dr Holmes been attending him.

And <how> Dr Holmes had let this state of things go on for
~~how many weeks!~~ six weeks, ~~The wonder is, as Dr~~
~~Sir William, thought, How many patients are sent mad~~
~~by their the family doctor every year, Sir William~~
~~wondered; Here was the fifth patient this in three~~
~~days who had been where case had been gravely mismanaged—~~
~~Oh these general practitioners! The harm they do~~
~~who had come to him from a general practitioner who~~
Here, for the fifth time in one week, was a

general practitioners

patient who had only ~~his family doctor~~ <him> to thank if he
took his
[ ]. On this subject of general practitioners, Sir William could ~~be eloquent in private~~. say much. ~~But~~ not of course to their patients.

"You ~~have~~ served in the war with great distinction, I understand" ~~said~~ Sir William mumbled, writing on a card, with his eyebrows raised, very sympathetically, Rezia felt;
~~He had a kind, nice, wise face, she felt. He would help them;~~
& she felt that he was a kind good man, ~~who would~~
like a father, wise, ~~cheerful, who would v considerate, &~~
~~who would make Septimus well.~~
~~One~~ She ~~had that~~ felt ~~that~~ filial, protected, cherished.
~~relieved, grateful, out~~ exposed no more. Septimus must feel ~~too,~~ that too,

It was a dull quiet room, grey & sombre; the doctor thought by these dodges, to ~~imply what he was incapable~~
take his patients in, ~~weakly as his taste was~~ <show his
sympathy>. ~~That was~~
his wife's ~~portrait presumably.~~ was a stupid woman judging by her portrait. He had married a
'dull stupid woman', ~~&~~ judging by her photograph, which was hung over the fireplace, ~~partly~~ in order to assert

the value which even Sir William attached to ~~the domestic life~~
family affection. But this war now. As Sir
that Sir ~~William spoke, it struck Septimus that~~ was writing about, on a
William pink card, very slowly: he meant, Septimus saw in a flash,
the great war, ~~of which is of course the war~~ of truth against
falsehoods in which Septimus was leader.

I distinguished myself ‘~~Oh~~ yes", he said, laughing ~~in~~ "very unnaturally",
in the war", Sir William noted.

"And ~~I see <I see that>~~ they ~~think~~ have the highest
opinion of you
at ~~the~~ <your> office" Sir William proceeded <murmured>
glancing at the letter
which M[r.] Brewer had written, ~~in~~ <couched in correct but> most
generous terms.
~~They~~ offered, to meet expenses, to provide a substitute, to keep
the place open; ~~in the most honourable way.~~ for Warren
Smith was "~~As~~ one of their ablest ~~assistants~~.
young men.

"Therefore I hope you have nothing to worry you
~~no anxiety of anykind, none of that~~ <no> financial anxiety
which
~~is~~ so often causes sleeplessness, & the other symptoms which
~~you complain of."~~ are troubling you," Sir William
murmured, slowly raising his eyes from his card, &
fixing them very gently but steadily on the patient.

"I ~~complain of nothing~~ <There is nothing the matter
with me, Sir William," said Septimus.
~~"There <Now>~~ we've touched something important" Sir
William noted.
But D[r.] Holmes tells me you don't sleep" he said.
Actually the poor fellow tried to get up. Its the name of
Holmes that does it, Sir William decided.

~~I am perfectly well. I am in lazy & vain."~~
~~wicked. I~~
~~"The damage done by general practitioners in nerve cases~~
~~cant be exaggerated" Sir William used to say to~~

~~There ought to be a law to protect nerve~~
~~The worst of~~ These general practioners <are the devil> is ~~that~~
~~they often~~
~~set the patients against doctors; make the it impossible to~~
~~persuade them.~~ the work twice as difficult.

so Sir William often said to his wife, <as he> wash~~ing~~<ed> his
hands
or snatch~~ing~~<ed> a meal; & It took him half his time to remove
the impression which ~~the patient had received.~~ they had already
made.
~~These sudden The change~~ The patient alternated between
moods of ~~depression~~ & exaltation & depression.
But you don't sleep, Sir William urged.
As an individual, ~~Septimus had~~ before ~~this~~ <the>
miracle.
Septimus had committed great crimes. <which must be
confessed.> This man ~~with his~~
~~pink cards & would must know <be> &~~ <so that he might>
write <them> down ~~on his~~ on
~~pink cards; to this~~ evidence on his pink cards.
~~But what were his crimes?~~
"I have lied. ~~I have been unfaithful.~~ I married my
wife without loving her.
Sir William ~~assured~~ pooh poohed all this <to the poor
girl, who heard> with a little nod.
This The real crime, ~~was more terrible,~~ for these were only evasions,
the real crime was far more terrible.
"I'll tell you the whole thing in a minute" he
protested. But what was it? <what was> This infinitely serious
crime, for which ~~had made him an outcast, so that~~ he had been
condemned to death by human nature, had fallen, had had
them on him, & Holmes had. ~~{card}~~ in the room, as an
executioner.
Give me a few minutes" he ~~said~~, implored.
"What ~~is~~ he is saying isn't true." Rezia ~~asked~~ whispered.
I am going to ~~talk~~ <take> to your wife <into the next
room,> for five minutes alone"
said Sir William; ~~taking <leading>~~ her into ~~a~~ <showing her the
way into> a little room which
"To seduce her, said Septimus.
~~Now~~ He was <left> alone.

~~He was now left alone.~~
~~He was amused to see that this remark,~~
Sir William flushed at this remark, as such men~~;~~ do when you ~~tell~~
~~them the truth.~~ speak the truth, which ~~is of course~~
~~our duty Septimus them~~ I ~~shall do now,~~ intend to do ~~now;~~
Septimus thought, feeling, as the door shut, again come
over him the ~~strange~~ exaltation, ~~of those who are about~~
~~to die the loneliness~~ of those who are outcasts, & look
back at the scene <which> still ~~can~~ performs all its functions
though now a vast silence had fallen, & only the clock ticked,
So they brought Christ before <his> judges, Septimus thought,
~~& he turned his head & looked hearing some~~ & again,
~~he was He had discovered the secret. returning again to~~
~~his~~ For ~~on~~ he had taken ~~upon himself~~ the burden on himself.
He ~~had to~~ <cd.> confess his sin; & then would be crucified: &
would pass through death ~~& rise~~: but what was the sin?
He had not loved—he had not loved—He had lied. Or was
~~it that he had pursued Isabel Pole once~~ it that he had
pursued Isabel Pole—round Bedford Square? ~~or~~
that evening!

~~Of course,~~ he was being watched by the man who
wrote things down on pink cards; ~~this was his last chance.~~
through the keyhole.

Nothing indeed ~~exhilarated~~ <was more remarkable> Septimus ~~more,~~
than the fact that this extraordinary sensibility which
could see through wood, could hear the crinkling of letters on his
mantlepiece, & in a moment if it chose interpret the
~~very~~ words of the sun beams, ~~must be destroyed.~~
~~enraged other people.~~ ~~would~~ <should> have to be destroyed.

~~There was this~~ Except of course

~~He would have to be destroyed, & yet he~~
He thought that he was ~~f~~ too good for the world, & that
goodness must be destroyed by the world moved him
almost to tears, not for himself; for he was already
~~merged, but~~ sunk, but for the whole vast prospect of
human misery, which like the trembling surface of the sea,
lay <spread> beneath him;
Sir William came back with Rezia, who had
been crying—naturally. She had been seduced.
"Your wife & I have had our little talk"
said Sir William,
Sir William is going to make you perfectly well"
said Rezia.
~~Oh~~ yes, <extremely yes perfectly> a little time, &
patience, ~~re~~ murmured Sir William,
who was writing a prescription.
There was something sinister in this alliance, for
Rezia had fallen clearly into the power of this man with
the grey motor car. They had ~~indecently~~ plotted some
conspiracy against him.
"There is nothing whatever the matter with me"
said Septimus. pink
But he says you are absolutely exhausted Septimus—
Rezia cried,
"I ~~dont~~ want you to ~~trouble . . . <yourself about
anything>~~ <leave everything to me> said Sir William
looking
up ~~deprec~~ warningly (for don't excite him dont argue
with him, don't speak to him more than you can help.)
he had ~~told <warned>~~ <told> her, in the next room, when he
had explained
very seriously & very kindly that her husband was in an
~~extremely ser~~ on the verge of complete collapse,
nervously &
physically, owing to prolonged strain of some kind,
probably the war, must be sent to a home at once,
which Sir William would arrange; they would
look after him perfectly; it would be a matter of months;
at first it wd. be better that she should not see him,

but <in the end he wd come back> he could get perfectly well;
~~that was certain.)~~
leave it all to me'—& he patted her hand.) Back they went)

Loneliness is a condition of human life; Marriage even leaves room for treachery. Get two human beings together & they will always plot against a third.

You can't really hurt me, Septimus said.

We don't wish to hurt you, Sir William replied.

I remain myself whatever you do.

But you are not quite yourself today, are you?

~~What was~~ <The> That vision of lying on the cliff, & the dead passing, music, & the secret, ~~which he had to impart?~~

~~You are the enemy, he said,~~ & this was the test
~~This man was the enemy.~~

You are the enemy, he said.

No, no, said Sir William agreeably.

~~But~~ why not speak the truth ~~for once~~? Septimus asked. for the last time?

Why ~~Need it be~~ <is it> for the last time?" Sir William inquired, quite casually.

"I shan't be here <We shant meet ~~see you~~> again.

I hope to see you several times.

~~Yes~~. <You want my mind This> your car must cost a lot to keep up.

~~My ca~~ That was your car at the door

~~Yes.~~ I have to visit patients all over England Mr. Warren Smith."

Nothing is <{——}> so profound as vanity. Sir William dealing with a lunatic ~~yet first~~ wished to impress. ~~even~~ a lunatic. He was at the top of his tree.

felt ~~some~~ unprofessionally, some human rancour.
And then, there was in Sir William . . whose father had been a
~~a~~ tradesman, a natural respect for ~~clothes,~~ breeding,
& clothing, ~~which this fellow~~ which shabbiness nettled; &
again more profoundly, there was in Sir William, who
had never had ~~time~~ to read <been to college>, a grudge,
~~overlaid~~ <deeply> buried deep
~~scrupulously,~~ against the ~~literate~~ cultivated people who
came into his room & intimated that doctors, whose
profession is a constant strain upon all the highest
faculties, ~~don't aren't educated & don't read~~ aren't
educated men.

So that he did ~~not~~ perhaps show his power a
little openly.

"We are going to send you to a home" he said.
~~where~~ you will be very well looked after,

"A home. One of Holmes' homes" said Septimus.

One of <u>my</u> homes, Mr Warren Smith".
~~But has <So>~~ human nature has the power to inflict ~~the~~ an
appalling <punishment;> ~~torture upon the fallen.~~—that the
stricken shall be at their mercy.

~~Holmes will torture me.~~

~~Thats <This> what the punishment is, Septimus thought;~~
~~& to be at their mercy.~~

~~He has condemned me. <I've lost the case.>~~ My
punishment is to
~~be~~ "I'm condemned then" said Septimus.

150
<u>280</u>
1200
<u>300</u>
42,00

[page 132 *verso*]

Sir William sighed a little wearily; & lay back in his chair.
The most exhausting part of a doctor's work is to try to remove f
~~some fixed~~ <~~These fixed~~> impressions which have fixed
themselves in the patient.
"Physically, yes," he replied with emphasis.
You are quite unfit to be out of bed."
All these distressing illusions, these voices, (for he
was satisfied that the patient heard voices)
will stop ~~directly~~ <when> your body is ~~properly~~ nourished.
The music & the voices & the revelations ~~would~~
~~depended~~ would be obliterated by this man,—
~~his gallons of milk, & his~~ his motor car.
Life is a succession of conflicts. Like waves they rise
ceaselessly, to be overcome.
We will have this out, Sir William" said Septimus,
hunching himself up in his chair, & making again
upon Sir William that somehow distasteful impression
of angularity, & ~~a~~ eccentricity . . . Yet he had
fought in the war. He ought to have been kept at home.
A fanatic, probably; ~~Yet~~ <But>, poor fellow, <he was> he had
been
through the devil of a time. Typhoid fever is a
mere joke to this sort of thing; ~~for~~ Sir William
never underestimated the gravity of a hurt
~~these damages~~ to that complex & mysterious
organ the nervous system: about which we know so
little he admitted; but ~~the~~ in this case ~~the physical~~
it ~~is~~ <was> ~~purely~~ physical, purely physical; he had
decided. The mind ~~itself~~ was sound.
By all means; we will discuss anything you like" he said.
He ~~never~~ <did not> hurr~~ied~~ his patients; ~~at~~ but how can a
famous specialist be unconscious of the flight of
time?
~~Say whatever you like.~~ "Say whatever you like"
he said.

This ~~extraordinary~~ <is an> opportunity which comes once only in a
lifetime: ~~to speak the~~ this <~~the~~> invitation to speak the truth.
But ~~it escaped him. what was the truth?~~
The truth, so vast & unwieldy pressed him forward, as a wave lifts a single swimmer, to dash him against the rocks.
~~"You're one of them the my enemy,"~~ said Septimus "Thats your wife—a stupid commonplace woman.
And here you sit, taking money. ~~Any well~~ My message—
(He thinks himself Christ, Sir William noted)
is—' he hesitated, "universal love."
~~I'm afraid~~ That doesn't include us" Sir William observed.
~~ironically~~ <musingly> looking at his wife's photograph.
~~But~~ <But> ~~I~~ don't ~~want you~~ to bother~~" he said & yourself about anything~~" he said good humouredly.
I only ask one thing of you—Believe that I know more than you do ~~about your state~~. Rest. Rest. Rest.
If you don't rest . . .
I shall go mad.
"Yes, you will go mad" said Sir William, realising that here was a case where it is best to speak plainly. The fellow was obstinate,
Why should I believe you? Septimus asked.
I am a doctor, said Sir William.
A knight, said Septimus.
"Septimus, Rezia implored,
~~"You're against me too," he cried.~~
~~You're both against me.~~ You're all against me.
Holmes you want to put me into your homes.
Holmes, Holmes, he repeated. Dr. Holmes."
There is nothing more difficult to deal with than ~~a patient's scepticism~~ this temper in a patient: ~~this~~

What is madness?
Why should I
not kill myself
Your wife
duty
cowardly.

Let him say whatever he likes" said Sir William with divine &
paternal gentleness.
~~Again he had another of these opportunities.~~
~~Dont you see,~~ Its you & Holmes, in conspiracy,
Septimus laboured to explain; ~~no no~~ <&> "~~He~~ waited, &
Sir William judged that he was listening <was positive that he
heard> ~~for one of those~~ <to a> voices.
half He had ~~that~~ <the> strained expression, ~~that~~ <the> absent
mindedness,
the tendency to sink into profound reveries. Even as
they watched him he changed from excitement to a
soft tremulous emotional expression. His eyes filled
with tears;
There's no death, he said.
A friend of his was killed, Rezia explained
~~He has come back;~~
~~My friend Evans was killed at Verney Ridge, but he
says" & Septimus continued as if he were reading a repeating
message, We have only to believe,~~ <The dead are all near us;>
Septimus
continued, as if repeating a message, in the fields of Greece.
Tell M[r.] Asquith. Universal love. To understand
other people. Even that bloody fool Holmes,
human nature, that is—
"He is completely unhinged. Sir William noted.
The question was, how soon could he be admitted? Where
to send him? ~~tonight if~~ Today is possible.
Rapidly Sir William considered homes & hospitals;
military & civilian; ~~Unfortuna He would be a~~
There would be difficulties in removing him. The
~~One must note. "Home" clearly was the wrong~~
~~Ho~~ Home, ~~owing to that had unfortunate associations.~~
One must avoid the use of the word Home. he noted
Now I want ~~let me~~ <to> speak to your husband alone for a
few minutes, said Sir William. The ~~serio~~
gravity of the suicidal impulse must be determined.

Septimus responded to the intellectual stimulus of being face to face, man
with man, the woman gone. He appreciated ~~the~~ Sir William's intention.
~~The intellect was All Let the intellect The final appeal~~
He intended moreover to test everything intellectually.
Here was the trial. ~~It~~ <His message> must be proved, intellectually.

"I want you to consider your wife" Sir William began.
His wife? I am no ~~longer~~ married."
~~She has thrown away her wedding ring.~~
~~You have She threw away her wedding ring.~~
~~"She thinks that you wish to kill yourself. I want to~~
~~assure her that she is mistaken.~~
~~He made everything <was at the> symbolical stage.~~
You have said things, I am sure without meaning them,
that alarm her. For instance, she has taken it
into her head that you mean to kill yourself.
We all have moments of depression. ~~I know.~~
~~You can't~~ "

One could feel the wind of this great mastiffs nostril
~~in~~ searching, snuffing. But ~~he~~ <that> should not discover ~~that~~
There must be caverns, recesses, ~~in the soul~~ places where one cd. hide
~~The~~ places one draws a curtain across.
~~The creature snuffl sniffed.~~
"It preys on her mind," said Sir William.
Every ~~sort of thumbscrew~~ would be applied.)
~~to~~ every torture to wring his secret from him.
~~There are moments~~ These impulses sometimes attack you? <come over you>
Sir William asked after waiting.
Thats my affair, said Septimus abruptly.
But No~~one~~<body> lives for himself alone, said Sir William.
I am not a regular ~~believer~~ <churchgoer;> myself, but ~~nevertheless—~~
~~we have no right to take our own lives. And~~
But ~~you are not a coward.~~" he looked at M^r^
Brewer's letter. You have a brilliant career before you," he said

Oh the humbug, oh the forms & ceremonies.—

Its the muffling of life that kills. The Sir Williams, the M$^{r.}$ Brewers, the
D$^{r.}$ Holmes'; so <with their> kindness ~~so~~ <their> gravity, ~~so~~ <their> sensi~~ble~~<e>.

It is the muffling up of life by Sir William, M$^{r.}$ Brewer, & D$^{r.}$ Holmes that kills. The thing itself is endurable, ~~n~~ but not its disguises. ~~Having Sir William would All~~ wrapped up in stuffing & arranging. these strange ~~there is a the blind;~~ They trample out a sound; Affection; ~~ambition~~; a brilliant career. ~~These are words that they have evolved. But the fatigue of making the connection between what the thing itself & its disguises~~ The words have to be connected with something real; the effort is immense~~ly~~ exhausting ~~fatiguing~~. But communication is life, communication is health. Evans commanded. ~~The Unless~~ The final secret has to be told or one is condemned.

"I—I—~~sa~~ Septimus began, stumbling & hesitating like a schoolboy who has forgotten his lines.

~~D Try to forget yourself, Try to~~ Think less of yourself, Mr Warren Smith, said Sir William. kindly however.

Yes? ~~said~~ Sir William encouraged him.

I have failed. I have lied. I married my wife without loving her."
"That is all one can say.
~~I want you to give me your word of honour that you will~~
~~make no attempt upon your life."~~
With all his experience of human nature, Sir William
could detect shades of ~~character~~ <meaning>: dispositions; knew when to
argue & when not; & it was ~~tolerably~~ evident that this
patient had ~~adopted an attitude of scepticism wh. made~~
~~it extremely difficult to deal with him,~~
~~was skeptical; introspective; would attempt was sceptical, suicidal,~~
~~was one of the difficult type. was skeptical; needed drastic treatment.~~
~~that the patient was obstinate, & needed~~
& here was a sceptical, difficult case, one of those cases that
getting commoner—~~young men of brains;~~ the war having
accustomed them to violence.

could detect shades of meaning, even in the most opaque—
muddled masses; could divine the ~~meaning~~ character;
& exerting this power, now turning it on in full on to the
man opposite, ~~he~~ determined that here was a case that
offered the most obstinate resistance, because the
patient was sceptical. would not submit,
offered an ~~instinctive resistance,~~ which, remotely, ~~Sir William~~
began to tell upon Sir William himself; leading him to
~~in the first place~~ to ~~pla~~ give up the attempt to see his patient
individually; ~~& then~~ he recalled all those powers which
were vested in him; ~~Perhaps~~ & could quite legitimately
allow him to master this sceptical spirit, & reduce
this slightest obstruction in the path of Sir Williams own spiral
career—for ~~the attitude was critical~~—to smoothness.
~~As Precautions~~ The patient would need, in other words,
very drastic supervision. He ~~became conscious~~ of the
~~of the flight~~ heard the half hour strike. There was
nothing more to be said.
"~~I will fetch your wife" he~~ He fetched

the patients wife.
It was settled; ~~the~~ he would make all arrangements:
She would hear from him by four that afternoon.
"Its going to be all right, perfectly all right—
He shook her hands, saying that, Sir William, the
judge, the saviour, the super man, in whose hands powers
of life & death were lodged, torture, isolation;
the great gaoler; the heavy compassionate man,
who had seen so much of this sort of thing,
bought his wife grey furs, made an excellent
after dinner speech, & was at the top of his tree.
~~Will he~~ get How long will it take? Rezia whispered,
as Septimus shuffled past them, down the stairs.
We dont know everything, Mrs Warren Smith.
Blankly, dismally, like a clap of thunder, or a
veil of cloud, she understood. "We know nothing"
Yet there was his motor car;
That takes a lot of keeping up" said
Septimus: & irrationally, ~~yet~~ she clung to her
husband against this portentious world.

[Review of "Memories and Friends" by A. C. Benson ("Mr. Benson's Memories." *Nation & Athenaeum*, 10 May 1924)]

[End of Notebook One]

[140-141]

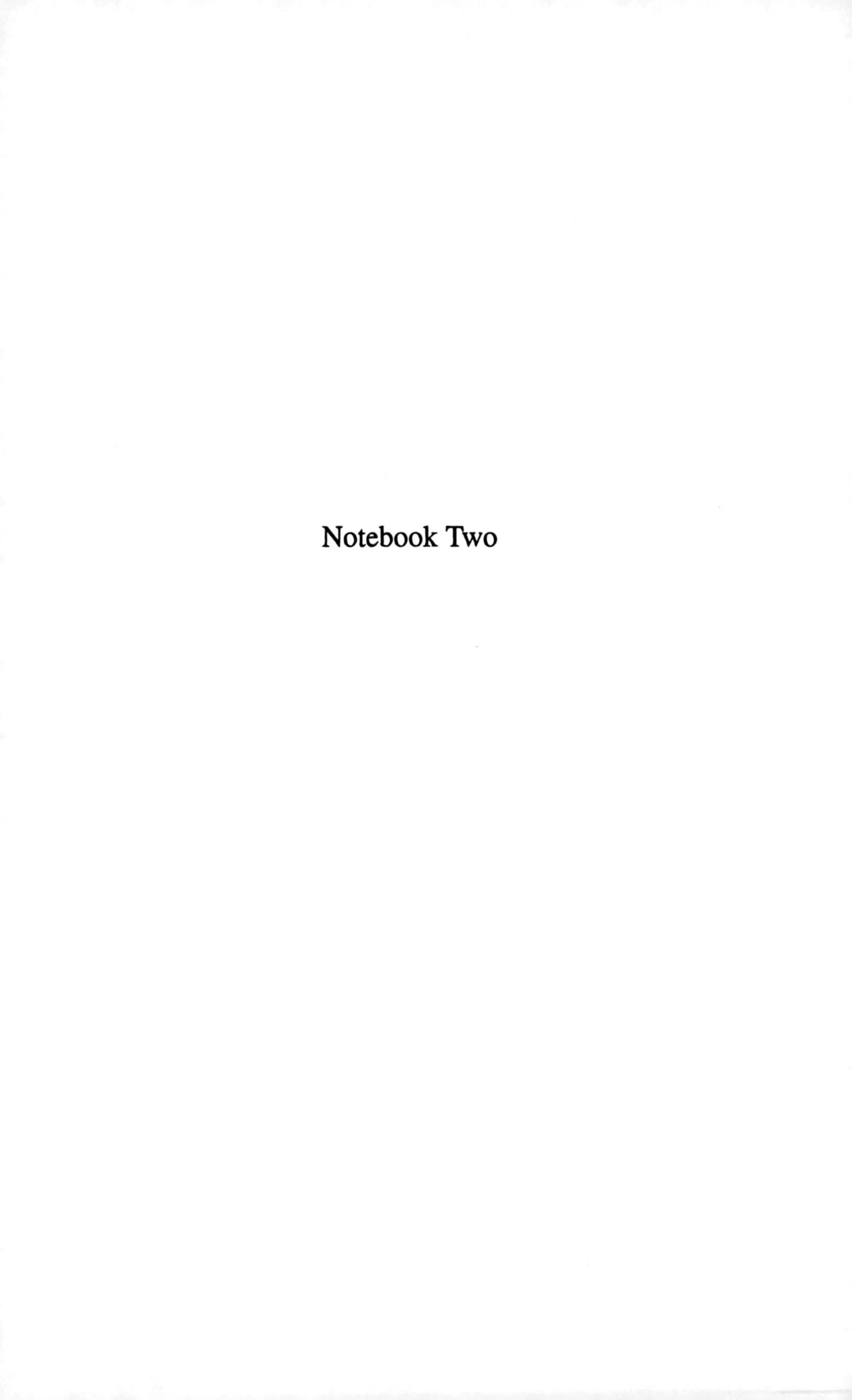

Notebook Two

7/7 = 5/7 ½

<u>The Hours.</u> or <u>M^rs. Dalloway.</u>
Good Friday. April 18th 1924.
Rodmell.

[*pencil*]
Shaftesbury's Characteristics
5th edition 1773 vol. 3. p. 5.
on change of style in the Lit of the
period.

150 (a delicious idea comes to me that I will write anything I want to
280 write).
1200
280 The truth?—was Harley Street founded on the truth? Was
40,00 that the root at the bottom of all these stately <formal> eighteenth
century
houses, ticketed with little brass plates in which were names,
with letters after them? Like exiles they <Mr. & Mrs. Warren Smith>
into were driven
~~down~~ Great Portland Street ~~to~~ seeking together some refuge, or
anchorage, safe from this voluble, treacherous, unstable sea of
specialists. Now indeed disillusionment had come to her,
who had asked filially for help, & ~~then~~ had been deserted
dismissed for until ~~the clock struck twelve, &~~ Sir William Bradshaw
~~received~~ them, Lucrezia had believed simply ~~in~~ that
~~being helped~~ by good men ~~if~~ <helped those> you were in trouble.
{But now—"I never hurry my patients."}

~~She had believed that~~ in the efficacy of tears, to
in ~~the~~ melt~~ing~~ of barriers: ~~in~~ <&> the community of mankind.
~~She had believed that it is~~ How did one laugh ~~otherwise~~
or trim hats ~~& then if~~ otherwise?

~~Spinning its <their> lovely web over the inner hollows,
shop tossed, the glittering skein from to shop across the
street; or hats, clothes, & diamonds; brittle as glass the
filaments stretched, upon which the & the race balanced
itself & the days traffic went forward, with music
wrought into it, & a desperate energy, a
courage which revealed itself to a her now, as she walked
down Great <Great> Portland Street, as the despairing effort of
soli the part of unhappy men. What, then, had she
believed?~~ How did one laugh?

~~Well, to begin with, one laughs out~~ She could
remember ~~laughing,~~ an ~~unreal world,~~ where
she would ~~it sit~~ take up the paper, & Septimus would take up
the paper & she would read aloud, & they would
laugh & laugh ~~& laugh.~~ But laugh at what?

of this that & the other, of their own accord, as sometimes in a little current, a bud, a twig a leaf, come together

And their happiness? ~~Well,~~ It was nothing whatever. It was sitting at dinner for instance, on a summer evening; a then ~~perilous f floating together of this that & the other—her the food perhaps, her face, a flotilla of litt exquisite <sail> little craft, which, with wonder, for how they came together one knew not, began one saw felt~~ ~~which came~~ floating of its own accord together. ~~roast chicken, this that & the other;~~ her looks perhaps; And ~~then it tinkled, it chimed; pass shivered & passed like a rose petal which~~ the ~~And so they came together, & the But why?~~ ~~They meet, on~~ Thursday say, at dinner say; & kiss & collide, ~~these~~ slide on; ~~& It was nothing whatever,~~ together, ~~And so then whatever one did or said was then a twig kissing another twig: & whatever he did, & the barrel organ & the old man crying Chairs & baskets to mend—But~~ There was an old man crying Chairs & baskets to mend ~~outside~~ in the street outside that evening.

And that was happiness, ~~But~~ But she had always believed anyhow that ~~underneath, people were bound~~ met; ~~together, & did,~~ in the stream ~~underneath~~ <beneath> these ~~things that seem~~ like little twigs & straws; ~~it is is deep; she had always believed~~ There was something that everyone knew about, ~~seriously~~: when they were serious. But no, Sir William said to her, denying everything. ~~making out that~~ And even now, walking with Septimus, she could see ~~how very very foolish, how strawlike <straws> in short,~~ that evening, & its folly, &

~~With~~ <But> such upbraiding, though corroding her ~~with~~ inwardly ~~bitterness &~~ flourishing like a sculptors chisel over her face, ~~so that~~ left the sunny houses untouched; left Sir William to dictate with extreme rapidity a series of letters & orders to Miss Stevenson his secretary. after all, after all, proportion, a sense of proportion—by what other guide can we live? If Sir William had ~~taken every patient to heart,~~ <lost that sense> ~~they how~~ could he have ~~served at all?~~ <helped the patients> ~~the~~ at all? Adept in

medicine, skilled in after dinner speaking, a very fair judge of ~~an~~
engraving,
& an amateur of billiards, how could the whole fabric have
been preserved save by ~~knowing~~ having ~~that sense to~~ in
perfection—~~the~~ <a> sense of proportion?

To his

~~He had given them~~ <patients he gave> three quarters of an hour;
~~He gave them~~ all
his knowledge; all his skill. And if, in this exacting science which
calls when the highest faculties of the human ~~mind~~ <brain>, the ~~patient~~
doctor ~~attempts to give more, in he fails invariably.~~
fails to maintain that poise of mind, ~~which that <loses his> sense of the
normal, forgets in some ill guided spasm of sympathy~~
which directs him, in spite of his sympathy (for the doctor has
~~his~~ feelings like other men) ~~to h weigh one thing with
another, & arrive, ruling out vagaries, & sym at the best
course to take, to respect the average <proportion> & to
only disaster would result;~~ no good would ~~happen~~ result.
<he fails in his profession,>
Health we must have; ~~& not the instability. bal~~ &
& health <just health)> is proportion; ~~And by proportion we
to realise with the And~~ Proportion, <divine proportion> is a measure
arrived at by the consent of generations of practical
men. Therefore when a man comes into your room &
say~~ing~~<s> he is Christ—a very common delusion—& has a
message, ~~& adds th which he cannot give,~~
as they mostly have, & ~~hints;~~ threatens, as they often do, to
kill himself, society appoints the doctor to shut him up
till he is cured. Milk is the great standby, ~~milk~~ with
raw eggs beaten up in it, <taken> every hour, oftener if possible, &
~~here everything depends on the wives who must be
firm, yet The more~~ Now Proportion, divine
proportion, ~~over~~ Sir Williams <goddess> standby, <had been>
acquired in
~~the rough &~~ the medical schools, in the hospital wards. The
~~in marriage w~~ catching salmon <in Norway> & in ~~marrying~~
<begetting one son by>
Lady Bradshaw, ~~with her~~ <who> ~~the daughter of~~ of a clergyman, who
~~was~~ took photographs. that looked almost professional.
Being thus instructed, & <duly> ~~carrying out her instru~~ seeing

one does not call
him mad, in the
old fashioned way,
~~It is all~~ <not> merely
~~why call it~~
Sir William
never ~~called~~ spoke
of madness—
always of a
sense of proportion.

in Harley
Street

that all her instructions were fulfilled, Sir William not only prospered
himself but saw to it that England should prosper too,
sequestrating her lunatics, forbidding the marriage of unfit
persons, & ~~all~~ making it almost impossible for any
patient of his to take active part in life until they
too shared his sense of proportion—<if they were men> or, ~~if~~
~~they were~~
Lady Bradshaw's if they were women, ~~Sir William~~
Sir William enjoyed the respect of his colleagues, the
affection of his subordinates, & the gratitude of the relations of
these dismal prophetic Christs & Christesses, who being
stricken with a sudden desire to prophecy the end of the
world, or the advent of God, or some other violent &
uncomfortable creed, had entirely upset the family <[ ]>
~~very~~ were much better employed drinking milk in bed.
Sir William was so comforting; so encouraging; so wise;
& Sir William took all the responsibility on to his own
shoulders, ~~&~~ for he knew—what is so often ~~difficult~~
impossible for the patients relatives to decide.—the
what is sanity, & what insanity.

for after thirty years experience

~~signed certificates, gave exemptions, & determined, what is~~
~~sanity & what insanity. kept them locked up; until~~
~~insanity yielded to sanity, to~~
~~This beneficent goddess~~
~~the death to life; & disps~~ said "This is madness. This is
sense"—Sir William being blessed with a sense of
proportion

This beneficent goddess has a sister, less ~~smug, but~~
smiling but more formidable, who is even now
the purlieus & engaged, in the heats & sands of India, the mud & swamps of
Africa, wherever in short the climate is the
devil & tempts men to fall from the true belief, <which is> the
~~Christian faith~~, <her own,> ~~she is & year in year out this~~
<is even now engage>
~~there she is this The sister of proportion whose~~
~~name is conversion is there hard at work~~
dashing down shrines, smashing idols, & setting up in
their place her own stern countenance. Conversion is

her name, & she feasts on the ~~hearts blood.~~ wills of the weakly,
loving power, loving ~~to lead~~, to impress, to impose,
adoring ~~more than anything to see~~ her own features stamped on
the populace. <faces.> ~~She stands~~ at Hyde Park Corner, <she stands>
preaching;
shrouds herself in white and walks penitentially disguised as
brotherly love through factories, & parliaments; <offering> help ~~she offers; but power is her demand;~~ <delight;> ~~her &~~ but desiring power,
~~sm~~ smiting out of her way roughly imperiously the
dissentient, dissatisfied, ~~blessing~~ bestowing her blessing on the
submissively ~~submissive~~ on those who, looking upwards, catch ~~in their own faces the glow <might> of her~~ from her eyes the light of their
own. This lady, had her dwelling ~~too~~ in Sir William's
heart, ~~covered~~ <tho' concealed>, as she mostly is ~~by some disguise which makes her shine~~ under some <plausible> disguise ~~which~~ not only
~~plausible, but venerable & awful, & if it~~ some venerable &
awful name: such as love, or duty, or self-sacrifice;
~~&~~ How he would work! How he toil to raise funds,
propogate reforms, unite institutions! ~~opened by Princesses, & inhabited by lunatics!~~ But Conversion,
the fastidious Goddess, loves blood better than brick; &
feasts most subtly, most satisfactorily upon some
ill conditioned son of a witch who has the temerity to stand up
to her. Lady Bradshaw, fifteen years ago, had gone under.
& profess a will of his own. Lady Bradshaw, fifteen years ago
had gone under. It was nothing you could put your
finger on. There had been no scene, no snap, no
breaking of wills; only the slow sinking, waterlogged, of her
will into his; Sweet was her smile,—swift her
submission; the air of the household <dinner in Harley Street>
was temperate & urbane.
bland. Only ~~a very slight dulness, or~~ as the evening wore on
~~a very slight dulness; no, it was uneasiness; the the air thickened; nothing stirred;~~ a very slight dulness, ~~no it~~ or,
was uneasiness; a nervous twitch, ~~indicated, what~~
a jumble & shamble & confusion, indicated what <it> was

I do not wish to ~~labour~~ <press> the point,
for there is not time, but I believe
~~that nine <all> novels out of begin try to~~
~~with a character, & that if~~
~~h though each novelist treats~~
~~character differently.~~ & that
it is for the purpose of giving character
that the form of the novel has been
devised. For other purposes it is obviously
too clumsy too verbose too little dramatic!

[page 6 *verso, pencil*]

wh lit his eye so oilily

really painful to believe—that the poor lady was lying.
Once a girl she had caught salmon freely; for fifteen years
desiring to minister to ~~that~~ the craving which Sir William had
contracted ~~as a boy at school,~~ for dominion, she had
cramped & squeezed, ~~&~~ pared & pruned, drawn back, peeped
through; so that without knowing precisely what made this
evening disagreeable, ~~or~~ <or> caused this pressure on the top of the
head; ~~It~~ <which> might be imputed to the furniture, <or> the pictures, the
or ~~something professional in the air,~~ or the
fatigue of a great doctor, whose life, as Lady Bradshaw said,
~~lying as usual,~~ was not his own but his patients,
disagreeable it was; ~~dull too, <alarming:> disheartening, &
enough to send you howling out into the street in search of
freedom, & making futile clutches with nervous fingers to
fr ward <lead> off the~~ & enough to send you howling out into
the street in fear of conversion.

That relief, however, was not allowed to his patients.
Converted they must be; {Sanity they had to achieve.}
~~Sanity they had to achieve. Life they must face.
And They had to adopt a sense of proportion for the
sake of those wives & husbands, whose sufferings, Sir
William would intimate, Sanity they must
achieve for the sake of their families.~~ There is the grey-walled
room, with the ground glass skylight, informed by all the
learning of Edinburgh & London, Sir William ~~addressed himself
daily to the profoundly difficult, p & painful task, of~~
did the job daily, & justly & humanely, & often got no
thanks for it, but made eight thousand a year, &
which he invested for his son, who was to go to the
University;

There in the ~~quiet~~ <grey> room with the groundglass skylight,
they heard ~~from Sir Williams lips the~~ extent of their
transgression. ~~It was~~ There ~~that~~ he went through that curious
exercise of the arms, ~~shooting~~ <shot> out the right hand clenched;
bringing <brought> it sharply back to his side with a smack.
~~which~~ <to> proved that Sir William ~~at least~~ <was master>—
controlled each action.
There some weakly broke down ~~in tears, while <at which>~~ Sir
William
most humanely looked away; ~~others~~ Here others,
~~rashly &~~ inspired by Heaven knows what intemperate madness,
~~first~~ charged Sir William to his face with humbug, or
questioned ~~what was~~ even more impiously <angrily> ~~the value of~~
life itself.
Why ~~not, for example,~~ live, ~~degraded, & dishonoured,~~ to the
~~tedious end, since what God~~; they ~~m~~ demanded? ~~&~~
Sir William <was inexorable; ~~he~~> replied that life was good.
~~He implied~~
Certainly, Lady Bradshaw hung over the mantelpiece in
~~evening dress,~~ & ~~it was reasonable to suppose that~~ Sir
~~William made ten thousand a year~~ was at the top of his
tree. ~~As for those who~~ But <to us,> life, they protested, ~~is~~
offers no such bounty to ~~us.~~ <Certainly it did not> He acquiesced.
And <perhaps> there is
no God. He shrugged his shoulders. In short, this living or
not living is a private affair of my own? ~~Here~~ Sir
William ~~was adamant.~~ <that> There was King George.
There ~~was~~ duty, & self-sacrifice, & humour & courage &
the family; ~~great disgrace, flight, cowardice; &~~
~~of~~ <all> which it appeased, ~~Sir William~~ had in Harley Street
a resolute champion, Sir William Bradshaw, who, had the
<belief> ~~had behind him, he~~ intimated, forces of all kinds, ~~legal, social,~~
which would see, he remarked, very quietly, that these ~~s~~
such ~~foolish~~ questionings, <impulses.> ~~were for they~~ <[ ][ ]> were
all the
result of a lack of blood, & physical exhaustion; spent
themselves in vain. And then ~~so stole~~ stole out

his income, it was rumoured, was £10,000 a year

from her hiding place & mounted ~~unmistakably~~ the throne &
~~inspired the eyes,~~ that <the> Goddess ~~who loves above all things~~
~~power,~~ &
whose lust it is to override opposition, & to stamp indelibly in
the sanctuaries of others souls the image of herself.
~~That~~ This miserable relic & rag of herself awaiting who came
came ~~bereft~~ fluttering before him bereft of shelter, ~~shade,~~ or
refuge, ~~should~~ naked, defenceless, received the ~~terrific~~
impression ~~stamp~~ of Sir Williams rage. He swooped: he devoured.
~~You're in my power, he murmured; And it was This~~ Such
decision, combined with humanity, ~~that proved~~ so ~~serviceable~~
endeared Sir William ~~so much~~ <greatly> to the relations of his victims.
~~patients.~~

Tick however said the grey marble clock in the consulting room:
tick, tick, tick., notwithstanding the fact that Sir William
was <now> downstairs, <was> ~~engaged~~ in eating his luncheon.
was pulling on his coat, was opening his front door, was
entering his motor car, ~~which~~ & driving away.
The clocks of Harley Street, where accuracy is rightly adored,
~~wher~~ were all <of> much ~~of~~ the same way of thinking; that it
it was very nearly half past one. ~~They had driven~~
~~decreed that With They had sliced up~~ The June day ~~between~~
~~them; divided it & baled <doled> it out in grains &~~
~~disposed of it was sliced up between them, &~~
~~had shredded the June day into between them, &~~
~~But~~ Shredding & slicing <nibbling> the June day into fragments,
they kept at it indefatigably. ~~nibbling at the~~ until
mound of time ~~which dwindled &~~ <was so far> diminished, that
a commercial clock in Oxford Street, whose hands are in
close touch with Greenwich, ~~announced a fact~~
spoke out loud. ~~It was half past one. Genially~~ it
~~spoke;~~ announced that it was half past one, spoke
genially, & fraternally as if it ~~gave~~ were a relief to
Messrs. Selby & Loundes to bestow that piece of
information for nothing. ~~Th~~ And while you looked
up at the clock, you read, almost automatically,

"Selby & Lowndes" written round the rim, & presumably the
~~know~~ name thus got into your sub-conscious mind, &
~~with~~ & subconsciously you were grateful, which gratitude
you liberated later by buying <off> ~~socks or shoes.~~ Messrs.
Selby & Lowndes socks ~~&~~ <or> shoes.

Miss Brush. So Hugh Whitbread reflected. <For> He had brushed the surface of
Lady ~~most modern~~ <many> theories,. ~~Without going deeply into life at any~~
~~point;~~ He had ~~in~~ brushed many surfaces: the dead languages;
the living; life in Constantinople, Paris, Rome; could ride & shoot, &
in his younger days had played tennis. Now, so the malicious
~~Walsh's & Sallys~~ asserted, he was head of some ~~<court>~~ department
for polishing ~~the King's <Royal>~~ boots, & could be seen on state
occasions
with a bunch of ribbons, a cocked hat, a sword, a
silk stockings keeping guard, ~~or checking tickets,~~ over what
~~was not apparent nobody knew. However, a little~~
~~information about the subconscious self & Dr Freud, m~~
~~had leaked into him, together with a miscellaneous~~
he had heard of ~~collection of facts from all sources. had leaked into him; undoubtedly~~
Freud, Stravinsky, ~~which was not surprising, considering <since> that he had been~~
& so on, since ~~afloat these fifty five years on the surface of London~~
~~society.~~ But nobody could question his <he looked the picture of>
chivalrous devotion. Moreover, since he had been
afloat on the cream of English society for fifty five years
~~some~~ all sorts of facts had <somehow> leaked in. He had heard of
Freud & Stravinsky ~~& so on~~. He had known Prime Ministers.
His affections were understood to be deep. And if he
was not ~~pre~~ connected with any of the greater movements
which had changed the face of the globe during his lifetime,
~~he had~~ one or two ~~sim~~ humble reforms <stood> to his credit.
~~One had reference to coffee~~ A coffee stall ~~perhaps~~ was one; perhaps
another had to do with the protection of owls in Norfolk:—
~~nor did any girl lose her place in his household~~
~~without being kept sight of <keeping his eye on her>.~~
~~{Altogher he had~~
~~his occupation; touched kept his ac & enjoyed his}~~
But this

~~but after all it is not this~~ in short his name figured with
~~sufficient regularity~~ <often [in?] [~~th~~?] [~~a~~?] [~~not~~?]>
at the end of <long> letters, asking for ~~subscriptions~~
money to protect, preserve, clear up~~, & paper boys~~ <letters on girls,>
~~& stamp out~~
abate nuisances. ~~for him to be in his~~ to be ~~liked~~
~~to pass through the world~~ And ~~he cer~~ lunched out, was
indeed now on his way to go through that ceremony which
habit made comfortable & old days rather sentimental
& conventions — with Lady Bruton in Brook Street. He ~~took her~~
desirable — must buy her flowers.
Ah but it was half past one!
A magnificent figure he appeared, pausing for a moment in
front of the great shop window. He regard~~ing~~<ed> ~~those~~ socks
&
ties critically. majestically, & yet with that slight
pucker between the eyes which ~~is the result~~ of
means that the {clock has struck: ~~that~~ it is time to go; ~~that~~
his — ~~indeed~~ the well trained body says <to the mind> On. Yet ~~he had~~ with
three or four thousand a year, could have bought anything;
looked at the world from that little eminence; but no one
dressed to match; but realised the obligations which
size, & health & wealth entail, & ~~behav~~ observed quite
scrupulously little courtesies & old fashioned ways which
gave a kind of quality to his ~~be~~ manner, something
to imitate, & to remember him by; for he would never
lunch for example with Lady Bruton, whom he had known
these twenty years, without bringing her, in his outstretched
in South Africa — hand a bunch of ~~flowers;~~ carnations; & asking
Miss Brushes' ~~brother~~ <her secretary> (Miss Brush was her secretary)
wh. for some reason — ~~taken~~ her brother
which — invariably remembered, & it must be imparted to a certain
Miss Brush who — ~~angularity on~~ Miss Brushes' ~~part that these enquiries~~
resented. — excacerbated her, & she ~~had didn't believe that Mr~~
never let on that — Whitbread ~~cared a straw for her brother; he was~~
her brother was — ~~<so much that she> was almost inclined to tell him about her~~
not — ~~brother, except~~
~~that she was almost killed her brother <denied once that she>~~ told a lie
once about her brother. & would have done so, had it not

seemed

Lady Bruton ~~observed all this grimly.~~
~~She herself preferred Richard Dalloway; who arrived at the same time, twenty minutes to two, that is to say.~~
~~But then she had known Hugh Whitbread for a hundred years.~~
who arrived the same moment.
~~Being very~~ <They were very> old friends; ~~friends of school & college; of a lifetime~~ <very old friends indeed.> indeed.
~~& said nothing.~~

Lady Bruton preferred Richard Dalloway, of course. He was ~~altogether made~~ <made of much> of finer material. But ~~she wouldn't~~
there was a great deal to be said for Hugh. She would never forget his kindness—oh years ago, he had been really remarkably kind. She sighed; ~~sharply,~~ impatiently, like an animal, who by some brisk movement has ~~reminded~~ shaken an arrow lodged in its flanks—such an arrow being for Lady Bruton her husbands <the governor> untimely death, years ago.
~~shooting,~~ in the East. ~~However,~~ <But> ~~the truth is that she was sixty; she was quite an old woman;~~ <However> The difference between one man & another is ~~not~~ remarkably little, granted the essentials. ~~Hugh's faults were sufficiently obvious. And at her age,~~
<She was> sixty two, ~~one wants a few simple things in one's friends—~~

old friends were old friends.

~~Nor had~~ She ever <had never> been good at that rather tiresome ~~essentially feminine~~ game which women like Clarissa Dalloway ~~used~~ to played incessantly—cutting people up, sticking them together. ~~Sir Edward, Lord Manning; M Percy W Wannof~~—The cleverest men of ~~their~~ <her> time—<had> ~~were~~ all ~~simple~~. been simple. It was in this very room that Sir Edward had got} She took the carnations with her angular grim smile. Nobody else was coming. She had got them there on false pretences—

to help her out of a difficulty

~~She showed the way. She was upright as a ramrod.~~

"But let us eat first" she said.
So there began a soundless & exquisite passing to & fro ~~from~~ through
swing doors of grey white capped maids, ~~women of discretion~~,
handmaidens not of ~~need & of act~~ necessity, but ~~rather~~
adepts in a mystery ~~which~~ or grand deception practised by
hostesses in Mayfair ~~at~~ <from> one thirty, ~~when~~ to two
when ~~they assert~~ with a wave of the wand ~~they~~
~~bid~~ the traffic ceases, & there rises instead this ~~e stra~~
profound illusion—~~how~~ in the first place about the food;
how it is not paid for; & then the table spreads itself
with glass & silver, little white mats & ~~small c~~
saucers of ~~glazed~~ <red> fruit; ~~the fire~~ burns, though it is
~~summer; wine comes, different wines; And all this is~~
~~ours; & with wine perhaps come the & the dulling of the~~
~~sounds,~~ & come ~~sudden visions;~~ twined jocund visions,
coloured, not plain, the fire burns; & with the wine
perhaps, & the food, (not paid for) come twined jocund visions,
~~which~~ like ~~serpents twisting & like serpents, wreathing up,~~
before musing eyes; speculative eyes, eyes now at repose to
observe—for example the beauty of the <red> carnations,
which Lady Bruton had laid severely beside her;
Let me say Do ~~try~~ <put> one, said Hugh, against your exquisite
lace.—the sort of remark ~~which presumably~~ you
might make if you had known your hostess twenty years.
<But> Miss Brush ~~never liked Hugh~~ thought ~~that sort of~~
~~thing~~ intolerably<e> ~~bad manners.~~ <bad taste.>
& then feeling

resting his fork, ~~& then feeling~~ Feeling apparently quite sure of himself,
Hugh Whitbread said, ~~leaning~~ "Wouldn't they look charming
against your lace?." Miss Brush resented ~~this~~ <his> familiarity
intensely
Lady Bruton raised the carnations; ~~she held with much the~~
but, holding them rather stiffly, (with much the same
attitude that her ~~great great grandfather~~ <the general> held the scroll of
white paper in the picture behind her) seemed set, fixed, entranced.
was the ~~Whether~~ <Now> she was the ~~great~~ <great> grand daughter, or the
great <great> grand
daughter of ~~Sir Miles~~ the general, Richard Dalloway was ~~never~~ not
momentarily not sure. Sir ~~Miles, Sir~~ Rhoderick, Sir Miles, Sir ~~Talbot~~ Sir
John— ~~He had it.~~ ~~He was~~ <The great great grand daughter> that was
it,
It was remarkable how in that family the likeness persisted~~;~~ in
the women ~~especially,~~ ~~Fanny Bruton was~~ <She shd. have been>
a Dragoon. [here?],
the leader of ~~An admirable soldier <leader> she would have made.~~ ~~had Richard~~
a forlorn hope; ~~Dalloway~~ a soldier; a leader of ~~men, generous, chivalrous—~~
he wd have sullen ~~absurd romantic~~, Richard Dalloway ~~was never blind~~
~~mu~~ cherished these romantic, chivalrous, ~~very~~ imaginative views,
served under her about ~~women~~ fine, well set up, ~~ruthless~~ old women of
pedigree; about their descent, which, fond of memoirs as
he was, ~~&~~ <indeed> ambitious of writing one, he ~~could~~ had at his
fingers' ends—~~He was no snob. Most people are~~
~~more or less pretty certainly the product of their environment:~~
~~was that birth matters; that the Br English are the best stock on~~
~~the whole in the world;~~ She <Fanny Bruton> came of one of the
oldest
~~most English~~ of families. ~~obscure & pigheaded,~~ <in England,
whose ~~name is~~ a token all over the world;>
~~though They had crossed in~~ & ~~even to look at her,~~
~~Their The military trade & even to look at her, one could~~
~~see one~~ & ~~was a one would~~ <& he wd have> like to ~~bring one of those~~
~~some of those young pacifists to look at her~~—
in his good humoured way. to bring some young
pacifists of his acquaintance ~~who denied~~ to lunch with
her; as if a type like that could ~~come spring~~
~~up~~ be bred <out> of ~~these~~ tea drinking amiable enthusiasts,
No, no. ~~You~~ He knew her home. He knew her people..

There was a tree, ~~whi~~ still living, which either Herrick or Lovelace, one or the other had sat under; down in Devonshire.

And so after considering whether it was the right moment to ~~introduce~~ <lay before them.> This ~~bother of hers,~~ question ~~which she wanted their advice on, because~~ it bothered her, & she would like to know, especially, what Richard Dalloway thought,—this question of drafting an appeal to the public for funds—if so, how to do it. ~~w~~ in what terms, & so on, Lady Bruton thought better not till we have had our coffee, & so laid the carnations down.
~~She gave her sigh. Nobody knew~~

And how's Clarissa? she asked.
~~Richard Dalloway, had~~ <It was> often ~~heard it of~~ said that Lady ~~Bruton had no women friends; though & Clarissa herself complained that made a grievance sometimes, of half in fun, of not being asked, of it sometimes, yet knew very well but the truth was that & as she turned the question out, & Richard remembered it as & it was true that she thought that Clarissa had hindered Richard rather with her lack of health & all that, so that she [ ] in her enquiries; Now she had no women friends; but she respected them;~~

Richard Dalloway had often heard it said that she did not like women; As a matter of fact she

"How's Clarissa?" she said abruptly.
Clarissa often said that Lady Bruton did not like her. Lady Bruton
had the reputation of being ~~polite~~ more interested in foreign
policy than in personal affairs, of talking like a man;
& of having had a finger in some notorious ~~hubbub~~ <intrigue> of the
80^{ties}, which was now beginning to be mentioned in memoirs.
Certainly there was ~~a table in~~ an alcove in her drawing
room, & a table in that alcove, & a photograph of
Sir Robert Muir, now deceased, <upon that table> who had
there written in
Lady Brutons presence, & with her cognisance, perhaps
~~upon <at> a very crucial moment.~~ upon an historical occasion.
advice, a telegram ordering the British troops to advance
~~upon a famous~~ She was loyal, & staunch, & well informed.
Thus when she said in this rather off-hand way "How's Clarissa?"
husbands had difficulty in persuading their wives, & indeed
~~were~~ however devoted were secretly doubtful themselves,
of her interest in ~~the feminine other~~ women, who often
~~were rather an impediment, were had rather prevented~~
~~their husbands from making the most of themselves~~—
got in their husbands' way, prevented them from
accepting posts abroad, & had to be taken to the
seaside in the middle of the session to recover from
attacks of influenza. Nevertheless, her enquiry How's
Clarissa? was known, even to Clarissa herself, to be
a signal, such as passing ships fling to each other, ~~of genuine~~
~~comradeship, interest~~ from ~~one~~ a well-wisher, from an
almost silent companion, whose utterances numbered perhaps
half a dozen in the course of a lifetime <but even ~~as~~ so she> {yet ~~went~~
~~silently &~~
~~steadfastly on & on &~~ would be honestly remembered when
~~with plain regret~~ when, as was bound to happen <at last> even to
this well set up martial woman, the ~~great~~ fog banks
swallowed her up & she went down, as, ~~however it happened~~
~~one~~ would <she would go down> manfully fighting. Strangely
enough, whenever
Clarissa saw her,} but signified, in their brief way, a
~~a sort of comradeship~~ <comradeship> recognition: ~~Of what?~~ Of some
community of feeling, ~~presumably, which united~~ them,
& went beneath these masculine luncheon parties, &

& united, Lady Bruton & M$^{rs.}$ Dalloway, who never met, &
often ~~gave~~ appeared, even to each other, indifferent or hostile.
"I met Clarissa ~~in the th~~ in the street this morning" said Hugh
Whitbread. diving into the casserole, anxious to pay himself
this little tribute of ~~having already~~ for he had only to come to
London, & he met people; but greedy too, ~~disgustingly greedy~~
Minna
~~Brush thought;~~ one of the greediest men she had ever known, Minna
~~Brush~~ Brush thought; ~~who <for she~~ who> observed men with
unflinching
rectitude, & was capable of everlasting devotion; being knobbed
scraped, angular, <& entirely> without feminine charm.

"D'you know who's in town?" said Lady ~~Wh~~ Bruton
suddenly bethinking her.

~~"Our old friend Peter Walsh."~~ I heard this morning—
~~O~~—our old friend Peter Walsh."
And ~~Ri~~ M$^{r.}$ Dalloway ~~beamed~~ <was genuinely glad;> all over, ~~so~~ Minna
Brush
~~expressed it to herself, being~~ thought, & M$^{r.}$ Whitbread only
thought of his chicken; ~~&~~

But then there was hidden from Miss Brush the
reason of <for> that charming friendly humane ~~merriment~~
smile which ~~lit up~~ M$^{r.}$ Dalloway's ~~face,~~ <sm smiled> when Peter Walsh
was mentioned; ~~& be the fact being that Peter had been
passionately in love with M$^{r.}$ Dalloways wife; she had
rejected him. how~~ <for> Peter had loved Clarissa, been refused,
~~been a failure,~~ gone to India, come a cropper, &
~~how could~~ Richard Dalloway ~~help feeling~~ was now
~~wandering about again,~~ on the look out, presumably,
for some sort of job, & Richard Dalloway had a very
great ~~feeling for him too.~~ <liking> for the dear old fellow too.

all three,

Lady Bruton, Hugh Whitbread & Richard Dalloway remembered
the same thing: ~~which was agreeable to <But> Richard Dalloway~~
~~how was c~~ (how passionately poor Peter had been in love)
but Richard Dalloway ~~also~~ thought ~~of~~ too ~~with the~~
~~how Clarissa & he had been married for twenty years~~;
about Clarissa. A ~~darker~~ depth ~~Cl~~ Minna Brush saw in ~~his~~
the ~~co~~ brown of his eyes; <she noticed> a ~~hint momentary~~ <the>
pause; a the hesitation;
~~one of those variations of expression which which~~
~~she thought~~ ~~She was~~ <which> interested her, as ~~Richar~~ Mr. Dalloway
always interested her, ~~& from~~ for what was he thinking, she
wondered, being unable to guess of course that he was
thinking how he would go back & find Clarissa, ~~waiting for~~
<in the drawing room,>
~~him,~~ —Clarissa whom Peter had so passionately loved
Ah yes, ah yes; his had been on the whole a very happy
life.

Minna Brush might years ago have fallen in love with
these silences, & her ~~own incorrect but~~ highly shrewd interpretations
of them. Now, ~~singularly aloof as she was,~~ <at 40,> Lady
Bruton~~'s had movements,~~ <had only to> nods, & she took the signal—
sunk ~~in what~~<how>ever deeply she might herself be, in these
reflections of a detached spirit, of a disinterested onlooker,
~~to~~ whom life could not bamboozle, because life had
offered her not a single trinket of value—not a curl, ~~not~~ a
~~shapel~~ smile, ~~not~~ a lip, cheek, or nose; ~~Austerely she~~
Lady Bruton desired them to hurry up in order that she
might get to business. And Parking was instructed, &
plates were changed.

[*pencil*]

Peter Walsh has come back said Ly B.

"Yes, Peter Walsh has come back" said Lady Bruton.
The idea of this battered wanderer returning at intervals to
their secure shores was vaguely flattering to them all.
But to help him, they reflected, was ~~a~~ impossible, because of some
~~fundamental~~ flaw in his character. ~~However,~~ Hugh Whitbread
~~reflected~~ of course would be pleased to mention his name to so-&-so
& so-&-so. ~~Already~~ He looked consequential yet lugubrious
at the ~~very~~ mere thought of the letters he would write to so & so & so
so about "my old friend Peter Walsh", ~~on~~ But it wouldn't
lead to anything—not to anything permanent.

"~~He's~~ in ~~trouble~~ <In trouble ~~aga~~ with his wife> Im afraid"
said Lady Bruton ~~briefly~~
~~trouble~~ with his wife." ~~But she was thinking~~ after all,—
deplorable as these ~~things~~ <affairs> are, they don't ~~somehow~~ count;

~~Richard Dalloway smiled. Of course this was what
they all guessed~~ They had all guessed that that was at the
bottom of it—"However," said Lady Bruton, anxious to leave
this subject, ~~on~~ "we shall no doubt hear the whole story from
Peter himself—"

~~I will get Evelyn to ask him~~ to lunch, said Hugh
Whitbread.

You don't know his address, I suppose?" said Hugh Whitbread
we will ask him to lunch." ~~slapp~~ & there was at once a ripple
~~For the flood of grey maids maids who watched so soundlessly~~
The address had lodged itself some where in the flood of
in the grey ~~soundless~~ <tide of> service which washed round Lady Burton
day <in> ~~after~~ day, out, ~~the~~ collecting, intercepting, ~~as~~
enveloping Lady ~~Burton herself~~ in a fine ~~tisse~~
tissue of ~~comfort~~ which broke concessions, mitigated
~~th~~ interruptions, & spread round the house in Brook
Street a fine ~~meshed~~ net, where ~~little~~ things lodged, &
were picked out ~~acc~~ accurately & ~~soundlessly~~ <intently> by
Parkin, ~~& who~~ greyhaired Parkin, who had been with
Lady Bruton for ~~fifty y~~ thirty years, & knew her friends by name,
~~Parkin knows~~ "M[r.] Walsh's address Parkin?" said
her ladyship. <&> He wrote it down for M[r.] Whitbread. who
~~ope~~ took out his pocket book, & ~~wrote down~~ raising<ed> his
eyebrows slipped it in among documents of greater importance.

Still the coffee hadn't come. Hugh was slow, Lady Bruton thought: he
was getting fat, she noticed. Richard always looked in the very
pink of <prime of health>
condition. But ~~at her~~ the whole of her being was setting
more & more positively & undeniably & domineeringly ~~upon~~
brushing aside all this trifling, upon that ~~topic which~~
subject which engaged her attention, not merely her attention
but that core of her nature, ~~that essential thing~~ that essential
part of her, that fibre which was the ram rod of her soul,
without which Millicent Bruton would not have been Millicent
Bruton, that ~~societ~~ scheme of hers for emigrating young
people of both sexes ~~to Canada~~ & setting them up ~~in a~~
with a fair prospect of doing well in Canada. She had
perhaps lost her sense of proportion, ~~it might be said.~~
Emigration ~~is not~~ <wore not> ~~had not to others the~~ same rosy
aspect to others that it did to her. It was not to them ~~the~~ <an> obvious
remedy, ~~the <a>~~ sublime conception; ~~which which saved England from
which that, after twenty years, it had become to her.
No; for of course, For But then, Lady Bruton had a military~~ <came of>
~~soul. stock, the~~ the liberator of the pent egotism,
~~which, like all~~ <which a> strong martial women, <a> well nourished
a well descended woman, a woman of direct impulses,
downright feelings, ~~&~~ <&> little ~~given to introspection,~~
introspective power, feels rise within her, once youth is
past, & must eject upon some object—it may be
emigration, it may be emancipation; but whatever it be,
this object round which the essence of her soul is
daily secreted, <be>comes naturally ~~to wear for her a
prismatic lustre, h in which~~ prismatic, lustrous,
half looking glass, half precious stone, at once the
soul of her soul, & the soul of rightness too.

But Lady
Bruton was
no writer

~~Lady Bruton cared more for emigration; & could be made to suffer more by an insult to this scheme of hers than in any other way.~~

~~But the trouble was this: When it came to writing, Lady Bruton was helpless knew herself to be helpless. She had tried, over & over again: She, had a so capable in every <other> way, could no more was like an old country woman crossing the Trafalgar Square at midday when it came to writing.~~

Emigration in short becom

[Draft of "Character in Fiction," a paper read to the Heretics Society at Cambridge, 18 May 1924, and based on "Mr. Bennett and Mrs. Brown," *Living Age*, 2 February 1924. A longer, revised version was published in *Criterion*, July 1924, and appears as "Mr. Bennett and Mrs. Brown" in *The Captain's Death Bed and Other Essays* (1950).]

20th May. Emigration in short becomes largely ~~Millicent~~ <Lady> Bruton.
But it was necessary to write. And ~~here~~ Lady Bruton
had no gift with the pen. One ~~A~~ letter to the Times, she used to say to
Miss Brush, cost her more <effort> than to organize an expedition to
central Africa, ~~for which kind of work she was singularly
fitted.~~ ~~In her~~ ~~From the depths of her weakness,~~ After a
morning's battle, beginning, tearing up, beginning again,
she used to feel the futility of her own womanhood, as she felt it
on no other occasion, & would turn gratefully to the
thought of Hugh ~~Whitbl~~ Whitbread who possessed—no one
could doubt it—the art of writing letters to ~~newspapers.~~
the Times.

{And so she was glad that he praised the soufflé;
~~She could not help~~ A being so differently constituted from herself
~~could not be conjured~~ had passions, which ~~could not be~~
one could not call simply greed, because ~~after all~~ they ~~may
be essential to its~~ might be part of this gift.} And
indeed Lady Bruton often suspended her judgement of men
in deference to the mysterious accord, in which they stood, &
no woman, to the ~~apparently~~ laws of the universe, so that it
somehow right— ~~Hugh wrote a litt her statement~~ Richard ~~& Hugh~~ advised
~~right relations to the~~ her, & Hugh wrote for her, she was sure of being in the
~~world~~ ~~right, in the queer way in which one <their> sex was right, & hers wrong.
Therefore she was glad that Hugh Whitbread enjoyed~~ the
~~soufflé~~; <Therefore:> She did not call Hugh greedy, because to enjoy
the soufflé in that rapt manner might be part of
~~the mysterious~~ <the> gift. And she waited until he was
~~really~~ <at liberty> ~~liberated from that the tyranny which~~, until he
was smoking, to ~~say, & she said it very~~ begin, & she
began very ~~ten~~ submissively to lay before them her
difficulty.

how she wanted to ask their advice.
Miss Brush laid papers on the table, & very soon Hugh Whitbread
had taken out a ~~smooth~~ <stout> silver fountain pen, which ~~as he drew it~~
had ~~I~~ now done, he said, ~~its~~ twenty years of service, &
~~therefore was~~ never failed him, which somehow appeared ~~rather~~ to ~~his~~ <the>
Hugh's credit, ~~of his just & humane & temperate life,~~ & to the
~~service to~~ credit of the sentiments which his pens expressed,
& was ~~drafting~~ <carefully writing> letters of the alphabet with
rings round them in
the ~~margins~~ <corners>, & thus marvellously reducing Lady Bruton's
tangles to formality, to English, to sense to grammar,
such as the Editor of the Times would respect, Lady Bruton
felt, watching the marvellous accomplishment. Now the
men argued. ~~And Richard was had far the better brain~~ of the
~~two.~~ Hugh was slow. Hugh was pertinacious. ~~Richard was~~
~~bold.~~ Richard said one must take risks. ~~in a matter of~~
~~this kind.~~ Hugh proposed modifications, in deference to
peoples feelings, which he said rather tartly. when
Richard laughed "had to be considered." ~~It was no~~
~~use putting backs up, he said,~~ & read out how "We are
therefore of opinion that the time is ripe for some
such measure" which Richard thought all stuffing &
bunkum, but no harm in it of course, & so Hugh went on
drafting sentiments <in alphabetical order,> of the highest nobility
~~sonority &~~
common sense. looking all the while ~~public spirited,~~
in <in solemn> contact with a larger world than that in which he
~~sat, letting his cigarette f go out, <&> frowning, sighing~~
~~occasionally & somehow sp in as if he were~~
for the good of the country, ~~he was prepared to~~ one
~~must sacrifice,~~—& summing up now & then the
progress they had made, until finally he read out
the letter, or speaking correctly, the draft of the letter
which embodied, so he said, the points arrived at, in
language <to> which no exception whatever could be taken.
"A masterpiece!" Lady Bruton exclaimed,

surprised as usual that what she meant could possibly be got up
so sublimely as that.

Hugh thought it necessary to add that he doubted whether <cd. not
be sure that>
the editor would ~~have~~ put it in. But, he said, he would drop
a line to ~~see so-&-so about it.~~
somebody.
And Lady Bruton who seldom did a graceful thing,
stuffed all the carnations into a vase with her own
hands.

& flinging them out again ~~said in a~~ called him "My prime Minister", & didn't know what she could have done without them, she said. They rose. Richard Dalloway ~~said~~ as usual looked at the General's portrait because ~~it was it was his serious intention to~~
he meant, whenever he had a moment's leisure, to write
a ~~history of biography, of~~ a history of Lady B~~ur~~<ru>ton's
family,—
And Lady Bruton was very proud of her family. But they could wait, They could wait, she said; ~~ev~~ meaning ~~by that~~ that her ancient family of military men, admirals, administrators, had been men of action ~~themselves~~, & that Richards first duty was to his country; ~~but one of these days when they <he> had time~~ as ~~they would have agreed.~~ but it was a fine face, she said, & all the papers were ready for Richard, ~~when Richard chose.~~ down at ~~Tri [ ] Af <Ald> p<m>ixton,~~ Aldmixton, when ever ~~he chose.~~
and then as ~~they were~~ <as> ~~she stood~~ they took their bowler hats in the hall, & Hugh was ~~exceedingly charm telling~~ <offering> Miss Brush some ~~discarded~~ ticket, ~~for something or other,~~ or privilege ~~or~~ of some ~~kind,~~ Richard ~~suddenly~~ turned to Lady Bruton & said "We shall see you at our party tonight" ~~W~~ whereupon Lady Bruton ~~looked blank, then looked like the magnificent— formidable woman~~ resumed her magnificence, which le letter writing had shattered, ~~& said~~

sort, which she did not appreciate

~~Whether she meant that~~ she ~~would~~ <might> come, or that ~~she~~ might ~~would~~ not; ~~it was impossible to say.~~ <come;> parties were not in her line.

~~And then~~ She went ~~slowly~~ up to her room. She lay, one arm extended, on
the sofa. She sighed, she snored, not that she was asleep.
only drowsy, drowsy & heavy, like a field of clover in the
sunshine this hot June day, with the bees going round &
about & the ~~cloud~~ yellow butterflies. Always she went back to
~~that~~ those fields, down in Devonshire, where she had jumped the
brooks on Patty her pony, with Mortimer & Tom. ~~She had~~ <She had>
~~loved horses. &~~ her brothers, <now> grey old men. ~~now~~.
And there were the dogs; ~~& so, relaxed in~~ There were the rats;
& there were the old people, sitting under the tree in the lawn,
little witches that they were!. always stealing through the
shrubbery so as not to be seen, coming back all bedraggled
from some roguery ~~And so, & so.~~ <And so.> Ah dear, she ~~remembered
remembered the whole thing~~ it was Wednesday afternoon,
in Grosvenor Street—~~she knew that. These kind men had gone,~~
these <kind> good fellows; Hugh Whitbread, Richard Dalloway, had gone
this hot day through the streets, whose murmur <growl> came up to her,
~~so hot in London at this season;~~ ~~And~~ power was hers,
& position; & income; ~~&~~ She had known great men; had
good friends; ~~been behind the scenes;~~ Murmuring London
~~pa~~ flowed up to her, & her hand, lying over the sofa back,
curled upon some imaginary rod or baton, such as her
grandfathers might have held, ~~wit~~ holding which she
seemed, drowsing<es>, ~~hang~~ & ~~ha~~ heavy to be directing; <&> ~~com~~
commanding; ~~somehow giving time;~~ this emigration
to Canada, ~~& getting her own way at committees,~~
~~so that drowsing<es> & heavy~~ those good fellows walking across
London. That territory of theirs, that ~~fair~~ carpet, Mayfair,

[Review of *Robert Smith Surtees (Creator of "Jorrocks") 1803-1864* by himself and E. D. Cuming. (*Nation & Athenaeum*, 21 June 1924)]

Flowers. Since he had doubts about his taste in solid objects,
~~he would buy~~ flowers; <it shd. be,> & so celebrate what was,
reckon things as you will,
an event. Yes, yes, he thought, massing the deep black & the blood red
tulips together, its the greatest mistake in the world not to ~~let people~~
say exactly what one feels. And he pocketed his sixpence or
two of change & went ~~on holding the~~ <off> his great bunch, ~~which~~
~~tapered to a~~ twisted into tissue paper ~~from which all the heads~~
in his hand, to ~~tell Clar Westminster, to his house,~~ to tell
Clarissa ~~that~~ <Here> ~~These~~ are for you because I love you. Yes he
intended to say it straight out, in so many words, whatever
people might think of him, "Here are some flowers . . . I love you"
~~upon~~ <at> which she would laugh; but he was going to make her
understand it. ~~He had loved~~ her from the first moment he
set eyes on her. ~~And though Peter Walsh might have given her in~~
~~some ways a more amusing time of it,~~ She would never
have been happy married to ~~Peter Walsh~~. anyone else.
And it struck him that ~~he was a~~ it was really a miracle, however one
looked at it, ~~after the war & one thing & another,~~ that he should be
actually going to open that door & find her. ~~And~~ One
feels these things, & one doesn't say them, he thought. Partly one's
lazy; partly one's shy. And Clarissa was—~~well, as~~ he
hesitated to cross; ~~he~~ upon which, being not merely simple minded
but having kept his simplicity undebauched ~~by all~~ <~~because of~~
needing of> the air
that had sung through his clothes, & ~~all~~ the turf his
stout boots had tramped, by the fish he had caught, the
pheasants he had shot, & the dogged pertinacity with which
he had championed the downtrodden & worthless in the
houses of Parliament—being preserved in his simplicity
yet at the same time made null too, ~~by~~ & ~~a little~~
speechless & stiff; ~~he—upon so thus, so,~~ now, hesitating to
his wife cross,
~~She Clarissa's~~ seemed to him ~~simply~~ a miracle. <So> A drop of gold
suddenly suffuses a painted window. He would tell her
that he loved her. And this he would say, ~~not~~
since the fates ~~had~~ willed it ~~so~~, not to any good elderly woman,

not to some admirable creature like Evelyn Whitbread, but to—to
Clarissa, who was

~~Very well, very well.~~ But it did make his blood boil to see ~~a~~
little creatures of five & six crossing Piccadilly. alone. ~~Richard~~
~~Dalloway~~ <The police ought to have stopped the traffic at
He once>
~~had no sentimental illusions about the infallibility of the~~
~~London police. He collected evidence against them; he had~~
~~reason to think that the London police force,~~ ~~But~~ He had no
illusions about the London police. He was collecting evidence
~~against them~~
of their malpractices, being one of those good fellows who
~~are never~~ <not> ~~taken~~ <see thru> in by starch & buttons & gold
lace & red tape, but
~~have a feeling for the~~ keep a <sort of> liking for the unfortunates—
for costermongers.—Why ~~shouldn't~~ they <not let them> ~~keep~~
<stand> their barrows in the streets?—
for prostitutes—~~for good Lord, nobody how can any man~~
~~blame them;~~ Good Lord, the fault wasn't in them, ~~but in~~
not in young men either, but in our detestable social
system. & so forth; all of which ~~was~~ any woman with
eyes in her head could see, ~~as this very~~ in the shrewd face,
in the upright ~~bearing~~ <carriage>, ~~in~~ the tan, the ~~brown~~ shoes, the
~~grey~~ clothes, the direct yet considerate ~~b~~ bearing of this
member of Parliament who was determined to tell his <walking
sturdily across the Green Park>
wife that he loved her, ~~& to give her a bunch of black—~~
~~red tulips.~~

~~Yet as for~~ This sprawling paper bag business in the Parks at
midday rather afflicted him; & young men lounging about with
girls.

The floor of the Green Park flashed & faded, as if a yellow lamp
were moved
capriciously
beneath. Now a whole family, perambulator, <baby?> bags, bottles
of milk, was
lit up under a plane tree; now ~~one~~ <a> solitary ~~man.~~ woman,
stretched in curious abandonment, as if she had flung herself in
~~abandonment,~~ on the earth. ~~to rid herself of some intolerable~~
tie ~~which the streets had inflicted on her, & now looked up,~~
~~from her island of sunny green,~~ to ~~with her chin propped~~ in
~~her hand, & her eye large & bright as~~ to observe
curiously, to speculate aloofly, to consider ~~man woman & child~~
~~as they came her way.~~ the why & the wherefores. from her
island of sunny green.
~~That was a jolly fellow with his flowers, she thought.~~
Bearing his flowers like a weapon Richard Dalloway
approached her, &
intent he passed; yet in this vast & bewildering procession,
where as the
preachers say we never ~~go~~ go the same road twice, ~~or~~ &,
of the myriads of faces we meet, <never> see the same ~~again~~
~~<once more>~~, where
death is the ~~lot~~ <reward> of each & this animation of legs & arms is
more proper to the grave, still there was time for
~~a spark of consciousness, a recognition of some sort, between~~
~~man & woman, & the a proclamation, an assertion~~
~~that he was taking tulips to his wife. a roar of~~ <a laugh>
laughter—
~~as if She did, in short,~~ ~~And the laughter of two people whom~~
~~social circumstances separate them,~~ ~~which being~~
~~between the socially separated, the unintroduced,~~
~~And the laughter be of two people separated by social~~
~~circumstances, who have not been introduced, is~~
Not that they would ever speak.

[Draft of "Thunder at Wembley," here called "Nature at Wembley" (*Nation & Athenaeum,* 28 June 1924. *Collected Essays* vol. 4, 1967)]

The man ~~had~~ was a ~~very~~ <all right> decent sort,' she thought.
Richard thought how the poor enjoy life.
Then there was Buckingham Palace, ~~& there too if you think of <which>~~
~~it as a <like a> prima donna, who has grown so stout that she can hardly waddle between the first violins on to the platform,~~
~~& is seriously impeded by a bunch of carnations,~~
~~& yet robes herself in white & stands out faces the audience,~~
~~though you may smile has its magnificence; &~~
~~which is not so bad, if you reflect upon the courage of painting yourself white when you weigh twenty stones;~~

(like an old prima donna facing the public, in white)

As for Buckingham Palace, you can't deny it a certain dignity./ nor utterly deride what after all does stand for millions of people ~~as H~~ for a symbol—Victoria—~~& the~~ & ~~the dolphins, the naked boys: <& her> fountains, & so on.~~ naked boys ~~& so on utterably detestable, & so Richard fountains—<dolphins! [   ] abound abound utterly abound>~~

~~Though heaven knows, Richard thought, a child with a box of bricks cd. have done better—~~
~~with a box of bricks could have turned out something better;~~
~~Only where people have been before you, buoyant, exulted, still laughing,~~ certain, ~~quite~~ certain, of meeting Clarissa;
~~&~~ opening the door, ~~& holding out his flowers~~; & now

wobbling over

~~adjust arranging, as he walked, a that possession~~, that congeries of impressions, which added to imperceptibly day by day, his philosophy, ~~to is a view,~~ was ~~his own~~ the treasure of his life, ~~its ballast~~ to ~~this~~ pure weight to this observation—how ~~its all moments, like this~~—happiness ~~is moments,~~ this.

~~To be certain: of opening the door;~~

To be sure, it doesn't last: But the folly is to let that interfere. I am a man, Richard thought; this is London, ~~1923;~~ June, 1923: all of which, seemed celebrated by the gentle swaying to & fro of all the little trees; & the firm statues, obdurate, fixed, cut in bronze.

[Review of "Unwritten History" by Cosmo Hamilton. (*Nation & Athenaeum,* 21 June 1924)]

To be sure it doesn't last; ~~happiness cannot last.~~ but the folly is
to let that interfere. No, it ~~should not~~ <should> interfere.
Out swung above his head the first tremble of the ~~soun~~ of the
stroke of the hour:
Clarissa positively jumped. Undoubtedly, she should
have finished her letter, ~~& the sound surprised her.~~
~~Old Mrs. Jenkinson.~~ Oh but it was no good writing; she must
telephone, she must wire. And really why should Mrs. ~~Mal~~
~~Masham~~ <Marsham>
~~Jenkins~~ interfere? Mrs. Marsham "knowing that dear Clarissa
would forgive her" ~~That was the first~~ page, "had found Milly
Henderson looking so ~~poor~~ down" & it ~~came out~~ <had discovered
only by asking,> that ~~Clarissa~~ had ~~<Milly did not>~~
she complained, that Clarissa had not invited her." ~~A to her party.~~
A party is <[was?]> ~~like the~~ stump of a tree with which you stir
<a [fire?]> ~~the mud.~~—
The leeches at the bottom of the pond conglomerate: the dull, the
drab; ~~the~~ the women without occupation; ~~the~~ were all afloat.

[Review of "The Life & Last Words of Wilfrid Ewart" by Stephen Graham. (*Nation & Athenaeum*, 21 June 1924)]

Out boomed the first stroke of the hour.
Clarissa positively ~~jum~~ <at her writing table> jumped. Why
should M$^{rs.}$ Marsham
interfere? M$^{rs.}$ Marsham "knowing that dear Clarissa
letter would forgive her" ~~had fo (that took up one~~ page) "had
found Milly Henderson looking so down, (only by asking,
for Milly did not complain) that Clarissa had not invited her"—
~~A party is the stump of a tree with which you stir the mud,~~
Would Clarissa invite her?" Why must she invite all the
dull women in London? She took her pen. But writing was no
good. She must telephone: wire. 'Hope to see you at my
party'. Send out Lucy with a telegram. Or send Elizabeth.
Elizabeth was closeted with Dora Kilman. ~~How~~
Down came the second stroke. ~~Really,~~ They might be
praying, if she knocked at the door. Anything more ~~wildly~~
~~infuriating~~—nauseating, she could not conceive<:>—Prayer, ~~with~~
~~that~~
~~woman.~~ at this hour with that woman. And the
sound of the bell flooded the room with its melancholy wave
~~For~~ She could ~~never~~ <not> understand ~~Elizabeth. It was~~
~~inexplicable.~~
~~her daughter.~~ Elizabeth. ~~hap~~ The receding wave gathered
itself together to fall once more; & she heard at the same
time distractingly a scratching, fumbling, ~~slam.~~ <which> with
overpowering dignity the stroke of three obliterated ~~any other~~
all. It was three. ~~o'clock. Nothing else survived~~
It was three. <She did not hear> ~~And~~ The <door> handle
turn~~ed~~; ~~&~~ <But> in came
Richard, ~~holding out his flowers~~ surprisingly. ~~with his~~
~~flowers.~~

The door handle slipped round & in came Richard surprisingly.
~~an~~ in the middle of the sound. He held out his flowers.
~~Oh~~ she had failed him, once at Constantinople.
He gave her <came up holding> the flowers. But then, Lady Bruton's had
not asked her lunch parties were said to be extraordinarily amusing.
He gave her the flowers. <~~raises~~ his raised his hand>
Elizabeth was praying with that
odious creature, Kilman. ~~All the dull frumps in London were coming to her party.~~ She was forced to ~~have them.~~ to ask all the frumps in London to her parties.
~~She~~ He kissed her.
~~And why? Oh but~~ {to relinquish, sink, surrender, & go down into ~~the depths where jarring worries were not~~ darkness.
& ~~then to rise with~~ was delight. She rose shaken.
Trembling she took the flowers; At once ~~in some~~} There arranged itself, in
the flowers, in the shell like mouth of the tissue paper in the nodding
(thoughts that came into her mind) something that ~~she would never~~ <Richard came into the room> always stand for this moment. <be Richard coming into the room.>
~~Ah, but she must not say "We had them at home." That he~~
~~Her memories did not She must accept the present <moment>; moment.~~
~~old, worn, undone by the trifles & sufferings & the nameless sufferings & agonies of this terrifying existence, as she was—by the aging of Elizabeth, & this impending party, & the great quiver of the strok bell—she must put that away & be simple with him; direct; For he said "I love. you." <he said> She took his flowers, &~~
—Yes, he had said it.
~~And now, very well; Ah yes, it was delicious.~~
~~Clarissa never said anything.~~
She never ~~said anything But it was~~ all right—
I shall put them up there, on the mantelpiece, she said,
Was it amusing? ~~she asked.~~ for she never said anything.
No: awfully dull.
And I had peter Walsh! she cried. ~~& & — oh theres~~
That damned woman here. ~~The woman~~ Kilman.
~~One moment, just before I go back.~~

& Mrs. Marsham—

Shant we sit down, for ten minutes, ~~quite~~ quietly, <?> said Richard. ~~It looked awfully~~ nice.

But she didn't like having flowers out of water; or that wasnt quite the right place;

He's in love again, she said. Isnt it awful? I feel his whole life has been such a failure. There he was with that knife—opening it, d'you remember? ~~And he said It's some woman in India: And he made me feel—~~ ~~Oh how~~ it <all> came back! ~~all day I've had that feeling~~— But why is it that he makes me feel—~~wretched~~? a failure too. ~~But, my dear,~~ you can't put them on that ridge. <They wont stand on that ridge Clarissa.>

~~But me tell me—~~<And I> didnt ~~I~~ treat him badly: ~~after all, I~~

~~Never, never. said Richard stoutly.~~

~~We should have been miserable.~~

[Draft of "Notes on an Elizabethan Play." (*Times Literary Supplement*, 5 March 1925; *The Common Reader*, 1925)]

[46]

They ~~were sitting~~ <sat> on the sofa together, looking at the mantelpiece, in
the middle of which, between the silver candlesticks, Clarissa had stood the carnations: It ~~looked~~ all looked very beautiful, very stately. as a ~~Half the furniture was <had been> moved away; the chairs set~~

~~The chairs~~ <The chairs> against the wall, for the party.

"He came straight to you, did he?" said Richard.

"Just as I was thinking of Bourton" And he's in trouble, going to get a
divorce, oh in love with some other woman out there.

~~What made you~~ ~~Why did you~~ get them?" she asked.

Why shouldn't I sometimes? give you something?" <the admirable Hugh gives Evelyn necklaces.>

Hugh? oh I met him

And then, it came over me. I might have married you.
And then, ~~& then,~~ Oh ~~he's a ghastly failure, wrink shrivelled;~~ <hes> quite old; & ~~somehow one~~ feels everything, is <such ~~as~~ as>
~~over~~; At the same time, so nice, you know, ~~so real~~—as he always was at the worst time; ~~so~~ honest. ~~Real, yes: perhaps~~ thats ~~what~~ <was> his charm." ~~was? making his crticism.~~

Saying things that make one feel ~~absolutely a crushed~~. wretched, vile.

~~And Hugh said he'd met you.~~ you met Hugh. too, in the street.

~~"I dont do that, anyhow,"~~

~~As they looked~~ at the roses, one moved apart from the others, suddenly;

Whats this about Elizabeth? Richard asked.

~~Only the usual thing.~~ Kilman arrives. <Elizabeth turns pink.> They go off together—

They

shut themselves up. ~~Such a~~ I suppose they're praying:

"Lord, Lord, Lord," said Richard, not that he liked it, but its no use interfering after all. ~~Not a bit of course~~—you set people's backs up.

~~But~~ "She's such a lump" said Clarissa. Besides she's rude to me, actually, in my own house. ~~She's no manners.~~

~~The poor creature to do without~~ <has no manners>

~~But~~ I don't want Elizabeth to do without." <have none>

~~And then~~ <Besides>

What does it ~~all~~ mean?"

Religion? said Richard.
~~Religion:~~ They saw the roses & the candlesticks & the chairs stood against the wall. ~~Since the windows were open,~~ The usual jungle of London sound ~~crossed~~ wove itself outside.
And ~~theres this bot nuisance about~~ <asking> Milly <Henderson>, said Clarissa—
~~I tell you all my troubles.~~ What am I to do about Milly Henderson? "~~Well, tell~~ it
~~That he~~ settled. And ~~La~~ Mrs. Marsham ~~should be told~~ to bring her.
~~That was disposed of.~~ <[ ]> if Mrs. Marsham ~~feels~~ wants to bring her.

He didn't like it; no, he didn't; but these things will pass over, if you let them.
She's such a ~~bore~~ <frump>, said Clarissa. Besides, she's rude to me actually
in my own house. Besides, what does it all mean?
"Religion?—~~the desire to conversion~~" Richard ~~mused~~
very slightly shrugged his shoulders, examining his hands, which were
clean, perfectly ~~kept.~~ clean—nails, ~~evenly~~ <all>
"And, said Clarissa, after a pause; what am I to do about
Milly Henderson?"
~~That wasn't difficult.~~ "Tell ~~Mrs. Marsham to bring her if she wanteds~~" As for that ~~how could it matter? a straw one way or another?~~ One woman <~~sad~~ Milly Henderson,> more or less at a party?—how could it matter.
"Ask her. Let Mrs. Marsham bring her."
"They were talking of Peter at lunch" said Richard; & <but> he could not
go into it; how ~~suddenly~~ he had felt that emotion: Ah but he had
said "I love you": he had put it into words. ~~He would~~ He was
~~took her hand.~~ intent.
~~Now~~ I must be off" he said, <suddenly> as if ~~he~~ were rousing himself.
And he got up, & he pulled down his waistcoat, & he
straightened his tie; & he ~~stopped~~ stood there looking, as if
he were making a note of it all, & she wondered
why. ~~Would he explain?~~
"~~What A~~ <Is a> committee?" she asked, as he opened the door.
Armenians" he said, in one word; or, perhaps it was
Albanians.
And really, ~~it was so~~ there is a dignity ~~in about human beings which is~~ in people; a solitude; even between husband & wife
a gulf; & that one must respect, Clarissa thought, watching him.
~~I respect it in Richard; he respects it in me,~~ for it is what one could
not part with, or ~~impinge~~, <take> without losing <one's> self respect, <one's> independence

passing away behind a pane of glass,

He returned ~~<carry>~~ with a pillow & a quilt.
"An hour's complete rest after lunch" he said,
dogmatically, quoting from a prescription; & disappeared.

[Draft of "Notes on an Elizabethan Play" (*Times Literary Supplement*, 5 March 1925. *The Common Reader*, 1925)]

~~Clarissa~~ <She> laughed. He would go on saying that to the end of time,
because a doctor had <once> ordered it. It was like him to
accept what Doctors
said literally. ~~It was~~ part of his adorable, ~~his~~ divine, simplicity.
~~pa~~ the thing in him she most loved, which no one had to the same
extent, which made him go quietly & do the thing, while she—
Peter frittered their time in bickering. He was already
half way to the House of Commons, to his ~~committee~~,
<Armenians> having
settled ~~all~~ her difficulties. That wasn't quite true. ~~though.~~
He ~~did not see the~~ did not see the drawbacks of inviting Milly
Henderson.
~~another single woman.~~ She would do it, of course, as he had said
that. Since he had brought the pillows, she ~~must~~ <would> lie down,
for a time at least. But—but—{what had come over her}?
Why did she suddenly feel, for no reason, <so> unhappy?
~~despising herself? not in good terms with herself anyhow.~~
As a person who has dropped some tiny stone, into the grass, ~~she~~ &
parts the tall blades very carefully, this way & that, & searches
here & there
vainly & ~~there~~ & at last spies it there at the root. she went
~~through this that & the other.~~ <the possibilities.> ~~That Sally~~
~~Seaton had said~~
~~years ago~~ <one by & [away?]> through this & that ~~possibility~~:
<said ~~out~~ one's not> ~~that~~ <how> Sally Seaton ~~had~~
said of Richard ~~he had a second class mind; & it was~~ true he
~~was~~ would never now be in the Cabinet; & it was true; how
Richard never would now discuss ~~important things~~: religion
was ~~one of the~~
an example: <No> It was nothing to do with Elizabeth. ~~she was~~
It was earlier in the day perhaps? ~~It was~~ something that
Peter had said, combined with something that Richard
had said that <&> ~~took away all her courage.~~ Oh parties!
That was it! Her ~~passion for~~ parties. They did
criticise her, both of them; very unfairly, very unjustly.
~~But~~ That was it; ~~yes~~ that was it!

Well, how was she going to defend herself?
She was now absolutely happy. She felt physically very
vigorous: They thought <(or rather Peter did)> that she
enjoyed her own
prestige & liked to have famous people about; <a great pride> was
well Peter might think she ~~merely~~ a snob <in [fact?]>; ~~Richard was thought it a natural,~~
~~<much more simple>~~
~~rather foolish craving for excitement.~~ how she loved

wh. was foolish, considering that her heart was well.

excitement. And both were quite wrong. For what she liked, of course, was simply, life.

She had an odd sense that she & life were alone ~~in the~~ <in this> ~~room together.~~

~~You're what I~~ Thats what I do it for" she said (being not merely alone, but since she was lying on the sofa, cloistered, ~~n~~ removed)

[*scribbles*]

~~Whitmonday~~
~~June 9th~~

4 or 5 scenes more.
Kilman & Elizabeth.
The Warren Smiths.
Peter.
London.
The party.

[page 53 *verso*]

Since she was lying on the sofa, <cloistered> exempt, ~~from any~~
action, ~~this~~ <the> presence
of this thing ~~w became~~ which ~~so~~ she felt, to be ~~her motive,~~
~~She <so> obvious became almost apparent. <physically existent>~~
~~The hum of the traffic~~
~~was part of it; the hooting of motor horns;~~ It had ~~a~~
robes of sound, the traffic, the motor horns; it ~~moved the~~
~~curtains; it had colour, <& was> &~~ <its> [ ] ~~for its colour; &~~
coloured; & had ~~sof~~ hot breath; & whispered. stirring <blowing
in> the curtains.
~~Could she explain it better to herself? more closely?~~
But Suppose Peter said to her, ~~yes, yes~~: <yes: yes.> But—<—these
parties—> whats the sense of these
parties? all she could say was—& nobody could be
expected to understand her. ~~That~~ They're an offering.
~~He would say that he could not~~ which sounded a
little mystic. ~~Still~~ <But> who was Peter to make out that life
was all plain sailing? Peter always in love; always in
love with the wrong person? Whats your love? she
would say to him. And she knew his answer—Its <how> the
only thing
of any real importance, ~~thing that matters~~, & <but> no woman <[ ]> ~~can possibly~~
<~~could~~ had> understand it <him>.
~~Once she might have been angry.~~ Very well. And
perhaps they didn't understand what she meant either.—about
life.
Certainly ~~you~~ <she> couldn't imagine <any man> either
Richard or Peter giving a
party—a party for no reason. ~~whatever.~~
But to go deeper, beneath what people said; (& these
judgements, how superficial, they are! how fragmentary!)
In her own mind, now, ~~why did she do it? & what did she~~
~~feel?~~ what did it mean to her—~~this that~~ <thing which> she called life?
Oh it was ~~a~~ <very> queer ~~thing~~—Here was so & so in South
Kensington:
& ~~Peter~~ <others> in Bayswater, ~~shall one~~ say, & ~~Richard W~~ &
somebody else up in Hampstead. And she ~~said,~~ felt,
~~(for this was her gift)~~ quite continuously a sense of
them ~~living on & on, & like that;~~ existence; & she felt,
what a waste; & she felt ~~how dearly~~; <what a holy> & she felt
~~I know I can help them;~~ if only they could be brought
together— ~~Life meant bringing together.~~
~~An artist did the same sort of thing presumably.~~

[54] [121-122]

And ~~So~~ she did it.
~~That was partly what~~ she meant. ~~And then the mystic side of it.~~
~~Any And she had that <had> feeling every moment of her life—~~
~~the day.~~
~~Why—heaven knows. But then why anything? It was an~~
~~offering she made~~; & And she did it because it was
an offering. Just as somebody writes a book after all.

[Draft of "Notes on an Elizabeth Play." (*Times Literary Suppplement*, 5 March 1925; *The Common Reader*, 1925)]

[56]

~~But then she had no religion whatsoever. <Why use religious words?>~~
~~She was without religion,~~
But she had no religion~~, no, her only instinct being that death is~~
~~the end; everything ends at death; ends it; for which reason~~
~~was~~ Only ~~some~~ that persistent sense of life; that woke with her in
the morning, & ~~went with her all day long;~~ was in streets & in
rooms, an instinct for bringing together, ~~the creative instinct,~~
~~not only~~ people, ~~only <but> things,~~ yes, or things.
~~Was it not perhaps her way of loving? her way of~~
~~giving as artists did when they painted, writers when they wrote?~~
It was her gift. ~~If she hadn't got that, what had she got~~
~~after all? But what made it odd was that she had~~
Of course she cared for ~~birth,~~ fame, & for birth. ~~She~~
~~& for success.~~ She was perfectly aware of ~~all~~ it:
as one might know that one ~~had no gift for~~ music; ~~<was~~
~~unmusical~~—>so
~~She knew Her faults, were silly So with her faults—her~~

She had the silent, the most annoying faults.

~~love of success, her~~ She loved success; ~~she loved m~~ <she
could bear>
luxury of some kinds; she said a million when she meant a
thousand; & as for keeping facts in her head—
Why, after all these years, she didn't know where Armenia was.
~~As for caring,~~ <& didn't care, couldn't imagine,> ~~genuinely~~
~~as Richard did, as Millicent~~
~~Bruton did, what became of subject races & whether~~
~~anything much outside England. And it all~~ seemed to her not
<But it didn't matter a>
to matter a straw. It was like water off a ducks back.
~~She was so ridiculously safe,~~

[Review of *Before the Mast—and After*—by Sir Walter Runciman. (*Nation & Athenaeum*, 12 July 1924)]

But all the same, to think that one day would follow another,—
Wednesday, Thursday,
Friday, Saturday~~—was enough that was~~ to think that one could go
out ~~&,~~ <& in the flowers run,> say to Hyde Park, ~~to think of~~
~~one's friends, & seeing one's~~
~~friends~~ to think of one's friends,~~—& then, how strange,~~ how, ~~indeed,~~
~~could one imagine & then, it would all be over. yes,~~
~~unbelievable, quite unbelievable, to think that it must end;~~
~~was it credible?, one day it must end; & then~~ how
~~unbelievable~~ after that ~~it seemed to think that one day it must end~~
how unbelievable death was! That it must end; & no one
would know how she had loved it all; ~~that she~~ how
~~she had~~ every moment—
The door opened.
Elizabeth knew that her mother was resting~~, &~~
She came in very quietly. ~~standing <& stood> still & straight,~~
~~like a child.~~
But she left the door ajar; & outside the door was Miss
Kilman, as Clarissa knew, Miss Kilman, on her macintosh
able to overhear everything that was said.
Miss Kilman stood on the landing. ~~outside~~:
~~Miss Kilman~~ <She> wore a macintosh for two ~~good~~ reasons;
first, <~~for~~ <it was cheapness> ~~economy~~; second,—after forty, a
woman needs a uniform.
She was over forty, & she was poor, degradingly poor.
Otherwise she wouldn't be taking jobs from people like the
Dalloways; from such people, who liked to be kind,—M^r.
Dalloway,
of course, had been kind. But M^rs. Dalloway ~~wasn't really~~
<had not;>
~~kind; she was did things for effect. was merely kind~~
had been merely condescending. She came of the most
~~worthless of all classes, She had everything she wanted.~~
~~Probably that was her home—that watercolour picture of a~~
~~house in a park. rich, with a smattering of culture.~~
~~They bought pictures.~~ Miss Kilman was looking at an
engraving ~~of a child with a muff,~~ after Sir Joshua
Reynolds. ~~And~~ <Why shd.> M^rs. Dalloway, ~~who never~~ spend the
afternoon lying down. ~~Why?~~ There was ~~nothing the~~
~~matter with~~ her. She had servants. Everything was

done for her. She considered that she had a perfect right to anything the dalloways did for her.

[Review of *Stendhal: Journal*, texte établi et annoté par Henry Debraye et Louis Royer, tome 1; *Le Rouge et le Noir*; *Vie de Rossini*, texte établi et annoté par Jules Marsan. (*Nation & Athenaeum*, 5 July 1924)]

[61]

~~She was an outlaw; she was a brigand~~; ~~she having~~ <she had>
been cheated,
~~of happiness; & she of happiness, & she had been~~
Yes, the word was no exaggeration, for surely a girl has a right to
some kind of happiness? ~~She had good sound working brains;~~
~~but~~ And she had never been happy: what with ~~her~~ being so
clumsy, <&> so poor. And then, just as she ~~was getting on, & might~~
~~had a chance~~ & might have had a chance <at Miss Dolbys school,>
the war came; ~~& she~~
~~wasn't going to hide pretend to~~ & she had never been able to
tell lies. Miss Dolby ~~found fault with some of her~~
~~thing she said in school.~~ thought she would be happier elsewhere.
~~It was perfectly true~~ <It was perfect> that her family was of German
extraction—<the name was hid in> Kiehlman, the ~~name had~~
~~been,~~
in the eighteenth
century. ~~And the foremis~~ So she was given the sack.
They turned her out because ~~she wouldn't tell lies. She was~~
~~History was her subject, &~~ She wouldn't pretend that the
Germans were all rascals <villains>—when ~~th~~ she had German
friends, ~~& the~~
when they had been decent to her, when ~~perhaps~~ the only,
happy days of her life had been spent in Germany!
She had had to put up with whatever she could ~~find~~ get.
Mr. Dalloway had gone into her case, & ~~had~~ allowed her to teach
his daughter <history>. Also, she did a little extension lecturing,
& so on.
~~But it <Then>~~ <But> Our Lord ~~had~~ came to her . . . ~~And really~~
~~Miss Kilman~~
~~pitied women like Mrs. Dalloway. She wouldn't change~~
~~places with her;~~ She had received the light ~~one~~ not
three years & two months ago; Now she didn't ~~grudge~~ envy
people like Mrs. Dalloway ~~their hap happiness~~: she pitied them.

~~But such was the complexity of her feelings,~~ her
~~She thought how much they had missed. Pity, rage, contempt,~~
boiled with in her.
~~But pity was not the emotion that seemed to make the pictures,~~
~~flowers, carpets of the Dalloways house seemed to roused in her.~~
~~She despised them whole thing. {Weren't there thousands of~~
~~people men & women out of work?} {With all this luxury~~
~~still going on, what hope was there that the world would~~
~~ever right itself, & the it was people like the Dalloways who~~
~~were responsible, he in Parliament, she leading fashion society~~
~~presumably (for Miss Kilman saw her name in the~~
~~Morning Post) & keeping everything back, parasites,~~
~~frivolous; so that if Mr. Dalloway were kind to her~~
~~if they did give her money, she felt that she it was she who~~

Pity boiled within her, as she stood on the soft carpet looking at the
old picture. With all this luxury going on, what hope was
there for the world, & it was the Dalloways & their like who
were responsible, he in Parliament, she leading society
(for Miss Kilman saw her name sometimes in the court gossip
<circular>)
~~so that Poor poor frivolous worldly minded creature~~!—
& spending her afternoons lying on the sofa. ~~Poor~~ She
pitied her from the bottom of her heart. Pity was a painful feeling.
~~This emotion Miss Kilman called pity;~~ <&> ~~When,~~ <Two
years & three months ago,> in a
<some high> state ~~like this, of bruised & painful heated~~
In a ~~emotion,~~ Miss
Kilman had turned in a church two years & three months ago.
She had heard the Rev. ~~P~~ Edward Whitaker preach; & the
boys sing, & <seen> the solemn lights descend. ~~& it And All~~ And
[ ] those hot & turbulent feelings had been ~~assuaged. had~~
<assuaged as she sat there,>
~~She felt, as she sat there, that somebody understood her.~~
~~She had wept~~ copiously, & later ~~she~~ had called on Mr.
Whitaker in ~~his private house.~~ person. ~~What had~~ <Who said that
it was the blessing of God.>
~~happened to her, as she sat in church, she asked.~~
~~He replied that~~ The ~~Lord had shown himself.~~ The Reverend
Edward Whitaker said.
~~And even now, as she stood outside Mrs. Dalloways.~~

~~drawing room door, on the soft carpet, looking at the picture,~~ ~~she invoked the help of blessing of God, prayed that for Mrs. Dalloway, & when Mrs. Dalloway came out with Elizabeth, Miss Kilman's eyes were suffused with emotion.~~

~~Never had Clarissa~~

And now she prayed for Clarissa. Again the ~~the~~ turmoil & rage & bitterness were soothed.

The Lord had shown her the Light. So now when the hot & painful
feelings boiled within her, this hatred, ~~or of this grievance,~~ <of> ~~against~~
Mrs. Dalloway, this profound ~~grievance~~ <grudge> against the world,
she thought of God. ~~Then her~~ She thought of Mr. Whittaker.
Rage was succeeded by calm. A sweet savour filled ~~all~~ her
veins. Her lips parted, &, ~~looking~~ standing formidable in
the landing in her mackintosh, she ~~so~~ looked with a
steady yet sinister serenity at Mrs. Dalloway who
came out with her daughter.

How they hated each other! That was Elizabeth's feeling.
She simply wanted to run away & leave them, because it
was so painful. ~~They couldn't understand each other;~~
~~to see them together.~~ And Miss Kilman looked so plain;
so big; so shabby. ~~It was as if they were~~ Her mother looked so
elegant, so supercilious: ~~But~~ <And> she <herself> could see
both sides;
& she felt that she was being torn apart, because
her mother & her friend hated each other.
But Miss Kilman did not hate Mrs. Dalloway; as she
turned her ~~beo~~ oddly lustrous eyes upon her, & saw her
~~pink small face,~~ her delicate body, her refinement.
She pitied her. And at the same there rose in her a ~~more~~
~~violent &~~ over mastering desire to ~~conv~~ overcome her, <to>
convert her.
Physically, she was so much the stronger. ~~In her But~~
if she could have felled her, it would have eased her. But
it was not the <[ ]> body; it was the ~~upright~~ hostile mock~~ing~~
soul that ~~<evaded>~~ she wished to subdue; to overwhelm; to make
~~act~~ feel her mastery. If only she could make her
weep; could ruin her; desolate her; take from her the
thing she most wanted! humiliate her! bring her to her
knees in acknowlegment of ~~my~~ <her> power. But
Miss Kilman ~~was~~ had God in her mind. It was to be a
religious victory.

[Review of *Stendahl: Journal*, texte établi et annoté par Henry Debraye et Louis Royer, tome 1; *Le Rouge et le Noir*; *Vie de Rossíni*, texte établi et annoté par Jules Marsan. (*Nation & Athenuaeum*, 5 July 1924)]

~~Clarissa was really shocked. This was a Christian—this~~
She was ~~woman.~~
~~<in> In touch with God! so common, so drab, staring at her in that fixed shiny way which made her want to scream, or to laugh! And this woman had taken her daughter from her! lent her books, taught her nonsense! And her own life was being exposed to something. her brutality. Hostile Everything fell about her in ruins.~~

~~2~~ 100
60. Clarissa was really shocked. This was a Christian, this woman.—
100 This woman had taken her daughter from her—~~No woman~~
20 ~~had a right to look so ugly.~~ She in touch with God!
~~280~~ heavy, ugly, common place~~;~~ She knew the ~~mystery~~ <meaning> of life!
~~Nonsense. And~~ But what does one say?
"~~You're going~~ You & Elizabeth are going out?"
Miss Kilman simply looked at Elizabeth.
No: one can't Elizabeth looked at the ground.
hate people. Second by second hatred crumbled; ~~& disappear <one can't hate people.>~~ Miss Kilman
became more & <& more> ~~more ordinary~~—an ordinary dowdy woman ~~pitiable rather,~~ poor, heavy—But what could Elizabeth find in her?
Miss Kilman ~~did not [consult?] who had very~~
said, just like a schoolmistress, ostentatiously & facetiously,
"Elizabeth has kindly offered to escort me to the Army & Navy Stores."
~~Nothing is~~ so Clarissa began to laugh.
How horrible, They all laughed. There was a pause.
Clarissa thought; ~~And so~~ <Then> off they went, down the stairs, Elizabeth & Miss
~~thinking~~ of love & Kilman, ~~who were,~~ Presumably they were in love? With an
religion, ~~in the abstract.~~ uncontrollable instinct
which is worst? Clarissa ~~went to top of the~~ leant over the bannisters & cried out,
Are you sure you've got everything for tonight? Remember our party tonight!"

But Elizabeth had already opened the front door, &
There was a van passing, & she did not answer.
Love & religion, thought Clarissa, going back into the drawing room.
How detestable! how detestable! for now that Miss Kilman was not before her, the old hatred came back.
And Miss Kilman walked as fast as ever she could, until, she reached Victoria Street, with her lips pressed.

~~The two great powers in <of> the world~~
For now that the body of Miss Kilman was not before her, the hatred ~~horror~~ of her came back: ~~&~~ And she had taken her daughter.
~~Miss Kilman~~ The most awful things in the world, thought

walking to the window coming back into the room, dressed in a mackintosh, out on the landing

Clarissa; seeing them clumsy ~~hot~~ <hot> domineering
hypocritical eavesdropping
tyrannical, jealous, ~~an~~ infinitely cruel & crushing,—
love & religion. ~~If there was anyone in the world she hated, it was Miss Kilman.~~ Had she ever tried to convert anyone herself? Did she not wish ~~well~~ everybody—~~that~~ <for instance> old lady whom
she always
saw climbing up stairs in the house opposite,—<merely> to be themselves? ~~Was it not mi the only service one could do them?~~ Let her climb upstairs, if she wants to; let her stop; ~~let her look out of the window;~~ <landing> then, let her, as Clarissa had often seen her, gain her bedroom, & ~~again~~ part her curtains, & ~~once more~~ look out of the window. ~~Respect that, thought Clarissa: And indeed~~ It was ~~a sight she never tired of looking at. It~~ Somehow, one respected that— ~~one~~ that old woman, looking ~~out~~ down into the street, quite unconscious that she was being watched. Yes, there was something solemn in it. But love & religion would destroy— That, whatever it was. ~~Was it~~ life, ~~that old woman, looking down into the street?~~ was it, something venerable.
~~The odious Kilman would destroy it. Yet~~ it was a sight that <alm> made one <almost> cry. ~~sometimes.~~

Love destroyed too. Everything that was fine, everything that was true, went. Take Peter now. There ~~a~~ was a man ~~so clever,—so~~ charming, ~~so~~ clever—if you wanted to know about Pope say, or Addison, what they ~~had~~ were like, what they had meant, Peter knew better than any one she had ever met. ~~It was Peter who had taught her everything she knew — Still she remembered things he had told her, had books he had given her—but & then he came & talked to her about love. The first vulgar, foolish, simple headed girl he met in the street he he fell in love.~~ He fell in love with ~~And~~ <But> then, look at the

think of peter in love;

women he loved, ~~a~~ vulgar, stupid, commonplace: & his appalling ~~egotism~~—he came to see her & he never talked of anything but himself. Horrible passion, she thought, degrading passion, she thought, thinking of Kilman & her Elizabeth, walking to the Army & Navy Stores.

Clarissa was concerned, & at the same time ~~for some reason~~ ~~too~~ moved, to see being alive,

~~Nevertheless, said the~~ Big Ben, struck the half hour.
~~the old lady opposite evidently remembered something~~ was
~~evidently~~ that the sound evidently ~~reminded~~ <warned> the old
lady opposite, ~~of~~
that she must no longer look out of the window.
~~It was a sort of mystery, this life that went on,~~ <It was a sort of mystery,>
She was now <to [many?]> forced to do,—what? Clarissa wondered, ~~gazing~~
trying to follow her as she <turned &> disappeared, ~~into the bedroom,~~
~~aft~~ with one gleam of her lace ~~scarf~~ <cap>, into the bedroom.
~~Thats all we see of each other,~~ Again, she had ~~that~~ that
~~no dou~~ odd feeling~~—what~~ Peter would ~~call that~~ <say it was> sentimental feeling—

pouting walking across the room sobbing—

but who was more sentimental than Peter, <himself> sobbing,
~~over his love affairs~~?—that ~~behind every second~~ <there> was a
~~great force,~~ a solemn enormous finger, <[had?] no> which raised itself
~~in the middle of ordinary things &~~ came down, down, ~~almost~~ in the
~~overwhelming in with a~~ sense of the ~~solemnity of~~ middle of ordinary things.
~~awfulness of living. solemnity of it.~~ <strangeness> ~~of being~~ alive. life. ~~Here she was~~ in one

room;

& across the street was She felt it here; that old woman over
there. As for ~~saying what it meant,~~ Perhaps to share this they

went

~~go~~ to churches?—Elizabeth, Miss Kilman? ~~for instance~~?
~~Only it was so odd to~~ <But why> go to a church? Why not <stay> here in this room?
Why creeds & prayers & mackintoshes? ~~Why not~~

Really to me, thought Clarissa; still watching in case the old lady might appear again; thats the mystery.—the old lady she meant; ~~&~~ <but> the supreme mystery, which Kilman might say she had solved, & Peter might say he had solved, but Clarissa didn't believe either of them~~—the ci~~
had the ghost of an idea <of course> ~~what she~~ meant was simply loneliness: That here was one room; there another; ~~&~~

Does

~~How do~~ religions <solve it> ~~people solve that~~? or lover~~s~~?
~~But some very clever man she had met at lunch had told her that~~

There was a clock that was always two or three minutes late.

felt, had
controlled her

How extraordinary it was to see the old lady moving away from the window!—as if ~~the sound were alt a~~ <this sound, this> she were
attached to the sound; ~~of the~~
She was now forced to move, forced to do—what?
Clarissa tried to follow her, ~~into the~~ as she turned & disappeared,

It was, ~~a~~
strange. mysterious.

& could still just see ~~the~~ her white cap ~~in~~ <moving> at> the back
of the bedroom.
It was as if an enormous finger ~~had~~ <suddenly> raised itself &
come down, down
in the midst of ordinary things; making this moment, ~~here at the window~~ solemn. She was still there, moving about, at the
other end of the room. ~~Why go to church then? Why not stay in this room~~? Why creeds & prayers & mackintoshes? when
~~Really to~~ me, thought Clarissa, thats the mystery;
The old lady, she meant, whom she could see going from chest of
drawers to dressing table. <She could still see her.> And the
supreme mystery,
which ~~Peter~~ <Kilman> might say she had solved, & ~~Kilman~~
<Peter> might
say ~~she~~ <he> had solved, but Clarissa didn't believe
either of them had the ghost of an idea of solving was
simply ~~loneliness;~~ <separation.> ~~That~~ here was one room; There
another. Did religion solve that, or love?
There was ~~one~~ <a> clock that was always a little ~~later~~ behind
~~than~~ the others. ~~It~~ Oh she must telephone at once,
thought Clarissa hearing it, to Milly Henderson.

~~& Elizabeth was heard her muttering.~~

It is the flesh, ~~thought~~ <said> Doris Kilman.
Prancing <flashing> ~~striking~~ & dazzling, jingling, crashing. &
roaring, the traffic in Victoria Street drowned clocks; but
~~And indeed Clar M^rs. Dalloway, Miss Kilman had~~ a
<habit> ~~sometimes <did> spoke~~ <of talking> speak aloud; ~~she~~
& ~~Elizabeth~~
~~heard the word~~ 'flesh.' There they were, crossing the
road, & Miss Kilman absolutely absorbed in what she
~~was thinking~~—frowning, talking to herself; making people
stare at her. Elizabeth had to take her arm.

Did religion—

But here the clock, which ~~was~~ always ~~two~~ struck two minutes after Big Ben, came shuffling in, ~~bearing in its letting fall~~ <with> a cupfull of odds & ends; ~~that it was half past three, & that~~ as ~~if it seems, trapesing lagging behind the that one must~~ which it dumped down ~~on the ground,~~ as if. Big Ben were all very well; with his majesty, laying down the law; but one must remember ~~really time~~ Mrs. ~~Marsham,~~ Milly Henderson, glasses for ices; as if time in his ~~march~~ were attended by ~~a troo~~ troops of camp followers with ~~their~~ baskets full of ~~broken meats~~
: as if ~~fro~~ the golden bar which lay flat upon the sea, turned to ~~were all~~ ripples & wavelets lapping & dancing; ~~as~~ erasing. confusing; & ~~it was~~ as of ~~confusion & chaos, one had to they a confusion of roseleaves, of bread crumbs fell fell variously over ones shoulders. as~~ <&> if one must jump in.

So troublously the half hour sounded. ~~But~~ Beaten up, broken up, ~~in Victoria Street~~ by the assault of carriages, ~~the~~ the brutality of vans, the eager ~~swarming~~ advance of myriads of professional men & women~~, in~~ little of the sound ~~was left in Vi~~ reached Victoria Street whole; & when Doris Kilman (who heard nothing, saw nothing, & was entirely absorbed ~~in a~~ conflict.) <muttered> ~~said~~, aloud, "It is the flesh" the sound died.

who appeared to be swarming upon some goal,

one must remember all sorts of little things, ~~as oh yes, laying down the law like that is all very well, it~~ which came flooding in, & lapping & dancing, in the wake of that solemn stroke, ~~that golden bar,~~ which lay flat upon the sea, ~~& lay~~ like a bar of gold, ~~One must Oh those letters,~~ & Mrs. Marsham. Milly Henderson; glasses for ices.

So troublously the half hour sounded. Beaten up, broken up, by the assault of carriages, the brutality of vans, the eager advance of myriads of spinning black coated men, flaunting flowery women, who appeared to be swarming towards some goal, little of the sound reached Victoria Street whole.

seemed to fall in innum

~~140~~—rent seemed to fall in innumerable fragments ~~among the people~~. on the
~~90~~ enter pavement.
~~60~~ interest Elizabeth ~~heard the words quite clearly~~ heard her say something,
~~100~~ money but saw that Miss Kilman was ~~speaking~~ talking to herself;
~~360~~ for her lips were pursed; her eyes protruded; so fixed were they.
~~400~~ What had happened was this; Mrs. Dalloway had insulted her;
~~250~~ That she expected. ~~But she had not been able~~
~~250~~ ~~What was deplorable, was that~~ But she had not triumphed; ~~as~~
~~she hoped~~; she ~~had could not~~ had not mastered her <the> flesh.
Ugly ~~&~~ big, clumsy—~~no unattractive, unfeminine—~~Clarissa
Dalloway, ~~in her insolence, for she was~~ & had laughed at her
for being that; & ~~she had that it~~ had revived the fleshly
desires, for she minded looking as she did, beside
Clarissa. ~~She knew she was awkward.~~ ~~She~~ Nor
could she talk as they did.

But why wish to resemble people <her?> she despised?
~~Why~~ She despised Mrs. Dalloway from top to bottom. ~~Her~~
~~day was~~ She was not serious. She was not good. Her
~~d~~ life was spent in ~~silly wordliness~~—silliness,—in going
to parties, ~~in dressing~~ up, or lying on the sofa. ~~Yet she had~~
~~never done a days work in her life. Whereas she, Doris Kilman,~~
Yet Doris Kilman had been overcome. She had very nearly
burst into tears. when Clarissa Dalloway laughed at her.
"It is the flesh—it is the flesh" she muttered, trying to subdue
this turbulent passion as she walked down Victoria Street.
She asked <prayed> God to ~~help~~ <come to> her. ~~Still The~~
~~insult~~ She could not
help being ugly; she could not afford to buy pretty clothes.
At any rate, she had earned her living since she was eighteen.
while Clarissa Dalloway— But she ~~refered~~ <prefered> ~~to~~
~~<would~~ ~~not>~~ think of her
~~any again until she could think of her with pity.~~ she would
~~think of steadily of~~ concentrate her mind upon something else
until ~~the~~ she reached the pillar box. At any rate she had
got Elizabeth. But she would not think of worldly things; until
she had reached the pillar box.

"It is the flesh" she said, struggling, as Mr. Whittaker had told her, with that ~~hot &~~ violent indignation, with the whole world which had scorned her, sneered at her, cast her off—beginning with this indignity~~—her great plain body, which could~~ the infliction of her unlovable body which people could not bear to see; ~~but it was not her fault; & then she had no charm;~~ Do her hair as she might, her forehead remained ~~like some bald;~~ like an egg. white, bald. And ~~clothes that were~~ No clothes ~~looked well on her.~~ suited her. She might buy anything. ~~Most women could bear to see themselves in~~ ~~And that of course means~~ <And> As a woman, of course, that meant ~~that no man will~~ never meeting the opposite sex. ~~Therefore She would never be <come> first. mean everything to anyone.~~ She ~~would~~ Never ~~come first;~~ would she come first with anyone. ~~Help there was none.~~ Sometimes it seemed as if ~~only~~ good, were all one lived for; ~~comfort; hot water bottles Mr~~ her dinner—her hot water bottle. ~~But no. One must fight. There had been overcome the flesh.~~ But one must fight; wrestle; vanquish, have faith in God. Mr. Whittaker had said she was there for a purpose: ~~yes;~~ But no one knew the agony! He said that God knew. But why should she have to suffer when other women, like Mrs. Dalloway—escaped. ~~He said that~~ knowledge ~~came~~ <comes> through suffering. said Mr. Whittaker.

They had reached the Tobacco department, of the Stores, & Elizabeth who found the glare of the street trying, entered.

[Review of "The Week End Book," edited by V. Mendel and Francis Meynell. ("The Weekend," *Times Literary Supplement*, 1 July 1924)]

[75-77]

~~They had reached the tobacco department of the~~ Stores
& Elizabeth who found the glare of the street ~~trying~~ entered.
the tobacco department of the Army & Navy Stores.
The cool brown atmosphere was at the moment bewildering,

struggling,
trying to
fix in her mind,
what Mr Whittaker

~~absorbed as to one <Miss Kilman> absorbed in this struggle, She stopped;~~
~~caught sight of herself in a looking glass.~~
~~He had said~~ that <had spoken to> ~~about knowledge~~ in his little back room,
with the crucifix on the wall. ~~She caught sight of herself in a~~
~~looking glass, hung between columns of cigar boxes. It is the~~
~~flesh, she~~ about ~~conquering burning~~ knowledge, about suffering.
& when she saw her own reflection in the looking glass hung
between columns of cigar boxes, she said it—
~~the~~ & said, with an odd serenity that it was the better coat
department she wanted; stalking on, through the
sweet department to the lift.

280
<u>21</u>

[78 *verso, pencil*]

Elizabeth turned into the tobacco department of the Army & Navy Stores.

Miss Kilman ~~had~~ found herself in this cool brown atmosphere, unexpectedly.
before she ~~had~~ reached the pillar box, ~~which rather took her aback.~~ She found herself among cigar boxes & looking glasses. while ~~It was~~ <She was still asking> Why should she suffer? <she asked> herself ~~Elizabeth~~
What did she want to ~~get~~ <buy>? Elizabeth ~~asked~~ <interrupted> her. It was a petticoat, she said, ~~with in her solemn way with her~~ <vehemently> & stalked straight on through the sweet department to the lift. ~~But let us consider, she said to herself as the lift shot up, being 'us', in her loneliness, two me women, one suppliant, the other stern; She had understood when she was in Mr Whittakers back room; & had reached the shore or safety; a sort of really she had been able to And stepping out of the lift she felt that she had~~
Up they went. ~~Then they reached the petticoats.~~
Elizabeth guided her this way & that, ~~to the place where~~ the ~~petticoats hung.~~ guided her as if she were a battleship, or gloomy leviathan; ~~or~~ She never said anything, & she chose ~~her petticoat~~ the very plainest petticoat, ~~as if she plain <dull> brown,~~
straight off, ~~despised the pretty ones,~~ & the girl serving looked as if she thought her mad.

Elizabeth rather wondered as ~~sh~~ they waited for ~~the parcel & the change~~

~~Of course Miss Kilman was so remarkable that~~

And suddenly Miss Kilman seemed to wake up. ~~for~~ She said ~~in her~~ that they must have tea. ~~She became cheerful, bri determined;~~ ~~She sat down at a table.~~ ~~She poured out tea.~~

Elizabeth ~~really didn't care~~ wondered whether ~~she was really hungry.~~ The truth was that Miss Kilman was hungry.

She ate pink cakes, as if an animal which lived in her suddenly became ~~absorbed &~~ gluttonous. And then on the table next them was a plate ~~full of~~ with different kinds of cakes. & ~~Miss Kilman~~ <she> kept looking; <&> considering, & was about

to reach over

take one when a lady & a child sat down at that table; & the child took the cake ~~at once in its~~

~~Did~~ <Could> Miss Kilman really mind ~~<be cross>~~?, Elizabeth wondered.

~~Yes~~ Miss Kilman did mind. ~~Not only was the appetite was curiously strong in her~~: ~~but <&>~~ the pleasure of eating was almost the only ~~unmixed~~ pure pleasure <she had>, & then ~~one~~ to be baffled even in that!

After all, when people are happy, ~~they have a reserve,~~ ~~<these trifles dont count;>~~ &

it ~~would be foolish of them to mind a trifle~~ They have ~~<Happy people>~~ a reserve, as Miss Kilman had explained to Elizabeth, upon ~~from~~ which ~~they can~~ to draw, whereas she was like a wheel without a tyre, jolted by every pebble; so she would say, staying on to talk after the lesson was over; Elizabeth thought in the first place that Miss Kilman had never told ~~a~~

<another> soul.

~~And then, besides these things,~~ & ~~after all, she knew so much.~~ And she made Elizabeth ~~think of~~ realise all sorts of things: ~~Miss Kilman It was only when she made her, that Miss Kilman~~ for instance about the war. ~~Miss Kilman~~ did ~~not begin it; but~~ the way ~~Mi~~ she had been treated was ~~an absolute scandal.~~ And then there was another point of view ~~of course;~~ ~~From~~ Her father & mother always thought the English right There were wounded soldiers about the house all day long. Miss Kilman made her ~~realise~~ <see> not that the Germans were right, but that ~~every~~ <no> one was ~~wrong~~ <right>. The ~~whole~~ whole ~~system~~ of government was wrong. They went to meetings together: ~~so~~ extraordinary people spoke.

on one of those Tuesday mornings when the lesson was over.
Elizabeth thought that it was an extraordinary compliment;
for she thought that Miss Kilman had never told another soul.

Oh she had made her understand that the world is an
extraordinary place!

Drop by drop the hot tea kindled in Miss Kilman
an egotistic exaltation; an ecstasy. ~~part~~ She divined through her
own brooding ~~though~~ that ~~she was losing~~ Elizabeth. was
wondering & ~~having doubts about her.~~ possibly doubting.
She saw people passing, ~~ges,~~ obsessed, nonchalant: ~~derided~~ she
saw herself; deserted; ~~& yet in her derided; but~~ neglecting all
her suffering.
But she would not lose Elizabeth! She would not give her up!
Elizabeth ~~said, wanted to go.~~ ~~She~~ was looking for her gloves.
She was not to go. ~~Are~~ Her own injuries were too vast to
admit of this ~~last~~ insult. Yet from all that boiling cauldron
within; what drops could issue? How ~~reach out to~~ <retain> this
sympathy; this girl; youth; ~~something~~ <that ~~was~~ so> one could
be fond of?
~~Her large heavy body crushed her down. Her body was so large, so clumsy; &~~ ~~Her hands were extended in a~~ <Her large hand
opened & shut upon the table.>
~~But~~ It was rather pointless, somehow. ~~That was the sort of feeling~~ Elizabeth felt. ~~Nothing seemed to happen~~—
Every now & then Miss Kilman ~~said~~ said something <made a
remark>; but
~~But~~ And then nothing happened. She had never felt that before—
that sudden misery. She was looking at the table.—
She saw ~~the~~ Miss Kilmans hand open & shut & it
became wrought into her misery: that nothing mattered.
She took her gloves. ~~And~~ Miss Kilman said, "I have not
quite done.

~~The life of a Lady.~~ ~~A lady.~~ ~~Mrs Dalloway.~~

~~So~~ Elizabeth waited.

~~All had was vanishing. Or~~ & As one thing went, another took its place. ~~Miss Kilman emerged; large, Elizabeth felt nothing whatever for her; or for anyone.~~ That was her feeling; & what ~~was left was so d~~ really existed now, as they sat at the table with Miss Kilmans horrid parcel between them, & the cups & the things, were miserably: ~~dull~~; nothing could ever be exciting & <again> ~~She only wanted to~~ ~~She~~

[*pencil*] A ladies portrait. A lady of Fashion.

Miss Kilman said; Are you going to the party tonight? It was like being accused of something. <Elizabeth> She supposed she was going.

~~There is no harm in them, said Miss~~

And ~~Miss Kilman said~~ <Miss Kilman> there was no harm in going to parties; but it was not a thing one could do very often, without its ~~being~~ being, she said, fingering the last inch of her sugary cake, a pity.

~~Unfortunately, Elizabeth~~ And Elizabeth ~~seeing~~ <saw> her ~~swallow,~~ open her mouth, ~~was disgusted, repelled—oh it was horrible!~~

She ~~finished swallowed & said, a~~ She ~~flicked off some~~ <wiped her> sugary fingers. ~~that & said <She saw that> She was making no impression. She was deserted.~~ <But> She could have wept. ~~She could have battered~~ with her hand; ~~Miss Kilman knew that~~ She looked, as she did so, into the heart of her misery, but was paralysed. Elizabeth would get up & ~~go~~:

Her cup was still half full of tea. She had not finished.
That her body dried by years of anguish ~~was going to~~ <wd.>
split apart; that
~~her voice would~~ she would give one <great> cry; that she would
grasp Elizabeth ~~tight;~~ <& express> ~~such that <so> she thought,~~
& so she felt; &
yet she could ~~say nothing; & Elizabeth was going.~~
~~She said~~ only <now> say things that annoyed Elizabeth. ~~She was~~
Pinioned to her rock; ~~& uglily, <&> clumsily ugly & clumsy,~~ she could
only grimace, & suffer & watch other mocking people pass, & feel
the time going. {~~Suddenly she would lose~~ <She was going to lose>
her temper.}
~~And~~ <But> she must control herself; ~~&~~ she must remember ~~how~~ her vows.
Elizabeth saw the red hand curl its fingers in.
~~In Desolate as She was, desolated~~; she was indifferent.
She would rather like to get up & go; but not if Miss Kilman
wanted to stay.
~~It is six years since I went <was> at a party.~~
I dont get asked to parties ~~myself~~" said Miss Kilman.
Why should people ask me to parties? ~~she went on.~~
I'm ~~elderly~~, & plain. I'm unhappy. ~~And I shouldn't go if
they did ask me it would only be out of pity.~~ Yet I
dont pity myself so much as I pity them. I
~~pity them~~" she said.
It ~~seemed as if~~ <It seemed> she pitied the people actually
there; the
~~waitresses, & the~~ ordinary people with bags & ~~lin~~ paper
parcels; ~~people~~ <waiting> with ~~pa~~ checks at the desks.
"I pity." Miss Kilman meant M^rs. Dalloway—
~~all~~ She could only say <again> this. "I would rather lead my own
life, in spite of everything. That ~~is what~~ That will be
your temptation— ~~You will be praised.~~
You will be offered every inducement to lead a
selfish frivolous existence. There will be
compliments, she said, And you will hear
serious things discussed in a <foolish> silly way. <&> You will
ask~~ed~~ to do this & that. <&> you will ~~be~~ find it very hard to

true ~~to the standards & ideals which <our>~~ the faith.

~~Dumbly like some meek creature who had been brought up to the gate & stands there;~~ not exactly understanding, merely living, & quite ready to gallop off, ~~the youthful~~ Elizabeth Dalloway sat.

"a selfish frivolous existence . . . temptations—true". Yes? was there anything more?

"Dont quite forget me" said Miss Kilman suddenly
<abruptly> with her
voice quivering.

~~Then~~ The dumb creature galloped away—right to the end of the field, wildly, in terror.

The great hand opened & shut.

~~For~~ Elizabeth ~~got up. got up.~~ turned her head. The waitress came. She got up, went off to pay the bill; came back, stood over the table; & ~~so they parted.~~ as Miss Kilman did not move; ~~so they parted~~ went. drawing out, Miss Kilman felt, the very entrails in her body, & stretching them in agony,
<as she crossed the room> &
& then with a final twist; then; ~~when~~ <something broke> she disappeared, <[taking the bill?]> Miss Kilman sat back in her
chair before the littered table with her hands before her. ~~Dully she was~~ suffused by shocks of suffering; <wh.> beat~~ing ticking one two three in her as she~~ through her body ~~as she~~
<one, two, three,>
sat there. ~~colossal clumsy yet dignified~~ There was ~~that <A> crucifix <hung> in Mr. Whittaker's back room.~~
Mrs. Dalloway had
laughed at her; ~~loneliness; suffering; despised; rejected; deserted,~~ the ~~loneliness & a crucifix;~~ <Elizabeth had left
her> ~~desertion; to be laughed at wherever she went; nothing remained.~~
A crucifix hung in Mr. Whittakers room.
~~And over it all, <Disappearing [soundlessly?] was> as if mincing <&> capering, <&> darting, went this straight body in a fawn coloured coat; skirt; that a round, rather pale face; brown eyes, set far apart; so it went; it disappeared; it was it was so beautiful;~~ beauty went; youth went.

She blundered up & marched across the room, awkwardly between the
little tables. She rocked ~~a little~~ <slightly> from side to side.
"Is this your parcel Miss?" somebody asked her,
thrusting her petticoat into her hands. She tried to pay
the bill; but Elizabeth had paid it. She could not find a
staircase. She ~~became~~ was hemmed in by dressing cases.
She found <blundered> herself in an enormous saloon, ~~with underclothes~~
with ~~fine~~ underlinen spread about. Through all the
commodities of the world, <[ ]> hung, stacked, grouped,
<perishable & permanent,> arrayed, variously
smelling; new sweet new sour she lurched; once she saw herself
full length in a looking glass; ~~hung between two~~ ~~There~~
She seemed to be trapped; At length, ~~out in~~ <she gained> the street, ~~she~~
~~stood by the kerb, looking at the omnibuses.~~ The
tower of Westminster Cathedral rose in front of her.—~~<which~~
~~was of course>~~ the habitation
of God, though ~~of course the Roman Catholic God.~~ There ~~was~~ <is>
God: there ~~was~~ <is> God. she said to herself. ~~But~~— Doggedly
she set off on ~~her astonishing~~ pilgrimage, to the Abbey; ~~to the~~
where ~~too~~ raising her hands in a tent before her face,
she commanded the respect of those driven into shelter
too; of the ~~oddly~~ variously assorted worshippers; ~~domestic servants,~~
now. ~~almost~~ divested of ~~character~~ social rank, as they
hid their faces; ~~& having discharged made their~~ <but once they
lowered them,>
~~communion, became~~ almost instantly reverent Englishmen.
~~some wished to see~~ the waxworks.

[Margin, beside "full length in a looking glass" to "tower of Westminster Cathedral":] among the commodities, the vanities, of the world.

[Margin, beside "communion, became" to "the waxworks":] some of them desirous of seeing

Miss Kilman held her tent before her face. Now she was deserted; now
rejoined. New worshippers came ~~to take the place of the old,~~ <in>
in from the street; <to replace the strollers,> & still she barred her
eyes with her fingers, &
tried in this double darkness, for the light ~~was~~ in the abbey was
bodiless, to aspire above the vanities, the commodities.—
~~hans & crin majors? Clarissa, Elizabeth; her &~~
to rid herself ~~of the weighty & cumbrous body~~ <of> ~~which~~
<the heats & chills> love~~d~~ &
hated <for> Elizabeth, ~~hated~~ <hatred> Clarissa; was despised;
<of that grinding despair [ ]> ~~& clumsy,~~ &
Her hands twitched. Yet ~~for~~ <to> others God was accessible.
The path to him was beaten smooth. Mr. Fletcher, <retired>
of the Treasury,
~~Mrs Gorham, widow of the <well-known> K.C., & Hubert~~
~~Beesley, who ap, a mere boy, approached him~~
quite simply {in this Abbey where they were accustomed
to worship; But ~~then, as Miss Kilman knew, though~~
~~her burden was far greater than theirs: But they were~~ not
~~afflicted as she was.~~ & having done their duty, lowered their
~~clean & kindly~~ hands, & leant back, ~~& wondered with a~~
looked at Miss Kilman, ~~not as~~ & ~~pitied her.~~ having
~~entered,~~ not quite left the underworld, thought of her as a
soul, ~~in the great army of souls;~~ as a being cut out
out of ~~<some>~~ immaterial substance~~;~~ ~~Miss This~~
After five minutes, ~~This she~~ Mr. Fletcher, at any rate,
could not help being a little distressed—he was the soul of
neatness himself—by the poor ladies ~~ext~~ <[ ]> untidiness; ~~&~~ yet
as he stood, gazing about him, at the white marbles—
grey window panes, her largeness, her robustness, her power,
as she sat there, perhaps shifting her knees, but never
moving her hands, impressed him, as they had
impressed ~~Clarissa~~ Mrs Dalloway & ~~Mr.~~ the Rev. Arthur
Whittaker, & Elizabeth above all—
For Elizabeth

For Elizabeth ~~was who was who was seventeen~~ <sixteen>
when ~~she~~ Miss
Kilman began to teach her history had never met ~~either at home~~
~~or at~~ anyone ~~with~~ so careless <in the first place> of her personal
appearance;
~~Perhaps then it did not matter? how~~ or so sure, or so
angry, or so well up in everything~~;~~ especially ~~about about~~
foreign countries. And then the state of England—Elizabeth
had never once thought of the poor. Her mother ~~did was~~
did all sorts of kindnesses to odd people; but ~~that~~ there
they lived, with everything they wanted;—Her mother had her
breakfast in bed every day of her life;—Lucy carried it up.
& she ~~did~~ liked ~~dull~~ old women ~~<simply>~~ because they were Duchesses.
~~She liked~~ <&> being descended from ~~Lord Stowmarket,~~ <the ~~Fre~~>
some ~~old~~ lord.
As for Miss Kilman, she said straight out "my grandfather ~~the~~
~~who was~~ <who> kept an oil & colour shop~~—thats how I knew",~~
in Kensington." All this came upon Elizabeth in a
clap that particular Tuesday when Miss Kilman suddenly
said that she had never known what happiness meant.
She was standing by the fireplace, with her bag of books in her
never would Elizabeth forget it; hand; & ~~she began to talk; & next time~~ <she stood talking>
she brought a book about
religion. ~~which she gave Elizabeth, Never had Elizabeth~~
<For> She said ~~that when she had come~~ how ~~it~~ the atmosphere of
the house distressed her; there was no ~~background~~, she said;
recognition of [values?], no ~~reli~~ spiritual ~~side~~ <things which >, ~~& Elizabeth had been~~ startled~~;~~
Elizabeth, & ~~opened her eyes to~~ all sorts of things—
~~her mother, her father;~~ <&> she went down to lunch, &
~~everything seemed different.~~ Perhaps ~~her father~~ cared
~~more than~~ her father & mother ~~seemed quite different.~~
& the way everything was done, seemed suddenly different
~~Miss Kilman lent her books.~~ Miss Kilman's books
~~by~~ about religion, however, ~~seemed~~ <meant nothing> to her ~~very~~
difficult. Miss Kilman took her to some church in
Kensington & they went to tea with a clergyman; but
it might be that she had no religious sense, owing
to her upbringing; & she had better begin, at any rate,

by trying to ~~acquire~~ <understand> the religious attitude. ~~of mind.~~ Elizabeth began

to ~~understand~~ <see> ~~saw through <why into> people~~ to ~~look at~~ <criticise> people

Her mother, her father—she thought about them, her mother particularly,
~~from~~ as she had never ~~thought~~ imagined that one could think of ones parents, ~~she Lunch parties, tea parties, dinner parties, there were always~~ For instance, those luncheon parties. of ~~rather~~ elderly people, what was <the> sense of them, considering the washing up & the expense, & ~~after all, they her mother was <had> not was had nothing <nothing> really interested in said very silly things,~~ & then <what> silly things her mother said~~—for she did say She~~ And then ~~anybody her father cam went on & on, boring people, with his hobby—stories about~~ could be so boring—she could see people yawning. with his old stories of Chatham & Burke; Off she went by herself; & then her mother would com~~ing~~<e> calling after her ~~to help~~ say that ~~the most exquisite lovely~~ the hamper had come, from Bourton, & the whole afternoon would go ~~in unpacking~~ <arranging> flowers; &
her mother almost in tears because the old gardener had ~~pi~~ sent her a bunch of sweet geranium, ~~remembering as how~~ it was ~~Miss Clarissa <her> favourite flower:~~ & oh how dreadful it was that Elizabeth ~~hadn't grown up in~~ <had never known> that garden!

"How escape? What could one do? Law, medicine, art"—~~the~~ <all> professions are ~~all~~ open to ~~the~~ women of your generation"
said Miss Kilman whereas she ~~had~~ <herself> had ~~to~~ no choice but teaching:~~—If she had had a choice,~~ <It was one of her grievances.> ~~She would have liked to chosen law, re probably, could had it been possible.~~

~~Probably~~
~~she wd. have~~

~~And~~ <But And> it wasn't as if ~~either~~ her father or her mother ~~put obstacles~~ <stood> in
her way. Her mother didn't want it; ~~she didn't like women's colleges;~~ but "My dear child, do what you like"—Yes, her mother never interfered seriously; ~~only it was~~ <it was> her only she was so ~~entirely~~ different. And her father thought it quite a good plan; ~~They were~~, Whatever Miss Kilman might say, <[being?]> very decent. ~~In fact~~ She adored them—~~But~~ <Oh> she wanted to get away from them. She ~~was~~ so ~~entirely~~ <utterly> different—everything was so different.

Who had been forced to teach; ~~& indeed one might do~~ anything.
~~You~~ ~~She had <have> abilities, Miss Kilman said.~~ You have great
abilities, said
Miss Kilman. ~~She brought old examination papers, &~~
And her father said of course if she wanted to go to college she might; &
her mother ~~m finally~~ agreed; her mother, so strange sometimes,
~~when she got into her that <her> silent mood & seemed to be quite~~
~~ready to allow when she seemed to watch,~~ ~~And she~~
~~but to want to~~ not arguing, but letting you talk; never
saying a word against Miss Kilman, or against religion; ~~or~~
~~but never nice insisting that but obviously~~ or against
college; ~~but &~~ ~~But she did hate them all,~~
But ~~<but hating> She hated them—one could see <that> she hated~~
~~them. Only~~
~~if Miss Kilman was in her house, she was her guest; & if~~
~~It was simply And even Miss Kilman had to~~
~~as she hated untidiness & all sorts of odd things <did hate things>—~~
~~untidiness for example;~~ but hating them; though
just letting you do what you wanted. To Miss Kilman she was
always very very nice: asked her into lunch; gave her flowers ~~once:~~
but Miss Kilman wasn't the sort of person to like flowers,
<squashed them all up,> &
~~being very busy, she couldn't waste her time sitting~~ talking—
& naturally hadn't any sort of small talk; & then
what interested ~~<Miss> her, bored <mother>~~ Miss Kilman,
bored her mother,
who ~~never knew any knew nothing about politics,~~ & Miss
Kilman was always at her worst ~~in then.~~ <with her> & lectured, &
~~became~~ looked very plain.

But ~~it~~ <this> was awful—"Really awful", said Elizabeth, as
~~people~~ very young people say things when they are excited, just
aloud, clasping at the same time either an umbrella, or
their hands; & ~~meaning~~ feeling, as they say it, that the
world is ~~the most~~ <more> exciting, ~~the strangest~~ <strange>
than anybody ~~the most~~ <more> wonderful ~~of~~
knew ~~places.~~ For here she was in Victoria Street.

280
200
56,000

suffocation & only these & more need to escape;

She was standing in Victoria Street, ~~having left Miss Kilman,~~
~~not wanting Miss Kilman,~~ free, quiet, ~~advanced, advanced somehow~~
~~beyond the an a step.~~ by herself. ~~into from~~ <for &> Miss Kilman
was ~~precisely <just> like other people;~~ there, in the Stores. Elizabeth
~~had no~~ was here; & it had been awful, when Miss Kilman said,
"Don't forget me" ~~to~~ to feel no emotion~~—to feel merely~~
~~only to wish to escape; & they <but &> as she escaped to feel~~
~~<she felt> happier & happier;~~
~~& then the to be out by on her own; free from Miss Kilman, & all~~
~~the effort, & the all the feelings~~
& now to feel as if Miss Kilman had never existed. And
~~since~~ she had nothing particular to do~~; why not~~ & she
might ~~d~~ go anywhere; ~~&~~ not home, ~~certainly~~ <oh> not, ~~home,~~ but
off—on top of a bus,~~—&~~ it didn't matter ~~much~~ which, <or> when.
Buses ~~came & went;~~ swooped; settled; were off.
She had no preference. She had not acquired any habits ~~yet;~~
~~or nor displayed~~ she had no features to speak of; {nothing
~~that led one anybody to one to~~ but a sunburnt mask,
~~white teeth,~~ slightly whitened with the finest down.} &
if nature had given her a beautiful body, ~~straight &~~
with the straight legs & fine ankles of a race horse,
so that Miss Kilman always thought of her ~~as a~~ moving, in the
open. her face was still ~~childish~~ <in doubt>; ~~&~~ more like her father's than her
mothers, <no doubt> ~~tending that is to say~~ <that is to say,> to the unexpressive; the
handsome, ~~the stable with~~ <But> Her eyes ~~would~~ were fine; &
~~(so~~ <as> Clarissa ~~had~~ said ~~a thousand times) &~~ with such
nice shoulders, back, ~~& ankles should she be a she~~
~~couldn't hel~~ & holding herself ~~perfectly~~, <beautifully ~~straight~~> she ~~certainly~~
must always look ~~charming~~; <nice;> ~~& Expression at eighteen~~
Quite lately especially in the evening, when she was
excited, she had looked almost beautiful in the ~~pure true~~
real English way, for hadn't the Dalloways been settled in
Lincolnshire ever since the flood? ~~so that they~~ There was a
greatgrandmother very like her. ~~As~~

And expression <which she lacked>, comes late—she was a little lifeless, heavy eyes, comes later.

There was ~~a great grandmother~~ an old ~~eighteenth century M^rs. Dalloway~~ <great great grandmother>
very like her. ~~And this lack of expression was~~ that she did not care more for clothes sometimes worried Clarissa; but perhaps it was as well. With all those puppies & ~~creatures~~ guinea pigs ~~always~~ <about> having distemper—
But that ~~showed she had, a~~ <her> passion for animals showed she had a heart, & now there was this odd friendship~~; &~~ ~~She had feelings: they And~~ Clarissa, ~~dining somewhere was much very much interested~~ <remembered>
~~by a saying of~~ <~~a~~ heard> old M^rs. Hilbery's,— <say> that the Dalloways were at
their best after forty. Clarissa anyhow was determined not to badger her. ~~Clarissa~~ Moreover, ~~about three o'clock in the morning, some when there is an a conventions about motherhood which~~ in motherhood there is much less blindness, ~~much~~ <much> more ~~of ordi the ordinary~~ discrimination than people allow; so it seemed to her, as her mind wandered from the pages of Baron Marbot,
about three o'clock in the morning, into the vast ocean, the ~~unfathomed, & never even attempted floods of life, fee feebly expressed margin, of reflections & intuitions which of life, in which she felt herself suspended,—as no doubt every other person in that street was doing—& extremely happy, very side awake, infinitely interested, her one dread indeed being death,~~

Imagine, this unfathomable, margin which was the margin of life; in wh.

lying there she felt herself ~~exquisitely~~ suspended; ~~among thoughts, visions, intuitions; which~~ like a fish, mute; & it amused her to think that next door some other woman was suspended, ~~thinking about her daughter; so~~ yet when they met, from sheer lack of words was it? or because they alarmed each other, ~~being~~ they would ~~just~~ pretend. You could not ~~say~~ speak the ~~"I have~~ truth, ~~however much you wished~~; & so like a solitary prisoner who spends his time scratching letters on the wall, ~~or~~ M^rs. Dalloway went on with her Marbot, quite aware that she was shut off.

thinking ho

Where was she going? Nobody knew her. Clearly, this affair, to be
grown up, & make an effect on people, ~~to~~ be someone, <be>
different from
anybody else, <other girls> was a tremendous undertaking.
~~She But then <And> why not be good?~~ Yet, if she had her way,
it would not be in London that she used this. vast gift, ~~&~~
which <seemed to> welled up, <to> as <to> her hands <as they>
grasped the rail, as she prospected,
from her ~~seat~~ front seat, the unknown ~~lan~~ quarters; but among
cows & flocks & ~~fields~~ & ~~country people~~ <peasants.>— ~~She would~~
It was the country she loved.

She loved children ~~too.~~ ~~But as for~~ Probably
something could be worked with milk, & clean stables; but
on the other hand, the ~~monotony of the~~ life might be dull.
~~That wouldn't be so~~ <Nor> in a hospital <[ ]>—where,
~~with luck,~~
~~she might in time control a whole school~~—there was always
~~excitement, always~~ responsibility. & She <became> was head of
innumerable wards. And then ~~& then~~— ~~But~~
~~It was~~ whether it should be a farm, or a hospital, became
~~not very important, in in the~~ indifferent, in view that is, of
~~a quite~~ <a quite> remarkable ~~experience~~ <idea>~~—One might be~~
~~good; one~~
~~might always do the~~ about ~~being~~ <being> good~~ness (they were~~
~~passing Temple Bar)~~
~~& just as they passed, that appeared so simple; &~~
which ~~over~~came <to> her just as they were passing ~~Temple~~ a
Great hoary white building; ~~which seemed to~~
~~stand for a &~~ how simple it was to be good; not bad; that was
~~that was the extraordinary idea, which~~ & ~~as they~~ were
<only> passing this building, ~~something~~ she had a vision of
millions of people, the people who had walked in London,
& ~~then~~ her giving back to the world what it had given
her; ~~a~~ very very strange it was, &

She ~~decide~~ was mistress of a thousand acres.

~~Such a view Somerset House received & the~~

Very strange, indeed, <one might think it> that such views should be proffered ~~dail~~
daily ~~by the young~~ from the tops of omnibuses to Somerset House; & the two paper-white churches which breast the stream of the Strand. So many ~~people~~ <ages>, Elizabeth felt, ~~sober men in the middle ages,~~ had worn these stones grey with the passage of ~~that~~ their feet; & it was quite different, she felt, ~~to~~ (getting down, ~~to here from in the~~ & walking towards Chancery Lane,) here from ~~what it in~~ <in> Westminster. It was serious & it was gay; & in short, she would like to have a profession. ~~Such~~
The feet of those ~~b~~ sages being ~~ab~~ for centuries about their ~~gay yet serious~~ activities, ~~the~~ hands putting stone to stone; ~~The~~ minds eternally occupied not with ~~more~~ trivial
worldliness, but with thoughts of ships, ~~for instance,~~ of ~~matters~~ commerce; of ~~the~~ books, <law> ~~perhaps;~~ ~~an~~ <or> of administration,— ~~compelled w~~ & with it all, ~~this dignity~~ <dignified>, ~~this you~~ joyfulness, ~~compelled not one girl but~~ for <the> ~~little courts~~ stately courts on ~~the right ran down to the river, compelled did~~
~~re stimulated not Elizabeth only but every sort~~
~~Elizabeth. but whose to vague prayer,~~
~~gave off a vigorous yet & strenuous <& solemn> & yet somehow solemn air;~~ & compelled ~~vows,~~ vague, unattended vows, ~~or~~ stimulated ~~one~~ <one> omnibus <load> after ~~omnibus not~~ another to make ~~a~~ some sort of return (Elizabeth felt that
she had been given so much) ~~for which would continue the~~
for the ~~gai~~ gaiety & the seriousness of the dead.

Strange though, ~~especially for one impassive, maternal,~~
~~<& maternal> & centred~~
that such ~~vows, or~~ impulses should form ~~so large a~~ past
of the thoughts of ~~omnibus~~ travellers~~;~~ as if ~~in~~ the sight of
buildings, without architects names, <of> shops with the same
anonymity
~~quality, there lived a general spirit, more of an intoxicating~~
~~stirred~~ had more power than single clergymen, &
~~&~~ individual books to stimulate what ~~was~~ lay, slumbering,
clumsy & shy at the souls sandy depths to break ~~wa~~
the surface; ~~&~~ without more consciousness than a child
has stretching & <or> sighing profoundly ~~in its sleep; only~~ it was
in the sleeping — no more than that, a stretch, a sigh; <then away> & then again,
down went the
impulse to the sandy depths. Elizabeth ~~was completely~~
~~ignorant of this part of London, & was~~ looked about her for
a clock.

She was a little awkward, thus penetrating on tiptoe, into a
<these strange> regions.
~~which had gen where she had no footing; Quiet & practical,~~
And she did not know her way. Every step she took up Fleet Street
was the step of ~~a val~~ some one who explores a strange house
by night with a candle, & is on edge lest ~~some~~ the owner
should suddenly fling wide his bedroom door & renounce ~~<ask her>~~ &
glare: — her for ~~<[business;]>~~ an interloper; nor ~~does~~ <did> she dare to
rummage up
alleys or into courts, anymore than ~~the~~ open ~~the~~ doors, ~~of~~
which might be bedroom doors or sitting room doors, or
lead ~~simply~~ <straight> to the larder. For ~~it was true that~~ no Dalloways
came along the Strand daily; ~~to do~~ never returned in the
glow of the late afternoon. ~~carrying bags;~~ She was a pioneer,
~~an outcast; a the~~ a stray; ~~throwing herself~~ venturing,
flinging herself upon the geniality ~~of~~ the brotherhood
sisterhood, motherhood, of this uproar.

Mrs. Dalloway.

Mrs. Dall

It seemed to her ~~as~~ good.
Indeed, ~~highly improbable as~~ though no girl ~~of her age,~~
loitering up Fleet Street ~~in~~ late on a summer's afternoon,
would consciously accept ~~from as the~~ from its traffic, & its
~~state base~~ stir & ~~its~~ the command to devote her life—
to the service of her kind {though Elizabeth would have
repudiated the suggestion, ~~&~~ perhaps it was wide of the mark,}
still there was in ~~the~~ her father's family the tradition of public
work; she was bound to receive, merely from the shape of
limbs, the ~~trusting~~ <&> ~~look in~~ her eyes, the devotion of her own sex;
& altogether might even now be gently setting her foot on the
first rung of the ladder ~~whose~~ which is crowned by the
comely & the stately, <the> abbesses, the Principals, ~~the~~ <the>
Head Mistresses &
~~Pr~~ other dignitaries, ~~for the most part uncrowned,~~ of the
~~rebu~~ republic of women. ~~Th~~ The uproar, ~~added to m~~
with an upper note added to it by an occasional barrel organ,
~~was of a perfectly proper accompaniment to all <such> dignified~~
accompanied dignified reflections; & if in some back room,
an old caretaker, ~~or dev messenger~~ devoted to the service
of ~~the~~ <her> firm, for half a century, had just breathed her last, &
her brother, ~~w~~ or whoever might be watching, had left her,
~~having accomplished this~~ with the sense that she, at any rate,
had brought off an act of supreme dignity. ~~an~~ This hot day,
& had opened the window & looked down on Fleet Street,
that uproar with the ~~rattling barrel~~ <hand> organ notes
rattling about in it, would have seemed to him ~~the~~
~~right, appropriate,~~ the right fare well.
[*pencil*] It was not conscious.

It was not conscious. There was no recognition of your dying
here, your
here making out a fine life's work; ~~yet No~~ It was almost indifferent; &
~~for that very reason, those whose eyes, not yet unhappy, clouded only with
a sort of wonderment, seek rested on the street, after having
noted scrupulously, laboriously the very last quiver of the dying lips,
were not outraged, not repulsed. It was to this indifference
that the one might most happily easily
rested on it without flung back into the~~
consoling. ~~So it, just consciously then <but> with the Forgotten,~~
Forgetfulness in people might wound; their ingratitude ~~de~~
corrode; but ~~not~~ this voice, posing endlessly throughout the
summers day, would take—whatever it might be. It would take} this
life; it would take this vow; it would take <the> van~~s~~, the
procession. ~~Then
man~~ It would ~~say~~ continue <wrap them round in [sky?]>—here
Elizabeth
~~not feeling free to go much further, &~~ having exceeded all the
bounds which her mother, who had a way of taking it
for granted that she did not go to certain places, or do
certain things, set~~;~~ her. hesitated. &

like fragments—
gentians, skulls,
~~perhaps~~ window
fragments in
some stew. &
eternal
glacier:

Never was she entirely without a sense of her mother's
presence. ~~This was especially so when she allowed tried~~ to
~~be Especially when she~~ They were so unlike ~~in~~ that when
~~Elizabeth~~ for they were so completely unlike that ~~on
often the~~ And that ~~of course,~~ was charming; it was childlike; ~~it was
all part of her innocence.~~ <it was> part of her innocence; ~~part
of~~ It tempered her fierceness; it ~~brought her~~ gave her

it attached her, ~~for the time being im firmly.~~ to the
exquisitely & firmly to home, as she called it: & in
her heart did she not think of her home as ~~something that~~ <a place>
not merely <of> comfort~~able~~, but of all these adorable odds & ends
doors, & cupboards, & old slippers; smells, echoes, effects of
light~~s~~ & shade, which since she had been born in this
home they still had, ~~could~~ no

~~Elizabeth~~ <She> hesitated: ~~She was~~ finally turned; & could be seen ~~returning retu~~ zigzagging her way ~~with an a tentativeness that marked her an interloper;~~ tentatively, for other people had reason to be here, she none? ~~back; &~~ towards home.

A ~~long~~ stretch of the yellow Strand ~~was blackened.~~ <went out; faded> Such ~~was the result, which of a cloud~~ For ~~a cloud~~ Such was the ~~almost unperceived~~ result ~~of an~~ of a ~~maneuvre~~ puff of wind, blowing a little shred of black veil across the sun; ~~this not that anybody~~ noticed ~~what was it.~~ For although ~~there was~~ the clouds were of ~~that~~ mountainous white, with golden slopes, & <had> all the appearance of settled habitations, ~~in a conference which~~ assembled benignantly,

280 ~~for good reasons,~~ in a ring ~~over~~ <round> London, there was a perpetual

200 slight going & coming ~~among~~ between them.

56,000 An attentive watcher could see signs interchanged, when, as if to

90 fulfil some great scheme, arrayed already, now ~~this~~ a

diminished summit ~~was <diminis>~~ dwindled, now a whole ~~py~~ block of

its head, pyramidal size. ~~like~~ which had kept its station unalterably, ~~advanced; seemed~~ <advanced or> gravely ~~to be~~ <led> leading the procession to fresh anchorage. ~~These were fine Certainty & a grave,~~ Indeed, ~~It There was no re quiet~~ <tired> though they seemed in their wills ~~ret~~ enjoying the repose of complete certainty, superficially, on the snows gold kindled surface.
nothing could be fresher. freer; ~~more quick to respond,~~ <ruffling, fadedly,> at any moment, it ~~might be time to~~ <they must> go, to dismantle this solemn assemblance, to ~~set up tents~~ & ~~fly, & Alive & nothing could keep them.~~ And ~~if~~ then, how irregularly & tremendously, ~~this~~ in spite of their own grave fixity, their enormous robustness & solidity, ~~baffled~~ <this> ~~baffling sun strokes, & sudden blacknesses, de brightened,~~ dashed a yellow stroke there; there darkness. Elizabeth, ~~having~~ had ~~crossed the~~ disappeared.

It was like the pulse <stroke> of some vapours, but irregular, pure.

An ~~puzzling~~ <ingratiating> habit, ~~Bernard~~ it appeared to
Bernard Warren-Smith,
who stretched upon the sofa with the inevitable bunch of grapes
beside him, a present from M$^{rs.}$ Filmer the landlady,
~~looked~~ watched the dazzling spot of watery gold ~~now~~
~~for bri~~ glow & fade with ~~astonis~~ the astonishing sensibility of
some liv<e>~~ing~~ creature upon the wall. ~~Ah but, that~~
~~old perplexity~~ As for that old perplexity, whether
the grass the flower, ~~the tossing green of the fragments~~
~~of the fragments of the trees the b~~ rugged green leaves
which the trees drew, ~~as if they were~~ <like> nets through the
~~have life;~~ & depths of the air,/ he ~~now rested secure in <the> procession,~~
consciousness, ~~not~~ of ~~any answer, but of the he had <it> was now~~
~~free from nibbling uncertainties; free no more~~ puzzled him
~~than a~~ no more. ~~He was perfectly content.~~ If
~~a~~ He was not puzzled: he was not distressed; he
might sink; he might ascend; momentarily at any rate
he ~~rest~~ floated on the warm waters, in the sun, &
~~as a~~ like a swimmer who has got far out,
~~could~~ hears ~~faint cries from the shore,~~ <dogs> ~~the~~ barking ~~of dogs~~ &
children ~~& the crying of children on the shore, & out~~ here the
shortly far off; ~~out there~~ <beyond> the sway & kiss of the ~~sea waves.~~ waves.

~~Nothing puzzled him.~~
He was not puzzled. It ~~seemed to him The goodness of nature,~~ & <At every moment nature>
~~her desire at every moment~~ to ~~create~~ <signifiyed> ~~enter~~ by some
laughing hint like that gold spot ~~on the wall or by~~—
~~beauty; of by great trees shivering, or by~~ her joy~~ful, &~~
her arm ~~under her ment,~~ her dancing freedom, ~~from which~~ &
~~yet was not~~ Yet concerned ~~itself~~ <herself> ~~with the~~ tenderly with the
~~miseries~~ of men, & ~~appeared, as walls like a~~ brandished
her plumes, shook her tresses, flung her mantle ~~in~~
one way after another, beautifully always beautifully,
~~outside, to tempt him, to console him, to sign to him,~~
~~this encourage, to <coming> like a free though she was,~~
~~yet coming~~ close to the window; ~~standing near, &~~
~~& though as if to until he came, she would then encourage him.~~
~~to encourage, to~~ ~~Of Her meaning was plain;~~
~~And~~ Rezia who was sitting at the table, ~~cutting a pie~~
twisting & turning ~~some shape~~ <a hat> in her hand, noticed him ~~not~~
~~that not~~ exactly ~~a smiling, but a look on her husbands face,~~
half smiling; ~~as~~ so that, ~~he was after all,~~ he was not
unhappy, ~~she concluded.~~ She drew out her thread,
placed it between her lips, knotted it, <&> ~~all the time~~
watch~~ing~~<es> him with the woeful integrity of some deserted
creature, ~~who~~ when he watched, as he was doing now,
something in the room, his eyes were quite peaceful; but ~~not~~
<~~they~~ were soft eyes;> ~~nobodys~~
~~his eyes:~~ ~~He was not himself.~~ eyes. <So> When he shut
them she felt ~~more restful,~~ <happier:> for

which went round
the wall,
there, there,
There,
her determination
to show—by
rightness, goodness,
beauty, beauty,
to signify beauty.
~~goodness;~~
~~beauty.~~
rightness,
goodness.

They were not his
eyes; they were
~~So stary, so strange,~~
anybodys eyes

~~They had~~ with a pallor in them, as if their ~~hazel brown~~ <blue green> had been mixed with water. ~~Haf~~ Mercifully, he shut them.

~~One could not be married to that.~~ It was not to that that one was married. She sighed, deeply, as if she were alone. & then, taking her hat, began her sewing.

He knew That she was there. ~~quite near to him,~~ Now she sighed; now she put down her scissors; now she turned to take something from the table. A little stir, a little crinkling, a little tapping ~~whispering~~ was ~~in the room.~~ about. She was there. ~~if he opened his eyes he would see her. But it was an effort,~~ a ~~very great effort~~ Through his eyelashes he could see her blurred outline; her little black body; her face & hands, her turning movements. at the table. She was making a hat for Mrs. Filmer's married daughter. ~~because~~ Her name was?—

"What is ~~the~~ <her> name ~~of the~~ Mrs. Filmer's daughter?" he asked.

"Mrs. Peters" said Rezia. "~~It~~ <I'm afraid it> may be too small—~~I don't know~~." she said. For Mrs. Peters, was a big woman, & not a very agreeable woman; & it was only because Mrs. Filmer had been so good to them, that Rezia wanted ~~to do something~~ to show that they were grateful. ~~Mrs. Peters <said> had a very sharp tongue <things>: she had the sort of thing Mrs. Peters did was to She had a very sharp way of saying things.~~ said the other day. She had come into the room the other day & found Mrs. Peters playing their gramophone.

"Did I tell you? Mrs. Peters was ~~in the room~~ <here> playing the gramophone when I came in the other day?" she said.

Oh how good that sounded!

~~She is not a nice woman. She is not~~
She did not speak to Bernard; to the air, to anybody.
~~But~~ It sounded to him astonishingly real, very satisfactory—M[rs.]
Peters had been in that room, playing the gramophone
~~Yet~~ She had moved <come in> about; she had taken the discs
in her hand; she
had wound up the gramophone,—but it was necessary to ~~define~~ <make>
There they were in the room, the very things. these impressions, ~~which~~ definite; ~~& in short~~ to look at the
things themselves; Very ~~slow~~ cautiously he looked at the table
on which the gramophone stood. First, he looked at the magazines
& fashion papers on the lower shelf; then at the ~~very~~ thing <itself>, the
with its green trumpet. gramophone. ~~itself.~~ And so on, at the sideboard, at the
bananas, at the engraving of the farm pond, at the
mantlepiece. All were extremely satisfactory
"~~I don't like her.~~ She is a woman with a spiteful
tongue", ~~so~~ Rezia ~~went on~~ <said>.
~~She Growing~~ more &
M[rs.] Peters ~~shared the~~ <wore> the solidity, the shiny ~~the~~
~~perfect truth~~ <true> ~~of the~~ <like> the
furniture. ~~And, therefore But~~ she <And she must be> approached
~~was more difficult~~
& Rezia; ~~& the~~ but gradually, cautiously, sipping the
relish ~~of~~ them at every shop. ~~enjoying what was not only~~
~~so enormously real,~~ gently tapping this ~~rat~~ immensity this
this solidity.
~~He wished to know~~ <What then did M[rs] Peters> ~~why she had~~
~~there: her history:~~ was
her husband's profession.
Ah said Rezia, trying to remember. Had M[rs.]
Filmer not said that he was a traveller, some
sort of agent, for some sort of company. ~~At present,~~
"Just now" she ~~knew~~ <said>, he ~~was~~ <is> in Hull.
"Just now",—There! That was Rezia
herself ~~speaking:~~ ~~"He~~ He shaded his eyes; so that

they might not be dazzled; or horrified by what ~~mig~~ some thing awful—some scowl, sneer, or deformity. There was none. There ~~w~~ she was, Rezia, familiar, in plain day light, sewing. not even looking at him.

After these glances at her, he was assured.

~~sewing~~ with the pursed lips that women have when sewing, the
rapt <set> melancholy expression. ~~But~~ ~~The~~ But ~~what~~ was there
any terrible about it? he asked himself, alighting again & again <a
second time, a third time,>
on her face, on her hands, for ~~she let him~~ <as apprehensively
at first> she sat sewing: No—she
~~& each time he was less afraid; each time reassured,~~
~~Life was absolutely commonplace: safe:~~ what was frightening,
& disquieting in life, ~~then,~~ since there she sat, ~~sew~~ in broad
daylight, calm, not beautiful, rather plain indeed, sewing?
And Mrs. Peters had a spiteful tongue: & Mr. Peters was in Hull, &
And why then shall one ~~attempt to be violently prophecy, or~~
firm, violent? those ecstasies, those vision, that tumult of
of feeling?—& rage & prophecy; & the misery & flinging,
~~scourged, an outcast: why all that, he wondered,~~
really state after state, high mountains; ~~v~~ death,
revelations; as he looked at Rezia, & shut his eyes.—opened
~~them &~~ & saw, dispassionately, those old vistas—high
mountains; death; ~~lone~~, & opened them, & there she was
methodically ~~arranging~~ <sticking> pins in ~~the~~ <to the pocket
of> her blouse?.

antelope,
zebra,
penguin,
pelican,
camel leopard
giraffe
lion, tiger
bison, buffaloe
monkey, hoopoe
ostrich marmot
mandrill &
    mongoose.

[page 103 *verso*]

["Nurse Lugton's Golden Thimble" ("The ..." *Times Literary Supplement*, 17 June 1965. *Nurse Lugton's Golden Thimble*, 1966)]

Why ~~even~~ <But then>, he thought, try to write down, or to
make visible <is not to be written down; no it was different>~~. A was~~
what ~~everyone had anybody in his senses has quietly, normally~~
~~is not of that kind;~~ & <&> ~~it~~ <he> ~~seemed~~ compar~~ing~~<ed> this
pleasant quiet calm,
with all the tumults of the past weeks, {~~really~~ he was ~~p is~~ violently
ashamed of his conduct.} which had raged in him; ~~& made him~~
~~swell & posture & attitudinise;~~ With shame he remembered
attitudes & ~~des sayings~~ <exultations.> ~~Even~~ What had burnt in him, or
pressed wedge like for deliverance, was now all streamed away.
~~How heaven~~ ~~Still, however, he thought holding~~ But why
should he be ashamed, he thought, looking at his foot ~~<sticking~~
~~out>~~ at the end
of the sofa, since ~~in this enormous~~ it is I; ~~I myself, one & the~~
~~same man,~~
~~who have been through all the stages of this~~ since
~~After all, he was a who made of~~ all stages were necessary, ~~in this~~
~~process of~~ living ~~life~~; & ~~he had gained, know~~ that immense toil,
~~when every that terrible ascent~~, had brought him ~~to this~~
~~conclusion~~ <here>; ~~&~~
~~never without folly & agony could~~ ~~to be quiet, at with Rezia.~~
~~There, & Mr.~~ Tremendous the journey seemed; the
~~But here, now, alone with Rezia, those But this was now & here & the~~
~~present moment: &~~ But here was the finish & ~~here was~~ the ~~only~~
<first> moment,
~~since~~ <for> years now, of certainty. ~~<that>~~ <When Rezia said
said how> Mrs. Peters played their gramophone;
~~yes; Rezia had~~ ~~when Rezia said~~ that ~~she~~ <had> ~~somehow ended~~
~~<his> isolation~~
~~And &~~ how Mr. Peters was in Hull.

As if she knew, by instinct, for she did not look at him,
how

~~to be talked of~~
~~like that at all,~~
that kind at
all,

those interviews
with doctors
vi

Miracle followed miracle: ~~all life one after another~~, painful, tremendous,
~~they rose & burnt, as if~~ one's like volcanoes~~;~~ or fire bombing; with
bitter smoke & rough flames; & then ~~this~~ <at ~~last~~> last ~~peace~~
~~this certainty,~~
was reached; ~~through them;~~ all was burnt out, & the daisies
<grass> grew;
for ~~H~~ he had a sense, as he watched Rezia, turning the ~~d~~ straw hat,
of a ~~<lying under>~~ coverlet of flowers.

She always tried <hard> not to look at him. It was not ~~to~~ marriage—
~~that was~~ it was not being one's husband; to look strange like that, &
always to be starting ~~or pointing~~ or laughing, or sitting hour
after hour, silent; or clutching her, & telling her to write. The
~~dining~~ table drawer was full of those scribblings ~~which he had~~
~~made her write.~~ about war; about Shakespeare; <about the
things in one's soul; & how> how there was no
~~such thing as~~ death: ~~For he~~ Lately he had ~~been~~ become
excited, suddenly, for no reason; & waved his hand, & seen ~~it~~
~~all~~ <things—>
~~work out~~ the truth: ~~of Evans had come~~ That man, his
friend who was killed, Evans, had come, he said—M$^{rs.}$
Filmer had picked up some of these papers; & what could she
think of them? ~~sometimes~~ They were reasonable~~; only very~~ [margin: what did the servant think of them?]
~~hard to follow~~; sometimes: sometimes quite mad. <But>
They were ~~only~~
never finished; ~~Before he had finished done one~~ his mind ~~w~~
And D$^{r.}$ Holmes always said that on no account was he to be excited.

or not. Some things she could understand; <others> ~~seemed to her quite~~
she could ~~not~~ make <neither> head <n>or tail of. And he ~~often stopped in the middle,~~
~~or changed his mind;~~ was always stopping <in the middle>, changing his mind;
wanting to add something; ~~as if there were some one else there~~ <listening, with his hand up;>
& once he <they> had found the girl who did the room reading
one of these papers, ~~& laughing.~~ in fits of laughter.
That set Bernard off writing about human cruelty; ~~lately~~
that ~~human~~ men tear each other to pieces: <the fallen, he said, they tear to pieces.> She had given up
arguing with him. ~~Once you fall, he was always saying,~~
Holmes is ~~on~~ you; ~~<merciless>~~ for ~~Holmes,~~ Dr. Holmes seemed to
stand for something dreadful to him—~~though indeed Dr. Holmes was~~ though why he disliked ~~Dr. Holmes~~ so much
she could not tell, since he was quite an ordinary man, ~~only kind, though~~ not very clever. perhaps. Then there were
these visions. He was drowned, he used to say, & lying on a
cliff, ~~&~~ He was listening to music. Really it was only
a barrel organ, or ~~one of those street~~ <some> man crying in the street.
"Lovely" he used to say. "Divinely~~" he~~ beauty~~ful~~" he used
to say, & then ~~he~~ the tears would run down his cheeks, which
was to her the most dreadful thing of all— a ~~strong man,~~
to see a man, a man like Bernard, crying. And ~~for~~
he would lie listening, until, for no reason, he was falling;
he would cry, starting & seizing hold of her, falling down, down,
into the flames. Actively she would look for flames, it was <seemed>
so ~~vivid.~~ <real.> But there they were, ~~sitting~~ alone; there was
nothing; it was a dream, she would tell him; ~~but one~~ <she would try>
~~could not go on, trying <but> like that.—She was frightened sometimes too.~~ she could not go on. Sometimes now she
was frightened too.

Holmes is on one, he was always saying good-hearted,

to comfort him; it was too great a strain

Of course, if she had been in Milan, at home with
people she knew, it would have been different.

holding forth.
Who was he talking to, Sally asked? <~~that~~ a distinguished looking> ~~But~~ Peter did not
man; know who ~~the distinguished looking man~~ <he> was. ~~Only~~
~~But Richard was <It was foolish> of course, Sally admitted, one <only> to say~~
~~pretend to know what~~
~~Of them all, said Peter,~~ <Of them all,> Richard seemed to him ~~to~~ the ~~most~~
best, Peter said; the ~~But Did one really know~~
other peoples' ~~anything about one's friends, Sally asked; & their~~
private lives, ~~was it not all~~
Really the best; the most disinterested. ~~He~~
But what had he done? <(Public work, she supposed.> And were they very happy
then, Sally asked, (she was very happy herself)
~~or~~ for, she admitted, she knew nothing of them, had
only jumped to conclusions, as one does, for what can
one know even of the people one lives with, she asked.
Are we not all prisoners? ~~Is it not~~ Despairing often
of human relationships she <often> went into her garden, ~~for~~ &
But no: <h> no got from nature a peace, a certainty which men & women
~~could~~ never gave ~~her~~. But he had always
preferred human beings, Peter Walsh said. Indeed, they ~~are~~
the young are beautiful, Sally said, ~~look~~ watching Elizabeth
cross the room. How unlike Clarissa! Could he
make anything of her? Not ~~much~~: <not yet: not ~~w~~> Peter admitted:
She was like a lily in its bud, Sally said; so
smooth, so stately; so full of promise; ~~for the future~~
But ~~<to>~~ Peter ~~did <could>~~ <did> not agree, ~~not for a moment, about~~
~~with th what she~~ about that—that we know
nothing. ~~of our~~ We know everything ~~on the contrary~~
he said. ~~We~~ At least he felt that he did.

Everybody? ~~For example he could tell Clarissa that he did not like~~
~~No, they~~ <Surely these> are enigmas, ~~said~~ Sally said; ~~for there~~
<& there> were
two ~~of them~~ <for instance> now ~~coming~~ <now coming> (it was
getting very late, ~~& Clarissa~~
~~if Clarissa~~ but she must wait to see Clarissa)—this
distinguished looking man & his wife: ~~the h~~ whom
Richard had been talking. <to> ~~They meant nothing~~ to him!
nothing whatever. ~~But~~ And Sir William
Bradshaw & Lady Bradshaw ~~passed quite~~ stopped:
always stopped to to look at a picture. Sir William always looked at pictures.
say something. He looked in the corner for the engravers name. Lady
It was a habit of his Bradshaw looked too. ~~And~~ Then they went. ~~But~~
on leaving rooms. They meant nothing to her, nothing whatever, people like
that, ~~she~~ <Sally> said. ~~What did he mean.~~

Oh but ~~they~~ one knew a great deal, Peter thought; more & more & more
every day one lived. Look, ~~look,~~ he said, ~~& there~~
~~After all,~~ And when one was young, it ~~was meant very~~
~~little~~ was too exciting; but now that one was old, fifty two to be
precise, (Sally was fifty five, but felt no more than twenty six)
~~now that~~ one could watch; one could absorb; ~~one~~ <understood,>
& it was
~~not true either that one had lost~~ <one did not lose> ~~one's~~ <the>
~~capacity~~ power to
feel (no, that is true, said Sally) ~~but for it~~
~~seemed to grow, but what happened was perhaps~~
It increased he said.
~~Indeed They don't feel~~ <she> Elizabeth feels nothing compared
with ~~as he sa~~ what I feel he said as Elizabeth
went to speak to her father, (who ~~said to <looked at>~~ her, grown up,
(& said ~~to her how~~ he had been looking at ~~the~~ her,
& ~~said to himself~~ <wondered> "Who is that very nice looking girl?"
~~for he had not known her,~~ & it was ~~his own~~ Elizabeth
grown up!) ~~which~~ & ~~Peter & Sally thought~~
Sally said ~~Elizab~~ They are devoted to each other, &
Peter looked, <knew that yes, of course> & felt certain of
course that that was so;
from the way they stood together; looking at the
~~people~~ going & leaving the rooms emptier & emptier, with
the chairs ~~all~~ turned this way & that & here a
little piece of lace on the floor, & a carnation,
& they were glad it was almost over, but
~~very proud~~ rather proud, & excited, &
Elizabeth ~~was~~ devoted to her father, &
~~thought~~ her dog was howling she told him,
but ~~re~~ <But> "You have enjoyed your party" Richard
said to her, & she said, frowning slightly,

Yes she had. ~~She had enjoyed at least she had enjoyed~~ what he ~~said to~~ her—it was a thing she would never forget, <but it was
his saying ~~that th~~ how he had first known her>
~~That he had thought she looked nice; & then~~
~~Peter could not must speak to them both, & so~~
~~he got up & Sally got up, & they Peter said We~~
~~know~~ Sally said, Richard has improved, you are right.
Let us go & talk to them, said Peter.

~~I~~ Let us, ~~he thought,~~ go to them, he thought:
~~For though~~ & ~~he felt,~~ as he walked towards them, this is <he ~~& felt~~>
one of ~~those~~ <the> moments, ~~which~~ this is one of ~~those~~ <the> events;
~~This~~ ~~I know possess this; I grasp this; he thought; And~~
But what is it, he asked himself, What is beginning to form in
me, & ~~will go on <& is> increasing & increasing; in~~ me, &
~~will at last over come me with an extrordinary~~
~~bliss?~~ & ~~making everything press on me until I~~
What is about to happen? By what name can I
call it? This terror, this ~~profound~~ ecstasy? It is
Thursday Clarissa.
Oct. 9th 1924 For there she was.
11.15.

<u>The Hours</u>

Oct 20th
1924

<u>Chapter One.</u>

Mrs. Dalloway said she would buy the flowers herself.
For Lucy had her work cut ~~of~~ out for her.
The doors would be taken off their hinges; Rumpelmayers
men were coming. And then, thought Clarissa,
What a day! Cant

What ~~an ecstasy~~ <a ~~miracle~~>! What a plunge! For so it had
always seemed to her, when, with a little squeak of the
hinges which she could hear now, she had burst open
the French windows ~~on & stepped out on to the~~
~~terrace of Bourton.~~ & plunged at Bourton ~~on to the~~
~~terrace~~ into the open air. ~~Like waves, like~~
How fresh, how calm, stiller than this of course ~~&~~ the
air was in the early morning; ~~rooks cawing, dogs~~
~~barking; & the sense, which naturally one lost later of this~~
~~& then & rooks cawing dogs barking; <&> & with it all—~~
~~but Peter Walsh she would say she~~ like the flap of a
wave; like the kiss of a wave; ~~for~~ & chill & sharp & yet,
(for a girl of eighteen as she was then) ~~how & so~~
~~little~~ solemn. ~~yes, solemn.~~ Peter Walsh would say—
whatever Peter Walsh did say—~~when he found~~
~~when he found her~~ "Musing among the vegetables?"
Wasn't that it? Peter who didn't know a rose from
a cauliflower. & 'preferred men to cabbages.' She
"I prefer men to cabbages". He must have said it
at breakfast, for her to be thinking of it on the terrace

one morning, ~~& then going <she had> out onto the terrace,~~ &
she had gone
on to the terrace, as she had done over & over again, ~~with~~
~~to escape, to look, to think it over, what Peter said & how~~ the
~~morning looked~~ & stood there, just for a moment, &
felt as she could not feel now, ~~at her age~~, that
something tremendous was about to happen, but ~~that~~
& so stood, & so looked, at the flowers; at the trees, &
wondered why, then, ~~that~~ this young man, whom they
hardly knew, should begin like that, to Aunt Helena of all
people, at breakfast. ~~Not to like flowers.~~ It was very
like him. And he would be back from India one of
these days, June or July, she forgot which, ~~& to be~~
~~perfectly honest~~ she ~~had never <for she> could not read~~ his
letters; they were awfully dry; it was his sayings one
remembered, his big pocket knife, his eyes; his
~~charm too~~: & his grumpiness; & when millions of things ~~were~~
had utterly vanished, a few ~~sayings~~. <things> like this. ~~which~~
brought back ~~to her that~~ about cabbages.

She stiffened a little, waiting for Durtnalls
van to pass. A charming woman, Scrope Purvis thought her,
Mrs. Dalloway, knowing her as one does know ~~the~~ people who live <next door> in
Westminster; a touch of the jay about her; of the bird; blue green;
light, vivacious, though she was over fifty; & grown
very white since her illness. <But> ~~Not that she saw him.~~ <did
not> For out
~~slid,~~ <There> She perched there; not seeing him, waiting to cross; her
lips pursed; very upright; ~~a & out they out~~

For having lived in Westminster how many years, now?
over twenty, ~~one knows~~ there is, even in the middle of the
night, Clarissa was positive, a particular ~~sense~~

hush; or solemnity, ~~or~~ an indescribable <pain,> sort of ~~apprehension~~
~~bef~~ suspense, apprehension (but that was probably her heart,
(—affected, <&> ~~affected~~ which was strained somehow) before Big Ben struck.
by There! ~~It boomed out.~~ Out it boomed. First a warning;
imposing musical, then the hour; irrevocable. Such fools we are',
She thought, crossing ~~now; &~~ Victoria Street <Gardens>: For heaven
only knows ~~how~~ why one loves it, ~~adores it,~~ makes up
this ~~astonishing adventure, even &~~ loves it so, ~~&~~ how one
~~or~~ how one makes it up,~~—presumably, everyone of us, not only well to do~~
sees it so, <making it up, building it round one, tumbling it creating it every moment afresh>
~~people,~~ but the veriest frump, the most dejected of miseries,
(drink had brought sitting in the door way~~—we all <all> [ ] that go along, as~~
them to it ~~she went along, like this, all make it up~~;
poor old dears) ~~want all being being~~ ~~one feels just as~~ ~~how could~~
<does she seem;> positively ~~they feel it too; they also; &~~ <do feel;> so, amazing, so
has that, ~~want it, enjoy~~ it, ~~must~~ have it, & can't be dealt with,
clings to that, whatever Richard might say, satisfactorily, by Act of
Parliament, for that very reason: ~~Life,~~ ~~they what one~~
~~life, its that, life's~~ <this> life; ~~she felt,~~ life; ~~the~~ in ~~their~~ peoples
eyes, in their energy, in ~~their~~ swing & tramp & trudge; in
the bellow & ~~the~~ uproar; ~~in the sudden calm too which~~
~~fell on her;~~ Richard was at that moment attending a
committee in the House of Commons.
there it is.

For it was the middle of June; &

For it was the middle of June. The war ~~might~~ was really done
with now, except for some one like M^rs. Foxcroft at the Embassy
~~last night~~ eating her heart out because that nice boy was
killed & now the old Manor House must go to a cousin; or
Lady Bexborough; ~~she~~ <who> opened a bazaar ~~with~~ <they said>
the telegram ~~<from the war office,>~~ in her hand:
how people ~~people~~ said; but it was over. It was June., ~~&~~ And though it was
suffer!— hot, it was fresh still; & gay, & stirring; already even at this hour,
of the morning, ~~after dancing all night,~~ <the> girls ~~taking their dogs out,~~
~~(as her Elizabeth would be giving their absurd woolly~~
~~dogs a run; & were~~ taking their <absurd woolly> dogs ~~out;~~ for a run; &
business [ ], & ~~visiting perhaps,~~ & Hurlingham or Ascot or
Lords or; & everyone dressed in ~~the thinnest possible~~
[~~&~~?] muslins & whites, ~~wait~~ <& pinks> & even the shops engaging too
with their ~~sprinkling of odds~~ & ends—old brooches, <old> buckles,
slabs of ice— ~~a picture or two;~~ <green weed> slabs of ice; & something more mysterious
green weeds, ~~in the air~~—whether it was the King <being> at Buckingham Palace; or
~~merely the dance & the stir which is June, of course, in~~
~~London; the plunging of the ponies, & the tap of bats, & the~~
~~running, & the shouting & the merriment;~~ &
or the sense of June in London; & polo, & cricket; ~~& horses~~; riding;
~~enjoyment; & with it all this peace.~~ For she had
turned into the Green Park. ~~Suddenly one could hear~~
~~the leaves rustle, & there was, almost more appropriately~~
~~suddenly~~ ~~than one could imagine, Hugh Whitbread! Hugh~~
~~Things~~ <all> summing themselves up ~~so; drop collecting; coming~~
down on
one in their mysterious way for no reason—no reason
whatever; so that one ~~said~~ felt this ~~it it~~ is it anyhow;
London, June;

[*pencil*]
For M^rs
D.

The king & Queen were at the palace. And everywhere,
though it was still
so early, there was beating ~~&~~ <a> stirring; galloping ~~bo~~ ponies;

Lords, Ascot
Ranelagh & all
the rest of it,

the tap of cricket bats & ~~all the rest~~ yet; wrapped in the soft
mesh of the blue grey morning air, which as the day wore on
would unwind itself <them> & ~~lif~~ & set down on their lawns &
~~their~~ pitches the <[flanneled?]> striving young men, & the
laughing

after dancing
all night

girls, <with all their parasols,> who even now were taking their
absurd woolly dogs
for a run; ~~& even now the shop doors were open, &~~

(after

~~the men coming motor cars were shooting out; & even now~~
at this hour ~~& old~~ discreet old ladies were shooting out in
their motor cars, ~~on errands,~~ <on err> ~~of the utmost discretion~~,
& already the shop keepers were fidgetting <in their windows>
with their paste &
diamonds to tempt Americans~~;~~ (& lovely they were too,
~~especially~~ the sea ~~greens,~~ the ~~fres~~ lumps of pure ~~colour~~
transparent <sea green> colour in their old eighteenth century settings
but one must economise, not buy things rashly,) &
& ~~it was adorable, & it was lovely;~~ & she, too, ~~who~~
loving it as she did with an absurd & faithful passion,
being ~~indeed~~ part of it, since her people had been
courtiers once, in the time of the Georges, she was going ~~to~~
<to have the party, her party; she was giving her party>

the veil; the hum;
~~the discreet hum;~~
~~the <slow> swimming~~
~~pea~~ birds; ~~the~~
in the pond.
& the & the
grotesque
poached
bird,

this very night, this June night to kindle & illuminate:
But how strange, entering the park, the ~~sudden~~ silence,—
then against the white government buildings who should
be coming along, ~~very~~ who more appropriately, but
Hugh Whitbread! H.W. carrying a despatch box with the
telegraph wires & the government buildings below

"Good morning to you!" said Hugh, rather
extravagantly, for they had known each other as
children. "Where are you off to?"

"I love walking in London", said M[rs.] Dalloway
Really its better than walking in the country!"

"We've just come up. Unfortunately to see doctors."

[*pencil*] Of course it was Evelyn his wife.

~~It m For <For>~~ That <This> ~~was the typical of the Whitbreads—"to all over—"to see doctors."~~ Other people came up to see
pictures, go to the opera, take their daughters out; but the
Whitbreads came "to see doctors"; ~~just about this time of year, always at this time of year.~~ Times without number, Clarissa
had ~~been to see~~ <visited> Evelyn in a nursing home; ~~she being For it~~ was it Evelyn again? Yes. Evelyn was a good deal
out of sorts ~~again~~, said Hugh, intimating, by a kind of ~~swell~~ <swell> or
pout of his very well covered, & extremely ~~w~~ handsome
large ~~tall well set up~~ excessivelly well tailored body
(he was always almost too well dressed but with his
little jobs at court, had to) ~~be~~ that ~~these~~ his wife had
reached ~~a time of life~~, <an age> or ~~had~~ done an <some> injury
to some ~~fu~~
woman's function, which he ~~kn knew~~ as an old friend
Clarissa ~~wa~~ Dalloway would quite understand without
requiring him to ~~mention~~ specify <Ah yes,> So she did;
<of course.> & she
~~promised to~~ felt ~~very~~ sisterly; ~~liked him, laughing<ed>~~ at him, & was
oddly conscious, as he always made her, of her ~~shoes~~ hat.
Not the right hat for the early morning, was that it?
For he always made her feel, she thought, as he
bustled on, ~~wav~~ assuring her as he went that she was
looking like a girl of eighteen, & he was ~~counting on~~
coming to her party ~~though unless~~ Evelyn had commanded
him to go, but if ~~he were detained by this,~~
he might be late, there was a drawing room, he had to
take young Claud—might he bring him?—& she
Evelyn next week ~~would be able to see visitors—~~
She always felt a little skimpy beside Hugh; schoolgirlish,

that this was one
of those cases of
[many?] to sour
women's [friends?]
or
has to be
rectified
wh. things not
serious ~~had~~
was incapacitating,

would ~~really~~
visit
count on a
visit the very first

but attached to him, ~~as one was to~~ partly from having known him ages,
~~though~~ & ~~seeing~~ <but she saw> the good in him, besides what
people laughed at—
his pomposity, his airs & graces. Richard was nearly driven mad
by him. And Peter Walsh had never to this day ~~forgiven~~
<forgave> her for
liking him: ~~And "The admirable Hugh"; For some reason they~~
~~always stayed at Bourton together; & She tried first~~
A strange incapacity men had, if there was a woman about, for
behaving even decently—she could remember scene after scene at
Bourton~~—always on Peter's side, for Hugh to do him justice~~
Peter ~~going off in a huff: & arguing,~~ Hugh of course not his
match in any sort of way, but still not a positive
imbecile as Peter made out; not a mere barber's block; ~~not a~~
~~he was~~ He was ~~very arrogant in those days, Peter Walsh; very~~
~~irritating: that He was very arrogant in those days,~~
~~Peter Walsh, very~~ <really> kind, ~~surely,~~ <truly> extremely
<extraord> unselfish. When
his old mother, ~~was (The most tiresome old thing that ever was,)~~
~~got nervous~~ wanted him to give up shooting he did it: & so on.
~~But Peter he~~ However~~—why had she ever asked~~
~~them together? For any goose could have seen that~~ nobody but a
goose would have expected them to get on. And Peter, after all,
however irritating, however infuriating, with his
perpetual moods, & his lecturing, & his way of blurting
out things merely to make ~~people~~ <you> uncomfortable,
his strutting; & was after all the
most adorable human being she had ever met. Not to be
made love to by—to walk with ~~an~~ a morning like this.
[*pencil*] Oh one's friends—how one waits to see things with
them.

~~extremely unselfish,~~ for when his old mother wanted ~~to go~~ him
to take her to Bath or to give up shooting, he did it—
he was ~~genuinely~~ <very> unselfish, & as for saying, as Peter did, that
he had no heart, no brain, nothing but the manners & breeding
of an English gentleman, that was only her dear Peter
at his worst, ~~grumpy, nervy, moody, with a~~
~~A moody~~ ~~Odious He~~ <And he> could be odious: ~~certainly:~~
very intolerant, ~~exacting;~~ very narrow-minded; always
scolding ~~telling~~ her, ~~not to be this that & the other & making~~
~~oh & they had said the most idiotic priggish things in~~
~~the whole world;~~ as they walked by the hour on the
hills through the woods; ~~& which talking talking~~ & talking, &
(with Sally Seton) ~~of everything in the world, &~~ or sat up ~~till the~~ <till all hours of
the—night> ~~over the~~
~~schoolroom fire with Sally Seton.~~ talking. Adorable, most
adorable of men! <indeed> not to be made love to by, but to walk
with on a morning like this—to see things with; ~~to~~
For they might be parted for <hundreds of> years, she & Peter; she
never wrote a letter & his were dry sticks; but all the
After she found herself same it would come over her quite suddenly, ~~oh~~ if he were
defending her self with me now; what would ~~Peter~~ <he> say? some days, some
from him: her sights, bringing him back to her, ~~intolerably;~~ <intolerable,
~~frivo~~ worldliness: her with such longing;> no,
longer painfully, for all the pain had long ago gone out of it,
~~but very happily, as if that were~~ the reward of
caring, after years & years, after bitterness, & unhappiness:
not that one's friends returned,—came back ~~w~~ in the middle of
[ ] St James' Park on a fine morning; ~~this or that~~
very ~~silly little~~ were ~~really~~ with one, as the past is;
[ ] ~~strangely with one; &~~ but very real. ~~And~~ <But> ~~he would~~
~~say to her,~~ with Peter, however beautiful the
day might be, & these trees, & the grass, & the
people sitting about & the children playing; & the
grey blue mist,—& ~~she sometimes~~ still she found it

~~sometimes almost~~ <almost> overpowering, the beauty of
London;
    ~~Peter~~ <Peter> he
~~always~~ never saw a thing. <at all.> He would put on his dear
if she told him   old spectacles
to.   ~~to look.~~ But ~~what~~ it was the state of the world that interested
him. The taxation of land values; Wagner; Popes poetry; &
~~people: their He used to say that he could read~~ the defects of her
own soul. She had the makings, he would tell her, of a ~~really~~
decent human being. But, he would say, you'~~re~~<ll> ~~bound to~~
    ~~<bound to> go under.~~
marry Richard Dalloway; <you'll> stand at the top of a staircase;
pour out tea. The perfect hostess—that had never
ceased to sting her—~~that he said~~ she had the makings of a
perfect hostess. he told
    But after all—such dialogues she ~~had~~ carried on with
Peter in India!—~~one must be one self.~~ So she answered him back.
So she tried to make out, & he was the only ~~man who made~~
human being who made her do it,
[*pencil*]
{a thing that certain people are so close
that they infringe each other's independence—

But, after all, what could one be except oneself? So she would still
~~argue~~ find herself arguing in <St> James' Park ~~of~~, after all these years,
with Peter Walsh, who was in India. Still justifying
herself, ~~&~~ making out that ~~her~~ she had been right; And she
had been right, too, not to marry him. For in marriage,
~~his~~ which is not friendship, a little licence, and
independence~~, of each other was necessary. Did she know~~
More must be between people living together day after day in the
same house; which Richard gave her, & she him (Where was he
this morning for instance? some committee, she never
asked what) But with Peter, ~~no~~ everything was shared.
~~everything~~ & it was intolerable, ~~to her anyhow.~~ utterly ~~exhausting~~
~~no freedom~~, & ~~a~~ when it came to ~~that morning~~ <scene> in the little
garden by the fountain—never should she forget the broken
spout & the water dribbling—~~then~~ she had to break with
him, ~~for both their sakes,~~ or would have been destroyed;
both of them ruined; she was convinced, though ~~when~~
for years & years she had borne about with her like an
arrow sticking in her heart, ~~the fa grief~~ <oh grief> & ~~the~~ <an> anguish &
~~the a sense~~ of the waste & folly of it ~~&~~ when, she heard, <& the
agony of that moment>

& <oh> the
horror of the
moment when

quite casually at a concert, <someone told her> that he had married some
girl met on ~~a ship~~ the boat going <out> to India! ~~However~~—
And that had been a failure; & his whole life had been a
failure—or ~~not what it might have been.~~ Unless, indeed,
as she sometimes thought, brought up as she was, so
conventionally with dear Aunt Helena, only caring for
orchids, & her <beloved> father, so ~~devoted, <strict> so timid, but so strict,~~
so timid, <so> heavenly & perfect though he was; unless there was in
Peter Walsh, & in most men, quite another side, which
she never even guessed at, & that was why he
despaired of her so bitterly in such <anguish> for not knowing what
love was. Cold, heartless, a prude. Never for a

could she understand ~~how~~ heis cared. <passion for her.> But
these Indian women did,
presumably. And she wasted her pity. for he was quite
happy., He assured her, ~~he was~~ perfectly happy.
though ~~Yet he~~ had never written his book ~~on Pope~~; never done
anything: & loathed India.
~~Well,~~

[*pencil*] Fed from a thousand sources as her life was, how pretend to judge another.

It made her angry still.

hoping for no reason, ~~But~~ Yet, fed from a thousand sources as her own life was,
ridiculous things ~~making her happy~~, <~~brimming~~ <filled> her with
ecstasy> & more nonsense often ~~making reducing>~~ her
~~making her~~ sitting whole days almost in despair, she ~~could not~~ would not say
~~of any one in the whole world now that this was what they cared~~
were; <that> they cared ~~for; or~~ ~~She would not lay down laws—oh no.~~
for this or that. ~~She would not say that Peter was~~ That they were this or that.
or the other. She could not account to herself even for a morning walk like this,
across the park, to buy flowers; ~~&~~ meeting Hugh Whitbread, &
being at once infinitely & intensely & radiantly happy; &
filled to the brim with unshed tears. & being ~~as if~~ were
floated out of herself by the beauty & the movement, & the sense of
London, & all agog, of course, to give her party; & being very
the omnibuses in ~~very old, a young girl; & being anxious to her finger tips, as~~
Piccadilly; ~~if those <she> were a knife in her which sliced through everything—it~~
~~was her people; & at the same time detached <outside of~~
wh. come ~~everything>, observant; &~~
dear & ~~for some reason, <cutting as> thinking of her childhood~~
sliced ~~all the time; & then, even~~
~~in the midst of it all,~~ The oddest ideas coming to her; ~~&~~
fragments of <old> poetry; & a sense of ~~the futility—or rather~~
of being out out far to sea, & alone; & blown on, very
dangerously, ~~for if she never lost her feeling that sen~~
~~sense of danger. sense that it is dangerous, very very dangerous, this~~
~~living even one day. A rope walker, & beneath death; so she~~
~~thought most people felt;~~ For
& its being dangerous ~~to live—dangerous, & exacting, &~~
~~unknown~~ <she had always the feeling of ~~a rope walker~~ . .
~~been~~ dear <it being very dangerous>>
~~And a man like Peter Walsh, was much cleverer than~~
~~she was.~~ to live even one day.

Not that she was clever~~; or~~

Not that she thought herself clever. How ~~could she~~ <she could>
have got
through life, ~~she often wondered, on the~~ on the ~~bare~~
few twigs of knowledge Fraulein Daniels ~~gave~~ <taught> her,
she could
not think. She knew nothing: no language, no history;
~~somehow, though she liked reading,~~ she scarcely read a book now;
~~except some old French memoir in bed;~~ music she loved, but
only knew enough just to strum if they were alone; & yet
it was to her absolutely absorbing: she could not remember
being bored; & ~~so, if it were so to her, without any~~
~~great capacity, (a thimble headed, chatter box, all~~
It was to her a perpetual miracle. ~~(What then must it be~~
~~to a man like Darwin?) Partly~~ ~~this life.~~

She had reached the Park Gate. And it came over her,
that she had a sort of genius, at any rate a natural gift, for knowing
~~quite a~~ people, easily, almost by instinct. If you put her in a
room, with anyone, <up> at once her back went ~~up~~ like a cats, or she
purred. Devonshire House, Bath House, the house
with the china cockatoo; ~~as they called it when they were children,~~
She had seen them all lit up once, ~~upon a time~~ <ages ago>;
& remembered
Sylvia & Fred & Sally Seton; ~~&~~ crowds & crowds of people, &
dancing all night; & the great waggons plodding
~~down Piccadilly~~ in the dawn; & driving home across the
park; She remembered throwing a shilling into the
Serpentine. But everyone ~~did that;~~ remembered; what
she ~~did~~ <loved> was ~~to exist now. Lovelier than ever~~ this;
in front of
her: <now> ~~the very moment~~. Did it matter, being ~~a stra~~
ordinary & <woman> a nincompoop, a ~~mere straw;~~ did it matter
She asked herself that no one would know, in fifty years,
that she; poor witless (as ~~her~~ old nurse called her) had
ever existed; did it very much matter, even to her, the

~~she had done nothing to be remembered by;~~ must, inevitably, cease to exist completely; ~~must things~~ all this must go on without her; ~~did it make one less hoping now; or~~ did ~~it~~ one <she> ~~wish for~~ resent it, ~~to be remembered; or~~ did it not become more & more consoling to believe, ~~as she believed in hi~~ <that> death ended; but, ~~mystically;~~ that nevertheless somehow, ~~strewn on the~~ scattered about the streets of London, on the ebb & flow of things, ~~this~~ even her life would go on ~~& on;~~ people surviving in each other, being parts of each other, not here Clarissa & there Peter Walsh; but ~~one~~ everywhere Clarissa, she being part, she sometimes felt, of ~~solitary lovely~~ trees, at home, at Bourton; part of old house there, ugly & rambling & all in <to> bits & pieces as it was; part too of ~~unknown~~ people; & ~~what could~~ be ~~more obvious than~~ she did not know; ~~&~~ <for> even if one had friends & ~~knew them~~ & cd. ~~say anything to them, surely was one not always caught like a mist on a branch there was always, about them & about oneself,~~
There lying between the closest friends mists, caught up on trees; what was she thinking, what image of silentce ~~dawn~~ in the country was she trying to recover, as she looked into Hatchards window & read, in the book spread open,

Fear no more the heat o' the sun.?

And below that was

& laid out like a mist between the people she knew well, who lifted
her on their branches as she had seen the trees lift up the mist,
~~which lay all round them,~~ but ~~only~~ it spread ever so
wide & flat far on the ground. What image of the white dawn ~~was~~
in the country was she trying to recover, as she looked
into Hatchards window & read, in the book ~~laid~~ <~~spread~~ tied> open,

'Fear no more the heat ~~of~~ o' the sun'?

Thou thy worldly task hast done, Mrs. Dalloway read.
Tears unshed, tears deep, salt, still, ~~w stood~~ stood about
her ~~being~~ for all deaths & sorrows; ~~thr there being~~
~~now, after the in~~ this late age of the worlds experience,
~~an~~ having bred in her, & in them all; all men &
women however frivolous they seemed, a sense ~~of sorrow.~~
<well of tears,>
~~flow many <or> deaths, &~~ sorrows; ~~& also, of course,~~
~~of~~ courage, ~~of the~~ endurance & vigilance; & a perfectly upright
stoical bearing.

Below ~~that~~ was <were> Jorrocks Jaunts & Jollities.
& Soapy Sponge. & ~~the~~ Mr. Asquiths memoirs; &
Cranford; & ~~hunting Big game~~ <Big game> Shooting in Nigeria, &
ever so many other books there were, but nothing
that seemed exactly right for Evelyn Whitbread in her
nursing home. Nothing that would ~~just~~ serve to
wile away ~~half~~ an hour, ~~&~~ <to> make ~~Evelyn~~ that indescribably
dried up little woman ~~feel,~~ look, as Clarissa came in,
glad, pleased; just for a moment cordial, before
they settled down again to ~~that~~ the usual talk about
womens ailments. How much she wanted it—
that people should look pleased when she came in—
Clarissa thought; & was annoyed to think. For

it was ~~not genuine;~~ <not genuine:> ~~that she was~~ ~~Peter said~~
~~that she lied. She~~
~~wanted so much to be liked, that she would do anything, &~~
And she would have ~~liked~~ <so much ~~prefered~~> so much
~~rather;~~ <rather> to be ~~one of those~~
have been ~~quite to be~~ one of those people, ~~who~~ like her husband,
Richard Dalloway, who ~~could not conceivably~~
did things quite simply; ~~instead of~~ who were not conscious of
all the shades & different feelings, but went straight forward on &
on, from ~~one thing~~ this to that, always occupied, ~~&~~
yet free & keeping themselves fresh; whereas, she thought,
turning to cross the road & go up Bond Street, she was
full of these detestable intrigues & sophistries of the
spirit: lies, evasions; ~~& so~~ dependent <too> on ~~the~~ what people
thought of her ~~& said of her; upon~~ their ~~being glad~~
then liking her; ~~& their~~ & ~~she was never~~ hardly ever
absolutely sincere, <or> ~~detached from the~~ absolutely
herself; ~~for there was always or unconscious of that~~
but ~~do buying~~ doing things to be liked; fidgetting, posturing
posing to make an effect (though no one was ever taken in
for a second) oh if she had had another life, she
would have been a different woman.

She would have been dark ~~& with beautiful eyes~~; ~~&~~
like Lady Bexborough with a skin ~~like a~~ <of> white
white velvet; ~~glove~~ crumpled; ~~& be moulded~~ <& beautiful eyes>; ~~not a pinheaded~~
~~& all those wrinkles.~~ As it was, ~~all~~ she could ~~say of~~
~~plume~~ only say that she held herself well; that she had
little hands & feet; ~~but~~ that

She would have been, in the first place, dark like Lady Bexborough,
with a skin of crumpled leather & beautiful eyes. She would
2,800 have been, like Lady Bexborough whom she admired most of all
women in the world, slow & stately; & interested in politics like a
200 man; & with a large country house, to entertain in; & very
11 dignified, very sincere. Instead of which she was ~~such~~ a
2,... ~~flightly~~ jumpy <flightly> creature; ~~she was~~ <a> narrow,
pinched, <pea stick ~~creat~~ figure> with a
250,0 ridiculous little face, beaked like a birds. ~~& she was far far too~~
300 ~~emotional~~. That she held herself well was true, & had nice hands &
11 feet, & dressed well considering that she spent little; ~~And~~ <But>
3,300 often now
this body she wore ~~seemed~~ with all its capacities, seemed nothing—
nothing at all; she ~~was~~ had the oddest sense of being herself invisible;
hearing, seeing, ~~th &~~ feeling with a passion, ~~of a violence,~~
~~an intensity that~~ of intensity; but herself unseen; unknown;
~~unnoticed~~; ~~&~~ there being no more marrying, no more having of
children; ~~only~~ no ~~more experiences, in herself, Clarissa Dalloway,~~
but only this astonishing & solemn & most tremendous
~~common human life,~~ progress: <on together in common> Bond
Street always
fascinated her—Bond Street early in the morning in the season;
Its flags flying & its shops; its resemblance to something
profoundly respectable in English life; ~~for~~ no splash, no
glitter; one roll of cloth where her father had bought his
suits for fifty years; & a few pearls; & a salmon ~~with~~ on an
ice block; that was all. {~~Yet~~ Yet it seemed to her,—
again, the result of growing old no doubt—a token of
~~the English who, of their~~ what she had loved; <&> what ~~a~~
~~th m~~ thousands ~~of men~~ had died for; ~~&~~ Only
far from thinking of death, she}

"That is all" M^rs. Dalloway repeated standing
for a moment to look in at a window, at a glove shop,
where, before the war, <~~they sold~~ one could buy> almost
perfect gloves.
~~And gloves she did~~ And her old Uncle William
used to say that a lady was known by her shoes & her
gloves.

(He had turned ~~in~~ <~~in~~ on> his bed one morning in the middle of the war
& said ~~he had~~ "I have had enough")

Gloves & shoes: but her own daughter, her Elizabeth, cared not a
straw for either.

M^rs. Dalloway went on, up Bond Street, to a shop where
whenever she gave a party, they kept flowers for her; for she had
helped the woman there, years ago. Her Elizabeth
~~notably~~ <really> cared ~~most~~ for her dog~~—a large bob-tailed~~ ~~sheepdog~~
most;—& that enormous & shaggy creature which had ~~the~~
one disease after another. If you took it out, it chased the sheep:
~~or it howled,~~ or it was run over; ~~or <or>~~ its fur came off in patches &
the whole house this morning smelt of tar; ~~Elizabeth far~~
~~more what attentive to Shag than~~ ~~For~~ Still,
better poor Shag than Miss Kilman. Better distempers & tar &
all the rest of it than sitting ~~w~~ mewed up in a stuffy bedroom
with ~~prayer~~ a prayer book. The astonishing mixture! Her own
daughter, her Elizabeth, she scarcely knew; marvelled at her almost
every day; the two things she, Clarissa, ~~really did~~ <could> not
understand—the passion for animals,~~—the~~ & this instinct
this religious instinct,—came apparently ~~by~~ naturally to her—
~~Elizabeth.~~ ~~They could~~ Why, it was ~~hopeless~~ <ludicrous>~~—if they~~
always wore a ~~went for a~~ wounded pigeons settled in their back garden
every day; miserable cats, who were only fit to be drowned in
~~had to be~~ a bucket of water ~~at once, or~~ she had no objection whatever
~~rescued.~~ ~~in sending them in a taxicab to the lethal chamber—~~
<sat on> the doorstep. ~~had to be fed~~ on hot milk ~~all night long.~~ were
fed on ~~herrings <hot f milk> in the~~ school room. ~~Moreover~~
How every day There were even
she spent fish— ~~But~~ Unhappy fish. But animals <were> after all
looking after them; could be <harmless> more or less accounted for; whereas to sit &
pray with that unwieldy woman, by the hour,
was ~~to say th~~ inexpressibly distasteful. It might
~~spoil Elizabeth~~ only be a phase—Richard said so.

It might be falling in love, which <every> one has to go through.
But why with Miss Kilman? She had a really ~~historical <able>~~ mind,
Richard said, & she had been badly treated; ~~but did mere~~
& one must make allowances for her; ~~so they were~~
~~inseparable,~~ Anyhow. They were inseparable, & her
Elizabeth, her own daughter, ~~could~~ went to Holy Communion
& how she looked, how she dressed, how she treated
people, who came to lunch, she didn't mind a bit.
~~To be religious &~~ ~~And the~~ Such kindnesses, ~~such~~ &
independence, sympathies, ~~which, sometimes, seemed~~ & ~~being sere~~
self control, & being determined never to inflict <ones own>
suffering on other
~~all~~ these ~~people—these were not the religious people &~~
~~these~~ were not in their line; it being her experience that
the religious ecstasy made people very callous, very
~~insensitive, just as~~ dulled their feelings, as public causes
had a way of doing too; for Miss Kilman ~~cared~~ would do
anything for the Russian; ~~for the poor;~~ <anything for an
cause> ~~it was only in~~
but in private inflicted positive torture, so insensitive was
she, so set in her own grievances.

Hour after hour, if you let her, she would talk about herself.
All men were brothers. For that very reason, one must hate
some of them, as one hated part of oneself—so it seemed to
Clarissa; who ~~simp~~ could not bear that unwieldy woman;
thought it a base form of robbery, this preaching to a girl
when one was supposed to teach her history: & her
appearance was so distressing. ~~Whatever the weather~~ <Year in,
year out>,
she wore a <green> macintosh; & she perspired; & she was
never in the room five minutes without making you feel
(She hated ~~every~~ ~~that~~ her superiority, your inferiority; ~~&~~ how poor she was,
~~kind of~~ beauty) how rich you were; how she lived in a slum; without
of every kind— a cushion or a bed or a rug or whatever it might be.
Poor, embittered, unfortunate creature!—all her
soul was rusted with that grievance sticking in it—
her dismissal from the school during the war,
And the odd thing was <that it was> the idea of her, not her, one hated;
for in the flesh~~, with her~~ there before one, ~~something~~ she, Clarissa,
almost always ~~began~~ <wanted> to laugh, comparing her, ~~fo~~
with the idea of her which presumably had gathered
into itself a great deal that was general, not particular to
poor Miss Kilman; had become one of those spectres with
which one battles in the ~~the~~ night; when the great wars
go forward; ~~the~~ had ~~become an awful bogey;~~
~~an idea~~; one of those spectres who stand outside us, &
suck up half our life blood; ~~a~~ strange products of the soul;
~~the conviction which one waits to impress upon other~~
people, domination, & tyrants; for no doubt, with another
throw of the dice, had the black been uppermost & not
the white,—she would have loved Miss Kilman!
But not in this world. No.

It ~~stirred &~~ rasped her, though, to have ~~such~~ stirring about in her
this brutal monster; to hear twigs cracking, & feel hooves
planted down in the depths of that ~~dee~~ forest, ~~where~~ the soul;
never to be content, quite, or quite safe, for at any moment
the brute would be stirring. This hatred; which, especially
since her illness ~~in had power to make her feel, running~~
~~all up her spine—precisely as if she were a cat—~~
~~spikes, shocks, tufts; a it gave her physical pain; to hate people.~~
~~This hurt her because of Elizabeth. Those tears which~~
~~it was a~~ & made all pleasure, in beauty, in friendship, in
being well, & being loved, & making her home ~~p~~ delightful
rock, ~~&~~ quiver, ~~shake~~ & bend as if indeed there were a
monster grubbing at the roots. But nonsense!
Nonsense, nonsense! she cried out to herself, pushing open
through the swing doors of Mulberry the florists; & advancing,
~~to~~ be greeted at once by button faced Miss Pim, who had
been ~~pu~~ put on her feet by Clarissa years ago.

There were flowers. Delphiniums; ~~roses~~; sweet peas ~~of~~
~~all colours~~; ~~tufts of~~ branches of lilac; & carnations—masses of
carnations. ~~It was wet & fresh &~~ There were roses;
in the wet warm, there were irises & lilies; Ah yes; So she stood among
deliciously smelling them talking to Miss Pim. And indeed, she was a kind lady;
shop having known her ~~for~~ twenty years, Miss Pim knew that—
~~Though she might look just like other ladies,~~ Ah yes, And
Mrs. Dalloway glancing about her among the flowers looked
drew in her beak like a bird; ~~looked~~ drew in her beak; looked so gay &
happy turning from side to side, among the irises & roses; &
the nodding tufts of lilac; Fresh they were, &
sweet scented; & frilled like ~~clo~~ linen ~~fresh from~~
clean from the laundry laid in trap; & dark &

passionate; ~~oh~~ & ~~in the &~~ & ~~then all the sweet peas in their bowls~~
tinted violet, or that exquisite white which is as fresh as a
~~sheet of paper;~~ ~~fresh & cool as a dairy it was;~~
& all the sweet peas spread in their bowls, fringed violet & white,
~~—then~~ as if it were the evening, ~~the simple fresh~~ & girls in
their muslins came from their ~~farm~~ house to pick sweet peas—
roses to stick in their hair; after the superb summers day,
with its almost blue black sky—its delphiniums & its
carnations, & its arum lilies—~~had~~ was over; & ~~they~~
~~with their it was now~~ that astonishing moment, between six & seven,
when the sky has no force in it, & ~~one~~ every flower—every
single flower in the garden—glows, whatever its colours may be:

by itself
spring
with a
magic flare

White, ~~ros~~ violet, red, deep orange; each flower seems to be
be burning, softly purely intensely; & the moths! How
she loved to see them ~~twining~~ in & out <round & round> of her
flower beds at
Bourton; ~~& the~~ <then the old> owl ~~calling~~ hooting

'Don't you get fearfully tired?" she said in her
charming voice— "standing? When d'you get your
holiday?
When do you find the time, she meant, to go out into the
garden & see all this! Roses & irises & lilies;
carnations, sweet peas; And

In September, madame, when we're not so busy"
~~And to~~ For it beat one down, it overpowered, it
did, really come out & like a wave, rise up & curl &
then sweep down triumphantly upon that hatred—
this beauty; this roses & lilies; this nodding [ ],
& pinks;

But who the lady was, over there, standing
over there in the window with her back to them?

by the red faced, button faced Miss Pym, who hands were
Monday always bright red, as if they had been stood in ~~the~~ <cold water>
jars ~~where she kept~~ <with the> her
flowers.

There were flowers; delphiniums, sweet peas; bunches of lilac;
& carnations, masses of carnations. There were roses; there
were irises & lilies. Ah yes. So she breathed in the earthy ~~wet~~
garden smell; talking to Miss Pim; who owed her help, & would
~~therefore always come out of her little box:~~ & ~~come out of~~ her box
always when M^rs. Dalloway came in;}; thought her kind, for
kind she had been, years ago; kind she still was, standing there,
~~turning~~ looking older, ~~now~~ this year, turning her head from side to
side among the irises & roses, & nodding tufts of lilac, with
her eyes half closed, snuffing in the delicious scent. And then,
opening her eyes, how fresh, like frilled linen clean from a
laundry laid in wicker trap they looked; & dark &
~~snipped~~ prim, the red carnations, holding their heads up, &
& all the sweet peas spreading in their bowls, fringed
violet, snow white, pale,—as if it were the evening, &
girls in muslin frocks came out to pick sweet peas &
roses ~~to stick~~ after the superb summers day with its
almost blue-black sky, its delphiniums, its carnations,
its arum lilies, was over; & it was the astonishing moment
between six & seven, when every flower—roses
carnations, irises, lilac, glows whatever its
colour—white, violet, red, deep orange; every
flower seems to burn by itself, softly purely
~~intensely~~ with magic fire.—in the misty beds,—
how she loved the grey white moths spinning over
the purple cherry pie, the yellow evening primroses!

~~W~~ Dont you get awfully tired, she said
to Miss Pym. ~~When~~ standing all day?
When d'you get your holiday?

For shadowy shop girls, pursued her ~~often, & hatred, which,~~ ~~as she~~ came
~~along the street had been~~ down the garden paths, ~~ugly as they were;~~
& hatred;
"In September, madame, when we're not so busy"
& that uneasiness ~~with~~ which thought stirred, raisi~~ng~~<ed> its head;
made the water ripple & tremble, & everything seemed treacherous &
insecure; & ~~then, thought~~ Mrs. Dalloway, ~~raising her head &~~
confronted this thought, this uneasiness whatever it might be,
& ~~at once stan~~ holding herself very straight, & looking very
bright, & then from all the flowers ~~this~~ a wave
rose, ~~a wave, a <& curle>~~ as if beauty being stored there, would if
you twirled it & flung yourself upon it, rise up, &
~~overwhelm~~—curled & swelled & she exalted born up,
when, on the very crest of it, out rang a pistol shot!
~~A crash!~~ a violent interruption!
"Really those motor cars," said Miss Pym,
apologetically, going to the window to look, & coming back ~~wi~~ &
smiling; ~~apoli~~ apologetically, as if it were her fault.

The violent explosion ~~which made Miss Pym go to the window,~~
which ~~&~~ Mrs. Dalloway start, ~~as~~ & Miss ~~Py~~ Pym go to the window &
apologise, came from a motor car which had ~~come stopped~~ <come
to a standstill>
~~burst its tyre~~ precisely opposite Mulberry's shop window.

People must notice, she thought; people, she thought, look~~ed~~ing
at the crowd,
moving off down Bond Street; the English people, with ~~all~~ their
children, & their horses, & <their> clothes. which she admired in a
way; ~~but~~ people they were to her; <only> faces, <&> ~~hats~~, bodies,
~~because~~ <but> & ~~she thought them hostile~~ this morning, they
were <she was afraid of them,>
because of that ~~awful~~ thing Septimus had said; he would
kill himself; an awful thing to say; Suppose they had heard
him? And she looked at the crowd.

~~Nine months ago, when they walked on the embankment,~~
Only last autumn she & Septimus had stood on the
embankment wrapped in the same cloak, &
Septimus reading a paper instead of talking she had
snatched it from him & thrown it into the river—
laughed in the old gentleman's face who saw them!
But then she was happy. Now they must get away, into
some Park.

"We must cross" she said,
Although his arm was without feeling, she had a right to it.
He would give his Rezia, who was so simple, ~~such~~ & so
proud of her hats ~~chatterbox~~ & only twenty four, without friends in England,
who had left Italy for his sake; a piece of bone.

The motor car proceeded with its blinds drawn &

The Queen going to some hospital, opening some bazaar,
thought Clarissa.

The crush was terrific. ~~it~~ <for> this hour in the morning. Lords, Ascot, Hurlingham, what was it, she wondered; for the street was almost blocked. The British middle classes, sitting sideways on the tops of omnibuses with parcels & umbrellas, yes, even furs on a day like this, were, she thought more ridiculous, more absurd, & in their own way more delicious than one could conceive; ~~she~~ with the Queen herself held up; ~~by a brewers van.~~ the Queen unable to ~~get past~~ pass. Clarissa was suspended on one side of Brook Street; Sir John Ruckhart, the old Judge, on the other; with the car between them; (Sir John had upheld the laws for years, & appreciated a well dressed woman) when the chauffeur,

~~Clarissa~~ She stiffened a little; ~~looked~~ so she would stand at the top of her stairs:

as they looked ~~an enormous~~ she would become perfectly silent; very ~~peaceful;~~ & in the still blue heights, a ~~quiet~~ string of gulls flew in a V shape across the sky, gu
& they saw a flight of gulls crossing the sky very quietly, just one gull leading. & then another,

For Dr. Holmes had ~~said to her~~ told her to make her husband (who had nothing whatever seriously the matter with him, but
<was> a little out of
sorts) notice things outside himself.

So, thought Septimus, looking up, they are signalling: to me. Not indeed, ~~in so actual words; but~~ indeed in actual words. That is, he could not yet read the language, but it was plain enough. This exquisite beauty, this divine loveliness, & tears
filled his eyes,
as he looked at the smoke words languishing & melting in the sky in & believing in him, in their inexhaustible charity, one shape after another of ~~astonishing &~~ unexpected beauty, ~~fresh creating a fresh, inf boundlessly, & signalling her intenti~~ & signalling their intention so to provide him, for nothing, for ever,
with
beauty ~~&~~ more beauty.

They were advertising toffee, a nursemaid ~~said~~ told Rezia: Together they began to spell "t . . . o . . . . f" "K . . . R" said the nursemaid, ~~standing at~~ & Septimus heard her say "kay arr" close to his ear deeply, softly, like a mellow organ, but with a roughness in her voice like a grasshopper's, which rasped his spine
wh.
deliciously & sent running up into his brain waves of sound.
concussing,
Indeed, <it was> a most marvellous discovery,—that the
broke.
human voice spoken in
certain atmospheric conditions, (for one must be scientific) can so quicken the ~~tr~~ very trees into life. Happily ~~(~~put her hand, with a tremendous weight on on his knee, so that he was transfixed, or this ~~beauty of the elm t~~ excitement of the elm trees rising & falling, rising & falling, like plumes on
& the color of the green shining & flickering & the sky [ ] him
horses heads, feathers on ladies heads, would have flaunted him away up into the air. ~~In short,~~ he was near madness; but mad he would not be. He shut his eyes ~~firmly~~, <he would> not ~~be~~ see.

But ~~light stole~~ in. <But> They beckoned, ~~the le~~ signalling to him that
they too were alive; leaves were alive; the tree was alive. The
~~bending & the bowing. shivering, quivering was~~ & the
leaves being connected by millions of fibres <with> to his own body
fanned his being up & down; & when the branches stretched it was a
statement. ~~&~~ Sparrows fluttering & descending in irregular
fountains
~~made a new were filled~~ <were part> in the pattern, & the blue &
the white & the
bulged out, clips black bars sharpened <blacked>, & defined themselves. Sounds made
harmonies with premeditation; the spaces between were as
significant as the sounds. A child cried; Rightly, far
away a horn sounded. All taken together meant the birth of a
new religion—~~a~~

Septimus, said Rezia. He jumped, as usual. People must
notice.

"I am going to walk to the fountain & back" she said.
For she could ~~not~~ stand ~~<no>~~ it ~~any~~ <no> longer. D^r. Holmes
might say
there was nothing the matter. But she could ~~not sit~~
_ ~~beside him when he did not see her & stared so,~~ not spend the
rest of her life with him alone; ~~when he sat~~ & stared so. ~~& never saw~~
her, & ~~turned~~ <made> everything terrible. Sky, & trees, &
children playing,
dragging carts, blowing whistles & falling down; all ~~were~~ was
terrible; & And he would not kill himself; & she could tell no one.
"Septimus has been working too hard" —that was all
she would say, for they did not understand him. He was a
great man. So love makes one solitary, she thought. She
could tell nobody; not even Septimus now; for & looking back, she
saw him sitting in his shabby overcoat alone, on the seat,
bunched up. It is wrong. <And it was cowardly> For a man
to say that he would
kill himself, ~~was~~ but Septimus had toughness: he was brave.
this was not Septimus now, She put on her lace collar, or her new
~~hat~~, & he never noticed; & he started, if she spoke, & he
~~thought~~ He was happy without her. Nothing could make her
happy without him. Nothing! He was selfish; so men
are. And he was not ill. D^r. Holmes

said he was well. She spread her hand before her. Look! her wedding
ring slipped. She had grown so thin. But she had nobody to tell.
Far was Italy, & the white houses, & the Milan
streets crowded in the evening with people talking, laughing,
out loud,
not half alive like people here, huddled up in bath chairs;
like paper flowers looking at a few ugly flowers. 'You should see the Milan
stuck in the grass gardens", she
said.
But who was she talking to? Unless it were Mrs. Filmer,
the landlady at their lodgings: There was not another human
being <she knew> whom ~~she knew~~.
So ~~it faded, the~~ <so her cry> ~~It~~ faded; unanswered; as the
sparks of a
rocket having grazed their way into the blue of the night
surrender to it, & even yield their fire to mount the
darkness. Dark descends; pours over the outlines of houses &
towers; bleak hillsides soften & fall in. But though they
are gone into darkness, the night is full of them; robbed of
colour, blank of windows, they exist more ponderously; give
out what the frank daylight fails to transmit; the
trouble & the suspense of ~~of~~ things conglomerated there in
the darkness; towers & men huddled ~~there with~~ in the
darkness; ~~& with dumb pain they endure,~~
reft of the relief which dawn brings <when it> waking the water
white & grey, spotting each window pane, lifting
the mist from the fields, showing <in> the red brown cows
<&> until all once more is decked out to the eye—
exists in fact. I am alone, I am alone, <she> Lucrezia
cried in Regents Park; as perhaps ~~in the~~ at midnight
when all boundaries are lost the country reverts to its
ancient formless shape, ~~without association, unnamed~~
as the Romans saw it when they landed, hills unmanned,
rivers winding they knew not where, with no common
shape <as yet> upon them,—she was in the darkness;
unsupported;
~~Mrs. Filmer~~ at when suddenly, as if a little shelf shot forth
& she stood out, she said how anyhow she was his wife, a

~~married woman~~—married at St Pancras Registry office nine months ago;

~~So she would~~ a married woman; his wife; who would never tell, never tell a soul that he was mad! But the shelf fell; down, down she dropped into the fire. He has gone, she thought, turning & running, gone & thrown himself under a cart! No: there he was; still sitting on the seat, in his shabby overcoat. He was talking.

Men must never cut down trees.

Men must not cut down trees.
Such astonishing truths, spoken for him, thrusting open his lips,
~~had a~~ came to him again & again, & he wrote them down on p
envelopes, <or> the backs of cards. ~~or made~~ Rezia was his
disciple.
The elm tree crinkling its bark signalled the message to him,
~~of its up~~ that it lived; the leaves dancing & spangling, signalled;
~~for there was no breeze.~~ ~~They moved of themselves. One~~
~~Scientifically~~
~~speaking,~~ One must be scientific: clear; ~~precise;~~ logical, ~~if one was to~~
at all costs. Certainly, there was no breeze: ~~Therefore~~ they signalled.
~~The fact was noted. Trees live.~~ They were about to speak—
the wildly dancing little leaf at the end of the branch; ~~bobbing up—~~
~~down,~~ was ~~about to~~ <branches> the stretching ~~of the branches~~,
the drawing
back, the sudden shiver of the whole tree; was the prelude;
to speak, & then, as he sat there with his pencil, a sparrow
perching opposite, chirped Septimus four or five times over,
quick friendly gay; & ~~then~~ went on, drawing its notes out
to sing freshly & piercingly in Greek words how
there is no crime. Make it known. Change the world.
no one kills from hatred. Make it known. Change the world.
Whereupon Another sparrow ~~flew~~ <perched> a little higher & together they
sang with
voices prolonged & piercingly that seemed to come from trees in
the meadows of life, beyond a river, where the dead walk;
& if he looked up from his card, Septimus would see them, the
dead, walking.
But he dared not look ~~at once~~ on the faces of the
dead, who were assembling, one after another, behind the
railings across the road. There was his hand, holding the
pencil; ~~he would look at that~~ & the dead were there.
But Let them speak to him first. Immediately the dead
laughed; faintly some of them; the laughter of other was
loud like clappers at the railings. It must be that his
spiritual climbed precipitous mountains; while close

to the railings the young laughed, in their muddy boots, noisily vanished. Evans laughed.

"What are you saying to yourself?" Rezia asked him. Was he mad then~~? But he could see a paper bag drifting drifting along, catching in the railings.~~
talking aloud? A paper bag drifted slowly along catching in the railings: ~~in He~~ Air currents. He must use his reason.

<upon [causes?]> He would
not go mad.

"~~But~~ There is nothing to be afraid of" she said, taking him by the arm, & making him walk through the enclosure where M^essrs. Spiers & Pond ~~have the~~ serve refreshments: & a ~~charming~~ darling little boy—she would never have children of her own—was drinking milk; looking over the edge of the glass at her, ~~slipping <leaning> on the lean~~ half lying on the table.—his nurse would have ~~him sit upright~~ none of

They must get away from people, Septimus said.—right away, over there; where, beneath a tree, two green chairs stood; & the long slope of Regents Park dipped, like a length of green cloth, with ~~smoke &~~ a ceiling ~~cloth~~ <veil> of pink & blue smoke, & far houses, & in the distance the hum of traffic; & on the right, ~~d~~ long necked animals, emus, ostriches, stretched over the Zoo railings, & a animal barked, howled.
[*pencil*] They sat down on the green chairs under the trees

There they sat down, under the tree.
"There is a God, said Septimus. There is no crime. Write it down" he said.
She would write it down, directly they got home.
As for the dead, he said—actually panting with the effort.
~~The dead; the dead"~~ Do not talk of the dead, she begged.
The dead, the dead" he said, in terror lest he
might see them; but the message must be given.
They are happy she said
They are quite close" he burst out. She
She ~~ta~~ started.
"Look, look" she implored him, pointing to a troop
of little boys carrying cricket stumps, one shuffling,
spun on his heel, & shuffling on, as if he were acting a
buffoon he had seen at the music hall.
Look at that, she implored him; for Dr Holmes
had said ~~above~~ he must be made to ~~take an interest in~~
notice real things: ~~take an interest in~~ go to the music hall; or
cricket—that was a ~~fine~~ <the very ~~thing~~> game, Dr Holmes said,
for ~~a~~ her
~~husband~~. A fine game, out of doors.
Look, she repeated.
Look, the unseen bade him, the voice which now
communicated with him, who was the greatest of mankind,
Septimus, lately taken from life to death, Septimus the
interpreter, the Lord who had come to renew
society ~~to . . . who had been chora~~ <who>, & lay like a
coverlet on the highest mountain top, ~~like~~ a snow
blanket smitten only by the sun, forever unwanted
suffering forever, the scape goat; the eternal, ~~Septimus,~~
sufferer from mankind; ~~above the~~ ~~Not that~~ I ~~do~~

do not want it, he moaned pulling from his eternal suffering, &
eternal loneliness, & ~~the crown~~ glory.

People will notice—<for> He is <was> talking aloud,
Rezia thought,
& ~~said~~ implored him again to look. But the boys had gone;
the Park was almost empty. There were only a few sheep.
Look at those sheep" she said.

But he was staring into the sky; at the
~~advancing, <&> deluging, communicating with each other,~~
~~Beautiful as they were, advancing, deluging, ruffled with gold, &~~
or stationary or marble,

~~Oh the beauty.~~ Again the beauty; <&> the composure, <&>
the splendour; &
~~the purpose~~. <as high> ~~High~~ overhead they passed; ~~the~~ pillar with its
ruffled edges, the footstool, the lovely ladies skirt
trailing across the sky, the sailing ships blown & majestic:
but not [strange?] ~~but~~ symbols they were & types of . . .
[symbols?] ~~Pardon me~~;
The way to Regents Park Tube Station—that was what
Maisie Johnson asked the young couple on the seat. ~~The~~
For she was only up from Edinburgh two days ago; this was
her first time out alone in London.

It was not this way; it was that way; over there,
Rezia exclaimed, seeming queer, Miss Johnson thought
~~They~~ Both seemed queer, Miss Johnson <she> thought. Not
English, & queer
very queer.

Everything seemed very queer. ~~Up~~ In London for the first time, come to take up
a post at her uncles in Leadenhall Street, & now walking through
Regents Park in the morning, this couple, on the chairs,
~~impressed her~~
~~made her~~ gave her a turn; the young woman being foreign; the
man looking queer; ~~which,~~ so that should she be a very old
woman, she would still remember, & be able to make it
a strange jangle
sound again among her memories, how she had walked ~~in~~
~~June~~ through Regents park on a June morning, For she was
only nineteen, & had ~~she not~~ got her way at last ~~&~~ <to> come to
London; & now how queer it was—~~there~~ this couple she had
asked the way of, & the girl started & jerked her hand, &
the man ~~& he~~ seemed awfully ~~queer~~; odd;
now ~~there everyone~~ all these people—for she returned ~~in~~to the
broad walk, ~~among~~ the stone basins, the prim flowers, & the
dogs ~~&~~ children & old men & women—invalids most of them
in bath chairs—~~all seemed,~~ <this morning> ~~after Edinburgh~~
~~people, so queer.~~
<as> the ~~became part~~ <sound> of that gently trudging vaguely gazing
breeze-kissed company; ~~& the~~ squirrels perching & preening,
~~&~~ the sparrow fountains; ~~springing for~~ fluttering for
crumbs (which a pink man in a long coat seriously
dispersed) ~~&~~ the dogs, busy with the railings,
busy with each other; while the soft hot air
washed over them, ~~the air of the br June morning~~
& lent to the fixed unsurprised gaze with which
~~universally~~ they received life, something
whimsical & mollified.

~~Maisie Johnson~~ with her big hands & red freckled face,
~~& eyes~~

Oh, she wanted to cry out—as she joined these
people intent with so little, floating buoyed on such
weak twigs—a stroll in Regents Park in the
sunshine; ~~obli~~ with their accumulations of cupboards &

& sideboards; evading death, or rather so intent on some hole in the
hearth rug that when he comes they scarcely know—Oh, she
wanted to cry, as she stood by the beds of coral hyacinth
her Cassandra cry of horror splitting the June day
(for the young man in the seat had given her quite a
turn)

Horror, horror, she wanted to cry (she had left her people; they
had warned her what would happen.)

This was life: <This was London.> Gazing from creased
eyelids at the
red flower beds cut like jam tartlets, old men with
women attendant stared hypochondriacally as if to
redeem years spent in feeble penwork by the sight of
plants blowing. Now it annoyed them. They
wanted to go home. No: to stay. They wanted—

Is this life? Maisie Johnson asked herself,
remembering Edinburgh.

If this were life crawling, staring, then she was
for death; (being big, strong, freckled, sandy haired
with those rather prominent, candid blue eyes which
like pan gelatine <can> receive an impression, unmodified,
save by surprise) if this were the truth the necessity
if the dull progress of days never plucked the
heart ~~out~~ <whole>, but beat it out spread it thin. At at
last the old body slack, yellow tinted, ~~lit~~ lie
like a lump to be freshened, browned by a world to
which it gave no glow: if this were life, well,
why hadn't she stayed at home?, she cried
wringing the knob of the <iron> railing; ~~&~~ And where was
the tube station?

That girl, thought Mrs. Dempster, who ~~had~~

saved crusts for the ~~grey~~ squirrels, & often ate her lunch in
Regents Park,
don't know a thing. & really it seemed to her better to be a little stout, a little

But Maisie Johnson ~~had~~ was asking the Park keeper where the station was—Regents Park Tube station.

M[rs.] Dempster watched her go, while babies in perambulators held their pink balls close to their eyes & frowned fiercely & flung them overboard, & gossiping nursemaids stooped & retrieved them, & scolded the arrogant boys; & thin M[r.] Stanton, walking for exercise, remembered how every Sunday, years ago, he had ~~d~~ crossed the park to lunch with Heythorp,—years ago, before books were written, good books standard books, & his wife had died. For life, thought M[r] Stanton, marching for exercise, is a damned queer business. It requires courage. And the past, which makes this walk by the ~~queer~~ absurd old fountain, half a dream, thought M[r.] Stanton, half a dream, he thought, & fell musing with his head on his breast, to the marvel of nursemaids, & he swung his stick, & ~~cried~~ laughed aloud, at the past, for there is nothing we know, thought M[r.] Stanton; but truth & courage he thought, ~~like a man in~~ & flourished his stick, like a man in a dream who
charges alone at the head of an
army, & routs battalions & storms the
citadel & ~~pla~~ plants his flag.

The hall of the house was cool as a vault.

Mrs Dalloway raised her hand to her eyes, & as the maid shut the
door to, & she heard the swish of Lucie's skirts, she felt like a
nun who has left the world, & feels fold round her the
familiar veils & the response to old devotions, ~~<&>~~ holding her
sweet peas to her face~~, dedicated she looked~~, The cook whistled in
the kitchen. She heard the click of the type writer.
It was her life, & bending her head over the hall table, she
bowed beneath the influence, felt blessed, purified, ~~&~~ saying
to herself as she took up the pad with the telephone
message on it, how moments like this, coming out of the street,
were <~~lit~~> ~~visible, to her,~~ <the justification> buds on the tree
of life, ~~the justification~~,
the summing up of existence; ~~as if~~ yet no one speaks of them;
~~the beautiful~~ flowers of darkness, <they are> she thought, as if some
~~pa~~ lovely rose had blossomed, for her eyes only;
~~wha~~ an odd provision of the private life, since not for a
moment did she believe in the existence of God; but all
the more she thought, taking up the pad, must one
repay in daily life, to servants, yes to dogs &
canaries; above all to Richard her husband, who was
the foundation of it—of the gay sounds, of the green
lights of the cook even whistling, for M$^{rs.}$
Walker was brisk, & on the day of a party whistled or
scolded from morning to night,—one must pay back
from this secret deposit of exquisite moments, she thought
lifting the pad.

Lucy stood by her, trying to say, how
"M$^{r.}$ Dalloway ma'am
Clarissa read. "Lady Bruton wishes to know

if M$^{r.}$ Dalloway will lunch with her today at two".

"M$^{r.}$ Dalloway, ma'am, told me to tell you he would be lunching out."

"Dear!" said Clarissa; & Lucy shared as she meant her to, ~~the~~ her disappointment;

X

Fear no more, said Clarissa; Fear no more the heat o' the sun; for the shock of Lady Bruton asking Richard to lunch made the moment in which had stood upright— that fine calm & ecstacy, ~~ros~~ shiver; & now as a plant on the river bed feels the water broken by a passing oar, she rocked in an agitation of jealousy.

Millicent Bruton had not asked her. No vulgar jealousy could separate her from her husband. But she feared time itself; & read on Lady

[End of Notebook Two]

Notebook Three

M$^{rs.}$ Dalloway, or The Hours.
July 31st 1924.

Mrs. Dalloway (or The Hours)

~~212~~
280 ~~If she had been at home among her own people it would have~~
~~1696~~ ~~been different~~
-424 ~~There was no one she could talk to.~~
~~59,360~~ ~~She did not want to look at him.~~
~~200~~ ~~And yet,~~ Perhaps she had done wrong; <but she thought, sewing,
-50 & not daring to look at Bernard, > Tired as she was, &
~~10000~~ without any friends in England, except Mrs Filmer, ~~for~~ she
how could she ~~had agreed to what Sir William Bradshaw advised—that they~~
help doing what Sir William Bradshaw advised, & saying
that they might fetch Bernard that ~~very~~ night—put him in a
<take him away>
home where ~~he would become perfectly well?~~ Sir William
had sworn to her, he would be perfectly happy, & ~~become~~ get
perfectly well. ~~She~~ But she did not trust Sir
William. ~~And she had not dared~~ <Never> ~~to tell~~ Bernard.
did ~~not~~ like him; & ~~She would have to~~ <She must> tell Bernard.
Still at moments he was quite reasonable; & ~~when~~ he had
asked, quite quietly, about M^rs. Peters just now. Furtively she
looked up, & had she not dreamt it all? Surely, he was
absolutely & entirely like himself? ~~Every obstacle had gone.~~
<lying there, looking>
She knew it, she felt it. He said,
~~That~~ Isnt that ~~rather~~ <on the> small ~~for~~ side?
He spoke ~~p~~ as he used to do: gravely; <& like a male,> & <for>
it was an old joke, of
theirs that he had a better eye for a hat than she had—
~~Oh but she hadn't any heart for hats!~~ Of course it
was small, an absurd little hat; but she had only done it to
pass the time.

Now, actually, he took it out of her hands. He
turned it round. He said it was a monkey's hat, &
M^rs. Peters was an elephant.

[*pencil*] ~~They had not laughed together like that for weeks.~~

~~260~~ It r rejoiced her, that!

~~250~~

~~450~~ ~~It was this poking fun that rejoiced her; <was so amazing,> for,~~
~~not for weeks had they~~

~~140~~

~~60~~ ~~just laughed, together,~~ been private together; ~~not arguing~~
~~60~~ ~~<laughing> or~~

~~260~~ ~~criticising, & shared that everything. at their own jokes.~~

~~200~~ Not for weeks had they been private together, laughing like this.

[*pencil ends*] ~~for~~ without bitterness, ~~quite calmly,~~ poking fun, ~~at~~ like married people. For all these weeks, ~~either he h~~ <there> he had been like a
stranger; ~~someone~~ living in his body. Now he was gone.

some one strange, someone wild, sad, strange,

"There!" she said, pinning a rose to one side of the ~~straw~~ hat.

~~Oh~~ But it was ridiculous; Septimus
~~Bernard Septimus put a~~

What have you ~~got~~ in your work basket?" he asked.

She had a ~~basket full of odds & ends: beads,~~ & ribbons, & artificial flowers, ~~among which he,~~ <& birds & tassels:> She tumbled ~~spread on the table.~~ them on the table; ~~which did~~ he ~~want~~? ~~His views were always definite.~~
~~He had no fingers—you <he> could not hold a needle, or~~

He began putting ~~one thing nex~~ together, a little bunch of <odd colours,> blues & yellows, for though he had no fingers, he could see things; ~~he could~~ & often he was right—sometimes absurd of course, but sometimes ~~right.~~ wonderfully right.

"She shall have a beautiful hat, he murmured. & ~~he went on adding~~ taking up this & that; Rezia kneeling by his side, ~~with her~~ looking over ~~&~~ his shoulders, ~~& at last she said, quite simply as~~
Now it was finished, except that Rezia must now ~~st~~ stitch the

250
<u>50</u>
12,500

[page 3 *verso*]

~~it together.~~
~~Why do you sigh like that? he asked her?~~
~~And it was beautiful, really beautiful.~~
~~Never had he done anything which filled him with~~
~~pride. He had made something~~
250 ~~Now And~~ When she sewed, although she did not exactly hum,
50 she had the air of a small kettle on the hob; ~~a little~~
12,500 ~~singing, in burbling~~ bubbling, mumuring, ~~always in movement,~~
& busy; ~~now~~ her strong little fingers ~~accurately~~ pinching &
poking; her needle flashing straight. And ~~as for~~ the
wild beauty of the sun might go in & out behind her;
& all those books (he had a certain number of Loeb classics,
Everyman classics, not very carefully arranged on a ~~n~~
fretworked shelf) might wait; ~~Respectfully, He figured~~
~~them waiting,~~ Shakespeare <was> tolerantly observing, Swift
saying
genially how he too could bide his time, Matthew Arnold
graciousness itself; for Septimus had now entered, he felt,
~~th~~ a pocket of warm air, one of those ~~recesses,~~ or sanctuaries,
hollowed in the heart of woods, where, by some ~~trick of the~~
inequality of ground, or arrangement of trees (it was <for he did
<must> his best>
~~absolutely~~ necessary still to check these exaltations by <be>
scientific
reason) ~~the~~ warmth & light remain, after dark: still one can see
the flowers; & the air ~~positively buffets~~ the cheek, like the
wing of some ~~sma~~ soft bird.

There it is, said Rezia, displaying M[rs.] Peters hat.
It will do for the moment, ~~at any rate. Then~~ Later I . . ."
~~Later?~~ ~~O dear~~ <Oh>, she remembered.
It was ~~rea~~ beautiful, ~~really beautiful, that hat~~. Never
had he done anything that filled him with such pride; such

a sense of the stability of the world.

{"But what is the time?" Rezia asked.}

"Just look at it" he said.

And, indeed, ~~partly~~ the hat, because they had laughed, ~~perhaps,~~
~~& because~~ & been alone, ~~lef~~ private together, seemed to her not beautiful ~~exactly—but how could she put it?~~ <no but> ~~but very~~ friendly: ~~some~~ how; ~~she would~~ Always like these colours. <always she wd. love that hat>

Wear it, he said.

~~And then, with this~~ She put it on.

But ~~Septimus,~~ I must look ~~very~~ <so> queer? she ~~said.~~ <cried> ~~to~~ running to the glass. ~~And then there was~~ Really she ~~so~~ couldn't be seen in it~~—& she put <took> it off when the~~ when there was a knock at the door,—She took it off; & took the Evening Standard from the maid, & shut the door before she put the hat on again.
~~Lately she had not given him the paper.~~

~~Oh somebody had made a very fine score.~~
~~While Septimus read the cricket news; she looked in the glass.~~
Oh she had forgotten! She oughtn't to let him read the paper!

And then of course ~~it happened; it~~ <what> always happened;
happened.
~~That~~ <The> small girl sucked her thumb at the door; Rezia went
down on
her knees; Rezia cooed & kissed; Rezia got sweets out of the
table drawer.
For so it always happened. ~~wherever she was; one thing after
another;~~
First one thing, then another thing. ~~At once, when she was there,~~
when she was in the room, ~~So Let her, then, just go on; doing~~ this, ~~doing~~ that; <& the
other> as
a the sun ~~streams, <beams,>~~ as the reed in a river [ ] out; for
there was
that kind of spontaneity, directness, good faith in every
movement, every word, as if her ~~will~~ being was the finest
veil on the surface of life, ~~driven~~ blown this way, that way,
~~by~~ ~~So~~ <&> up & round & moving & skipping round & round the
room she went, playing some game; ~~& so it was good~~; so
~~it was right. So lying here he could go on forever.~~ What
did the paper say? ~~Surrey was~~ all out.
"Surrey all out" he read aloud.
"Surrey all out" she sang,—it was some game with
M[rs.] Filmers orphan grandchild, that they were playing—
making little pounces, little rushes; ~~shouting~~ the child stamping
& screaming with laughter.
~~And far away, far away it sounded, when the~~
The better to enjoy <it> this ~~entirely delicious~~ <perfect>
delight, this entire bliss;
this & complete ~~bliss~~ <beauty>; he shut his eyes. But only
with not seeing ~~anything,~~ the sounds became fainter,
stranger, ~~like <the> cries f~~ sounded like people on the outskirts
of a <the cries of seeking for a [ ]>
in a game of hide & seek, who have but for wood, <who have not [ ].> going further away &
passing;. not seeing
And when he ~~opened~~ started up wide awake, what did
he see? The bananas on the sideboard. Nobody was
there. Rezia had indeed settled on the floor, <behind him,>
with a book.
These appalling truths clapped naked to the soul, have their greatness.
To be alone, that was it, ~~to be~~ alone for ever. the unescapable
fate, the doom pronounced, in Milan, when he came into
the room, where they sat, cutting out buck ram shapes, with

their scissors: the punishment of his sin; ~~this~~ which he must pay by killing himself.

~~So there~~ he lay, half raised, staring at that sideboard,
with the fruit <in front> ~~&~~
the oval looking glass. Not a sound reached him. Nothing was happening. He was alone <exposed> on this vast eminence,
~~this cliff.~~
~~extended,~~ stretched out; but as for visions ~~of—of a cliff.~~ This
was no
cliff; he lay on ~~org orange~~ <yellow> plush, not turf; ~~in~~ Mrs.
Filmers first
floor sitting room. ~~And there, was in the was the black screen~~
had
~~with blue bulrushes <birds> painted on it; but where~~ but no
he ~~had seen faces~~ they were not faces, they were birds ~~&~~
~~bulrushes. nest~~ flying ~~about~~ among bulrushes.
And there were no faces, ~~no~~ on that screen, merely ~~blue~~
<painted> swallows
~~&~~ bulrushes. ~~Here he~~ And the voices, the dead, Evans &
the rest of it: probably a mouse had squeaked, or some
curtain rustled. ~~But here at least was naked truth,~~ Here
was ~~nothing the truth.~~ Deluded he had been; a fool.

Such was the brain—source of all delusion

<There is> Your mother ~~is~~ calling ~~for you~~, said Rezia.
~~He could supply quite accurately what~~ That meant. It was
~~presumably~~ about six; the child must have its bath; <now> ~~unless~~
~~the she would cry; at the Mrs. Filmer would &~~
~~her mother would say that grumble it had to have its~~
~~bath before they began cooking.~~ or there would be no
hot water for washing up. ~~And~~ at the door Rezia
went through the whole ~~of the~~ <of the kiss> routine; <of>
kisses; promises;

~~But~~ She had to take the child downstairs, "I'll be back in a
minute she said
~~And~~ This would be the moment then to carry out that
troublesome affair—~~killing oneself~~—with a knife, or a
gas tube; ~~or some according to his promise.~~

For ~~he thought, putting one foot on the floor, & stretching himself,~~
there's ~~can be~~ no point in it. Obviously, ~~without illusions,~~
~~life is~~ without visions, <these dead> voices, ~~those~~ <the>
fifty years or so of life
all of wh. were untrue

before him would be torture, boredom; ~~&~~ there was Rezia to be considered. That one thing after another of hers—what was it?—a hat (look at ~~the hat now~~, <it> on the table~~—a very <the>~~ ugly hat) a newspaper, a child;—she had the gift of it; could do it; would always do it, ~~unless~~ Among the things Bradshaw had said, was that "Duty to your wife . . . marriage ties—" & so on.

[*scribbles*] So he was left alone, with the screen, the coal scuttle, & the chiffonier.

~~And~~ There was nothing petty in it. In justice to the gods it had to be admitted that ~~this~~ a naked soul in emptiness, looking ~~at nothing, is~~ out at emptiness; ~~is not h can exists~~ <has its independence granted it>
~~by itself;~~ can support itself; {they have not tampered with its ~~independence.~~ All props withdrawn, ~~still~~ it exists; it
Lamp out, suspended But the air is ever so many degrees below zero, & ~~a~~
one ~~that~~ numbness, ~~which they say is painless,~~ must end in ~~that~~ ~~the~~ <that> death which they say is ~~painless~~. ~~They have not~~ ~~Anyhow, he~~ had without pain. But, <the gods> as a human being, he had
had his rights.

~~It was really The Gods~~ <Rightly, at this pass, They> ~~showed~~ had withdrawn; ~~completely;~~ <they had left him; let air pour into> as
~~as if to say they knew that this pass had~~ ~~Still there remained,~~ ~~or began <But> now, to dawn, with this the consciousness of the souls~~
in loneliness, ~~power to exist independently, a wild vision of escape. hi <there~~
in escape, ~~came the desire to test it, in for the,>~~
~~of flight, on & on, alone, an escape. as if having this <the> door one fell against, opened.~~

~~However~~ On his own shoulders was the burden, & ~~That was real, that~~ <the> screen; ~~&~~ was real, & the coal scuttle was real; & ~~there were no~~ they ~~had allowed him~~ <& in> ~~Now in~~ all truth there is satisfaction he thought; &

Monday
11th Aug.

So he was left alone; with the screen, the coal scuttle, & the
chiffonier
There was nothing petty in it. In justice to the gods it
had to be admitted that a naked soul ~~in emptiness~~
looking at emptiness has its independence, ~~can support itself,~~
All props withdrawn it exists. But the air is ever so
many degrees below zero, & must end in that death which
they say is without pain. ~~But he had had his rights.~~
~~The screen was real; the coal scuttle was real; since~~
~~This would be the moment then to carry out that troublesome~~
~~affair with a knife or a gas tube.~~
~~For It was a question of "duty to one's wife".~~
~~"Remember, you have a duty to your wife."~~
~~Still one <But> may be~~ the sideboard is good, ~~&~~ the plate of
bananas is
~~it is~~ good . . . Here, however in her impulsive way, Rezia
~~flung the~~ burst into the room, chattering,
And then, she stopped, ~~frozen, presumably. And <His words>~~
~~Bradshaw had~~
~~said Remember, you have a duty to your wife . .~~
Some letter had come: everybodies plans were changed. Mrs.
Filmer
would not be able to go to Brighton. So the machine
was in perfect order; her ~~power~~ gift of living worked;
whatever odds & ends you put into it. "There is <was> no
time to write to ~~Mrs.~~ William". And really
Rezia thought it was very very annoying, & she snatched
up the hat, & she thought one might perhaps . . . just . . .
~~a~~ make . . . a little . . .

Her voice ~~It~~ died away, ~~her~~

~~So~~ Nor ~~could anyone ever say that~~ suppose that the

~~judged him.~~ ~~Reach as he might, he could not catch the~~
Stretching as far as he could he caught the last sounds of
the contented melody;~~—could hear sighing, stirring, trembling,~~
~~the~~

But after all, why trifle? ~~Why~~ ~~His duty remained; even~~
somewhere at the back of his mind ~~he knew the very words~~
<~~there~~ was>
~~which that an order~~, a statement issued by human
nature, to the effect that ~~it was your~~ <you had a> 'duty to
~~remember~~
your wife'; &, Bradshaw had added <another about> ~~this~~, 'a
brilliant
career.' ~~As for resisting <&> Such <were the> momentous~~
~~decrees;~~
~~were no longer to be resisted. Laws that one obeyed;~~
~~considering~~ ~~In short, Rezia, Bradshaw & Holmes~~
~~edicts~~ & a third about cowardice; & in short ~~no more~~
Bradshaw & Holmes between them having decreed him an
unfit citizen, & Rezia ~~being~~ having her own life.

Ah! Damn! she cried. (it was a joke of theirs—
her swearing) the needle having broken.

One thing after another—hat, child, Brighton, needle
she had the gift of ~~it life~~ it!

She wanted him to say whether really she had
improved ~~it~~ the hat. ~~So~~ ~~Sitting~~ <She sat> on the end of the sofa.
~~The~~ ~~Why are~~ "we are perfectly happy <today>" she said
suddenly,
So very true, with her hands up to her ~~hair~~ <hat>, as if ~~really~~ it was so
~~strange~~ true; /she must say it
And ~~never~~ indeed~~—though she had this dreadful thing,~~ <her>
secret,
that he was to go away tonight, that Dr. Holmes was to
call, it would not be very hard to say it, & she would
say it, when he had told her what was wrong with
the hat.

[Drawing at bottom of page of a square sitting on a longer line. The square is marked at the top left and right hand corners with short vertical and horizontal lines, respectively.]

[page 11 *verso*]

For now she felt as she had felt when she saw him first come in &
sit down, ~~taking off his hat & r~~ rather on the edge of his chair,
~~looking rather~~ in a cafe, looking about him, An English man,
~~but not~~
not <one> the large, ~~men, whom ones, but~~ <men> whom ~~some~~ of her
friends admired; for he was always thin; ~~but fair like an~~
~~Englishman, with thin, with a beautiful fresh colour, &~~
for he had a beautiful fresh colour; & with his big nose, his
bright eyes, & his way of sitting, <resting> hunched, & his
large knuckles,
~~hands,~~ he made her think ~~of some~~ she had often told him—of a
~~young~~ bird; & then so very gentle. Always with her he was
gentle, though he might be strict with ~~his~~ men. She
had never seen him wild or drunk, only suffering sometimes
through this terrible war, but even so, when she came in
he would put it all away. And anything, anything, in the
whole world ~~that she thought n she could tell him, & his~~
~~being so much older, &~~ any little bother, with her work,
~~or~~ anything that struck her to say, she would tell him; ~~as if~~
& he quite understood. Indeed though she loved her
father & her sister, it ~~was~~ could not be the same; Being
older than she was, & being so clever—how she loved his books!
how ~~he~~ patient he was teaching her English}—how serious, ~~& he~~
~~then getting her a copy of Shakespeare &~~ wanting
her to ~~understand it, before she even knew her letters~~
read Shakespeare with him before she could even
read a child's story!— <being so much more experienced.> he
could help her; ~~as~~ he
~~could teach her; & she yet she never felt younger~~
She never felt ~~ever~~ that it mattered—that she was
not so highly taught; & indeed she ~~never~~ could help him too—
all <this> came back to her ~~now, as if~~ sitting at the end of the
sofa; not

There she was perched on his feet.

There she was perched on his feet, She held her hands to her hat
{in her unconsciousness, pensive, white,} waiting for him to
say, did he
like the hat or not, ~~yet like & waiting, & falling,~~ he felt, as she
waited, ~~where, being without consciousness of her body,~~
that he could follow the flight of her mind, swooping, perching,
like a
bird, from branch to branch, ~~in~~ sitting there in one
of those loose, lax unconscious poses which came naturally
to her, ~~not un~~ <so> ~~absolutely~~ easy was life was to her; &
if he spoke ~~at once~~ she smiled; no start; nothing but a bird
settling; lightly, ~~to the second.~~ its little claws at once on the
Hence their pet branch. Some days, anyhow in Italy, she was almost wild;
names. They were danced, sang; anything made her laugh; & yet—that
was her charm—never loudly, or, if you wanted her to stop,
~~sitting~~ at her table before you knew it, there she was, at rest, demure ~~always~~,
generally with feeling your thought. ~~She did not understand it.~~ She
something in her ~~was not could not~~ {It was not like a man, f understanding
hands what you said. It was not like Evans}

And Holmes accused him of cowardice. "You should
~~think rather more of~~ <consider> your wife" & so on.
~~But oh those authorities~~—Holmes ~~&~~ <the> ~~Bradshaws~~ will
Bradshaw too, ~~pronouncing opinions, was~~ an authority upon marriage;
with the photograph ~~Bradshaw too.~~; but ~~why in~~ with Rezia ~~there~~, <was at the end of
of <u>his</u> wife in. the sofa.> holding her
Well, there ~~hat~~ pensive, attentive, & yet not very far sunk in thought,
she was. ~~even Holmes himself was~~ ~~she seemed, in her~~
Court dress on ~~Holmes was~~ ~~[Dallow~~?] There she was.
the mantelpiece; Would you forgive me if I had done something wrong? she
Remember your asked
wife. And she told him, ~~how~~ <what> that morning, ~~Dr~~
Sir William had told her; how ~~she had he~~ <there> would
was a ~~bea~~ house in a beautiful garden, just outside

London, where he would get absolutely well But they will not let me see you for six weeks", she said: there shd. be nothing that

It was, indeed, very odd that Holmes & Bradshaw should have the power to separate them.

Have I done wrong? she repeated.

Septimus was perfectly calm; he seemed just to be thinking.

Indeed, perfectly reasonably he asked her when they were coming:

& what would it cost?

~~But~~ Mr. Brewer had been so extraordinarily kind—

(Brewer's been so kind, Bradshaw's been so kind, & Holmes too, <had been so kind>

he murmured) ~~But Holmes, he said, rousing himself,~~

(quite But he did not understand; & he was weak. ~~he spoke~~

& he wanted her to explain to him—Holmes had said there was ~~n~~ nothing the matter with him?

~~But~~ ~~D~~ Sir William says ~~for~~ that you are very very ill.

And really—that was the extraordinary about Rezia—

she believed;— "Sir William" she called him.

A ~~man~~
Lady Bradshaw had three feathers sticking up on the
top of her head.
That amused them.

The argument:
The believer.
but not altogether.
Her argument that one must believe
(time passing)
One must believe in something.
But in Holmes or in Bradshaw?
You cant go on prophecying:
The table drawer full of nonsense.
He reads half a page: about the dead;
It is nonsense.
It is quite true what she says.
To begin all again.
To build up this vast edifice.
The terror of Holmes
She hears him come.
He jumps.

XThat Holmes & Bradshaw
have power over anyone
who tries to commit
suicide

It is ~~the~~ an offering, a
Silly absurdity: something that
people ask of one.

Looked at her
as his ~~someone~~
fellow victim.
They did demand of
them
both this sacrifice—
for being too happy?
for some crime?

The sense that they were one
flesh.

She called him "Sir" Wiilliam; ~~she believed in Sirs.~~
'Sir'—she believed in Sirs.
"That <a> man whose wife wears ostrich feathers ~~in her hair~~—"
he said.
Rezia flinched, for she remembered how ~~cold~~ <when> Sir
William
~~had seemed~~ when <[he?]> he said goodbye; so that the whole of
her life
& everything in the world, had seemed not to matter one scrap,
until she got out into the street with Septimus again.

~~But all this laughing & sneering. was useless.~~
~~It would all <should not> begin again—this~~
He must know better than we do, she said.
But why ~~had~~ this 'must.'~~—why~~ what had he done to
get ~~Re~~ Rezia into his power? She hated him. Yet the
shades of terror were on her. ~~One~~ It was not fancy; a chill, a
paleness was now over them both: ~~as if~~ <&> she knew
what hung over them.
~~We have to do what he says, she~~
They ~~will not~~ <won't> let you ~~kill yourself,~~ <stay
here> she ~~added~~ <said>
when you say you are going to kill yourself"
Ah! ~~That was it.~~ She had delivered him over
to them. <&> Dr. Holmes always has porridge for
breakfast if he weighs less than eleven stone six; &
Dr. Bradshaw's wife wears three ostrich feathers in her
hair. Everything that was his, was now in their
power.
But she would not let herself be frightened.
Even though he lay there panting in a kind of agony.
~~It was this terror of Dr Holmes, again.~~
It ~~is~~<s> ~~all very sill~~ <silly, its> silly of ~~you, Septimus~~, she
~~said.~~ repeated.

~~She called him~~ ~~'Sir' William;~~ ~~She believed~~
This great brute with the wide nostrils would be snuffing all over him
soon; ~~this blood hound~~. He ~~would burn everything before they~~ came
into every cranny; every secret place.
Anyhow we'll burn—we'll tidy up" he said
pointing (& it seemed to have made him <seem older,> shake all over—) to the table drawer
~~She brought~~ ~~We w~~
She brought him all the papers, which were there,
things she had written for him, things he had written. She
turned them out upon the sofa. There were diagrams
among them too; little figures with sticks for arms, against
~~jagged lines~~; ~~[—]~~ circles traced round sixpences & shillings,
~~jagged lines~~, ~~As for the writing, really~~ He could not
understand quite what he had meant.

And the writing—that poetry; which had formed itself on his
lips as he lay in this room before those burning mountains ~~&~~
Well, it ~~that was <appeared to be> nonsense. too.~~ What was it about?

with marks himself made on paper against the [king?]

~~But~~ They had been ~~an~~ illustrations ~~of~~: notes ~~to mark down~~ <of>
~~meanin~~ revelations—which he was to lay before Mr. Asquith; ~~this~~
childish scribbling. He began to read his writing. ~~with Rez~~
pointed with his finger for Rezia to read too~~—What had it~~
~~been about? did it mean? It was insane. all about~~
~~death, nightingales; it was~~ Together they read those strange
ramblings—wild they seemed, incoherent, yet like flakes falling
in front of ~~some~~ cauldron of fire had a light on them,
recalled him to moments of ecstasy ~~visions, had some~~
~~stirring power, which though they were nonsense, utter nonsense,~~
~~suggested a signalled to him, sunk~~ right away ~~now~~ an
~~like But all that must go. He so &~~ could just make
their signal to him, ~~& then faded into gibberish: insane~~
~~words, in—yes, These These words~~ (They
could just convey to him—But ~~she was crying~~ <Rezia> laid her
hand on
~~She didn't like~~
them. ~~She couldn't~~
~~hit Its not all nonsense, he said~~
& ~~kept one~~ <He> pointed to one sentence. But she did not
see how <written> ~~wrung from him one wild~~ <still> night, there
was a
quiet in the words; written at dawn;

It is so silly, she said suddenly, and so it did seem to
her,
~~First~~ you laugh at Dr. Holmes, ~~then~~ you laugh at
Mr. Brewer, ~~then at~~ you laugh at ~~Dr~~
Sir William Bradshaw. But they are just
like ourselves.

She would put all these papers carefully away
She said, in an ~~ev~~ envelope. She would
tie them up (for she had no envelopes) with a piece

of silk.

And indeed it seemed to her silly.
"Because somebody might come in for a moment & say of me
~~thats~~ <[hes?]> a fool: or of you."
So skilled <~~quick~~ clever> was she, <with
her fingers> that ~~to~~ putting things together
that a packet like that, of odds & ends, she put straight—
tied up ~~whi~~ without looking scarcely. sitting beside him.
Never had he seen her look like that—
the floating flower? The ~~drow~~ cut rose? No: she was a
tree in the moonlight; a white flowering tree; ~~or~~ with
a ~~lovely serious~~ face looking <out> through the branches.

about the dead singing behind rhododendron bushes; ~~about learning;~~ how to
be polite; how to travel; ~~how to many~~ reflections on dress; ~~some~~ on
books; characters of Mrs. Filmer; ~~whole~~ poems addressed to Dr.
Holmes; & Evans, Evans, Evans; sheet after sheet
of his messages — was copied down from his voice; ~~when he had~~ whispered ~~from~~
as he had — <them>
~~among the dead.~~ from behind the screen. Did they mean nothing.
Shame & wonder & at the same time an extreme excitement &
ecstasy possessed him.

---

a stern face, the face of a prophetess, a lawgiver—
dealing justly with <human> observations, human frailties;
~~the~~ a sorrowful face; for ~~the truth was that in these last
weeks she had~~ <having> suffered terribly <[ ]>; & had ~~surmounted,~~ <climbed> ~~what
for~~ he could see it, ~~the~~ to a height—this of accepting
~~Holmes & Bradshaw & the rest, <people>—which put was utterly
beyond him;—& perhaps she had gave her~~

"There!" The horrid things were tied up.
They were finished; they were done with.

"Now"— She was ~~quite~~ composed; <~~she was~~ even> gay;
~~she felt~~ conscious of his ~~eyes eye on her,~~
attentions, ~~&~~ of their being as she called it "married people";
that is to say, when she got up to go into the bedroom—
put his things togther, he ~~said~~ looked at her—kept
looking at her; & she came back &, obviously, one needn't say it,
he liked to look at her, for though sometimes he ~~never~~ did not
notice her, as a woman, for days, sometimes it came over him; he
liked her to be by him.

"~~And~~ what does he want?" she said,
kneeling down & calling him by the name of that
Italian crow, which, being malicious & a great
destroyer of crops, was like him.

He wanted to know: the time.
It was ten minutes to six.
When they were coming.
soon after six.

& then to explain, as simply as possible, that he had endeavoured
to write down, in those papers, ~~a version~~ an account of the world; <his feelings>
but it did not appear to be ~~quite right~~: reasonable; ~~but that~~, her
view, (& he called her by the name of that restless & inquisitive
little Italian bird which hops, pecks, ~~in~~ pops in & out)
was far more so; ~~but only to hold it genuinely, as she
held it, was beyond his strength impossible for him at
present.~~

Whereupon she got up & went to pack his clothes.
but hearing voices downstairs, & thinking it ~~likely~~ probable
that Dr. Holmes had called, ~~she went~~ <ran> to prevent him coming ~~in~~ <up>.

~~Septimus heard her.~~ He heard Dr. Holmes, voice on the staircase
presumably protesting.

My dear Lady, I have come ~~to see your husband~~ <as a friend>.

~~There~~ She would let him pass. They would force her—
She cd. not let him pass.

Whereupon Holmes wd. say, that Septimus was a coward

~~The hounds were on him.~~

Getting up rather unsteadily, hopping indeed from foot to foot, he considered ~~that Holmes really did make any other way of escape out of the question.~~

Mrs. Filmers nice clean bread knife ~~that~~ No, one
He couldn't use that. The gas tube? That was
a long business. Really thought Septimus hopping
about the room, I've left this all ~~till~~ too late—
But he always had put things off—packing for
example—never could put in his razors till the last
moment— Rezia had probably packed his razors.

There remained only the window. It was to the window that the
joint hands of Holmes & Bradshaw pointed; to this tiresome,
troublesome, & rather silly ~~pr~~ business of opening the window &
getting onto the window sill. ~~But~~ he did not want to die.
He did not want to kill himself. Life itself, ~~was~~
was admirable. To breathe, to feel the air; it
cooler now, after the heat. There was a man in the
house opposite staring with ~~his~~ an expression of
horror, of terror, at him, Septimus.

There he was, sitting in the window sill.

An offering" he murmured, with some
idea of <thought> ~~an altar~~ in ~~his~~ mind—the window sill was an
altar; & so ~~with~~ in the belief that he was giving up
to humanity what it asked of him he sprang
vigorously, of his own free will, on to M^rs.
Filmers ~~basem~~ area railings.

but it did not matter, & she knelt by him: ~~& then got up &~~
& ~~they~~ Then she got up

So ~~there~~ it had to be done.
with something maternal in it, ~~as if she said will~~
~~knew that there was no~~ as if through giving birth she had
had her children about her.
reached this sanctuary, & had ~~at last~~ <learnt how to>
accept~~ed a~~ Holmes &
Bradshaw ~~A~~ Miracle! ~~Renunciation!~~ Triumph! But
~~only to be achieved by the heaven born, & by them~~ at the
cost of some enormous renunciation; ~~too great~~
some staggering ascent with ~~suf~~ weights upon <on> one's
shoulders, on one's head
up & up. ~~He was too~~ It was not for him:

No, it did not matter, she said kneeling by him.
These ~~little~~ divisions, ~~inflicted~~ <are made> more by words than
anything;
~~divisions~~ & ~~solitudes~~ ~~To~~ <Let them> be silent—alone.

he could see her, like a little hen, wings spread.
fluffing out. But Holmes would persevere. Holmes
would persevere. Putting her aside with his
thick powerful hand, Holmes would ~~come~~ get past her;
come up, stairs: open the door;
~~Rather a Coward,~~ In a funk eh? Holmes
wd say. Duty to your wi

Rezia ~~managed to keep Holmes behind her.~~
Came into the room, keeping Holmes behind her; saw the
window
open, heard the crash; ~~&~~ She did not want to turn away, go
into the next room, wait; ~~I will come for~~
~~while Dr Holmes ran~~ She had seen everything; she knew
everything. ~~He has done right, perfectly right, she~~ said to
D$^{r.}$ Holmes, & Mrs Filmer ~~fell over~~ <ran> into each other on
the stairs.
~~Then~~ Mrs Filmer made her sit on the bed in the back room.
~~And now & then~~ <And> she, Rezia, said He has done quite
right. He has
done quite right; at intervals, because M$^{rs.}$ Filmer
~~wished~~ <wanted> her to say something~~, & Dr Holmes took
charge of
everything.~~ ~~There was a great deal of running up &
down stairs. As for the rest, he had~~ nobody could hurt him now.
~~Poor~~ D$^{r.}$ Holmes <came in>—poor Dr Holmes~~—he~~ was trembling
all over ~~&~~ as
white as a sheet.

~~And~~ While they were whispering (Dr Holmes & M$^{rs.}$ Filmer)
that nice old clock ~~began~~ struck One, two, three.
How sensible, how comforting; ~~how beautiful too, as if it were~~
four five—how beautiful too, that voice; & then ~~Oh dear
how~~ to please Dr Holmes she had to drink something, but ~~just~~
heard ~~&~~ the clock ~~struck~~ <strike> six.

A rather austere sound. That Wordsworth had written with
extreme ~~beauty~~ <beauty> about ~~Duty it~~ the stern daughter of
the voice of
God, she did not know or had forgotten; all her knowledge
was hand-to-mouth ~~&~~ fragmentary; ~~but~~ whereas, to hear
St Pancras, or whatever the clock was, striking six on a

on a summer's evening, one would surely think ~~two things~~;
that there was either in the sound <itself>, or in the
~~cunning~~ <minds> of the human
race who made it, an enduring belief, which they had arrived at in
common, which Wordsworth had expressed, & women whose
learning hardly rivalled <that of> the birds of the air, ~~attained,~~
yet attained, by unknown means; ~~a friend of laughter, tears,~~
~~<so> that, in short, when the clock struck it spread its hands~~
~~over a scene, which made up of the most contradictory~~
an understanding, ~~elements, &~~—
~~a friend~~ <a common> of laughter, <~~or~~ of> tears; something in
short universal. One could
believe in that; ~~&~~ &, further, trans~~fer~~pose this sound,
which so soon ceased, ~~into~~ up into the sky; see in
white clouds, dark clouds, the violet of waves, beneath, the
same comforting suggestion, ~~that the of peace; certainty;~~
That diversity is united, ~~the truth~~ & ~~enough~~ certainty enough
attained to cover the wildest & ~~fierce fiercest~~ questionings
of the least proven spirits.

Rather an austere sound, far, far away.
She had had no education; all her knowledge was hand to
mouth fragmentary. It was just the sound, or something in
the sound, which, compared with all this thumping & whispering,
~~[could?] floated out~~ seemed to her stern as Septimus
himself was; outside, <untouched> It seemed to her that all this
hurry scurry would soon be over, & then, ~~parting~~ opening the long
French windows Dr Holmes, ~~had artfully mixed with~~
~~who distrusted clear thinking on such occasions~~ had mixed
a little opium <morphine> in her draught—her husband was
horribly
mangled—would not return to consciousness—she must not <ask
to> see him)
~~he~~ he took it upon himself) opening these windows, ~~she would~~
~~step out~~ into the garden out she would go.
In her morphia trance, Mrs. Filmer waving her apron,
for she was half ~~distracted~~ & <wandered off—at intervals—
what she> was expect~~ing~~ed to see ~~a~~ bloody
body brought in~~)~~ seemed to her all part of that white garden
at dawn
~~with the lilies & clo sunflowers, & whatever they might be doing,~~
~~(for she~~ A strange sense she had of leaving here on the bed her,
body; & here, that is to say in her ~~mind~~ <head>, being out of doors.

Not that she had any education, or could ~~in such stresses,~~
add to the clock striking in that aloof way, which yet was so
consolatory, words; words of poetry, or biblical
words~~, or~~ It was a flag; it ~~was the how~~ she had
~~seen~~ seen once a flag slowly rippling out, from a mast,
perhaps at Venice. ~~Of~~ men killed in battle,
~~Perhaps she was thinking; &~~ carried through the streets,
were so saluted; or it was ~~simply~~ the shadow of
clouds; ~~Such happy things, such~~ for of her memories of

<young woman poor thing>—most distressing—how cd. one have foretold it? nobody cd. have foretold it? A sudden impulse—he could <did> not consider himself in the least to blame. He would have acted <similarly> the same way, he said ~~Mrs~~ a stranger in the hall, so the ambulance was coming—wd. not allow them to bring in a bloody body

most were happy.

Being really shocked, Dr Holmes had given her, perhaps a ~~the~~ shade more <morphia> than he meant. He had never been so upset in his life. But no blame attached to anybody.

~~It was a~~ Everything must be left just as it was.
nothing touched . . . the police would judge for themselves.
~~Probably he would die in the ambulance which was~~

He was not suffering: poor chap. But why the devil,—. A young
fellow in the prime of life—what induced him? Dr Holmes
could not conceive.

He ~~came~~ <called> to her, & she, putting on some scarf, ran
down, out
~~along a lane,~~ through cornfields—onto a hill, where could it
have been? some where near the sea; for there were ships,
~~there were~~ gulls; & ~~there was a <the> sound of waves splashing;~~
~~&~~ butterflies coming up over the cliff, ~~And then she fell asleep.~~
~~Sunshine & cloud passed over her. & he sat <was> beside her~~
However, there they sat, & in London too, there they sat,
&, half dreaming came to her through the bedroom door, rain
falling, <went> ~~various~~ whispering, stirring, among corn
[shocks?] ~~sounds~~,
the caress of the sea,—as it seemed to her, ~~a hollow yet~~
~~awful voice, murmuring, wings~~ pillowing them in its ~~hand~~,
shell, & murmuring to her, {ceaselessly benignantly
maternally} ~~how she was~~ safe ~~now~~; laid ~~now~~ on the shore,
strewn, she felt, like flowers, {on some tomb.} bunches of
bright flowers.

~~For He~~ is dead, <(in that tomb indeed)> she said,
smiling at the poor old woman,
who guarded her, with her honest light blue eyes staring
<fixed> at the door, &
her redd~~ened~~ <thin> hands clutching her apron. Mrs. Filmer
pooh poohed. Oh no! oh no! And not for
worlds would she have gone into the next room. They
were carrying him away now. ~~And Oughn't his wife to be~~
~~with him?~~ Ought she to be told? Ought she to go ~~too~~ to him?
But they must do as the doctor said.

~~And~~ This medicine made her sleep. She was asleep.
~~And~~ or so she seemed, when Dr Holmes, <who was to convey the>
looked in—to say—What could he say?
She was hardly conscious: The shock, on top of a

long strain; a ~~fore~~ foreigner too: she did not understand in the way or
what was said to. ~~Let her~~ Let her rest~~ing~~.
~~English~~ woman would. ~~Of course~~ If the man <husband> should ask for her, she
could come. & She saw the out line of D$^{r.}$ Holmes ~~sob~~ passing
through her eyelashes. She wondered drowsily why Septimus had so hated him—
& oh dear, she would find it out, she would find it out—

That tears relieved sorrow was one of Holmes' beliefs.

~~And~~ absorbed in a dumb talk, ~~&~~ '& shaded with great rocks,
all echoing the sea sounds, ~~with~~ <& with> white birds, <&>
white flowers, &
~~the round her,~~ in her eyes, ~~there~~ she ~~lay~~ <They lay> ~~put to him~~
~~some~~ asking him
all these questions, things ~~that it~~ <it> came into her head ~~to~~
~~say~~.—oh she didn't mind what ~~she said.~~

[Margin: This sort of thing telling him whatever]

As for the ambulance, containing Septimus, Dr Holmes
& two attendants, it sped, lightly, with a beautiful
clean efficiency to the hospital, bearing some poor devil;
someone hit on the head, struck down by disease, knocked over
perhaps ~~by~~ a minute a go at one of these crossings—as
might happen to oneself; ~~And~~
~~And~~ The light high bell had only to sound; ~~&~~ <Traffic let it pass.>
~~There was something~~ Perhaps it was morbid; or was it not
touching rather,—the respect which they showed this
ambulance, with its victim inside—men & women, all
rushing from their offices, ~~cast a glance at it;~~ yet intently
bethinking them, as it passed, of some wife; ~~some~~ or,
presumably, how easily it might have been them there—
stretched on a shelf with a doctor or a nurse—
Ah, but thinking became morbid, ~~directly became sentimental~~
sentimental, directly one began conjuring up doctors
~~nurses~~, dead bodies; a little glow, ~~came~~ of pleasure
~~in them~~ succeeded in this thinking /warned one, ~~n~~ not to
go on with that sort of thing anymore.   Fatal to art,
fatal to friendship;   ~~Of course, one~~ And yet,
thought Peter Walsh, as the ambulance turned the corner, though
the light high bell could be heard, down the next street, &
still further, as it crossed the Tottenham Court Road, <chiming
aloud the truth> still
I ~~could~~ have that in me which—he meant he ~~had~~
could dissolve in tears. Why, heaven~~s~~ knows. Beauty of
some sort ~~pes~~ presumably.

[Margin: a sort of lust too ~~over~~ the visual corpse]

230 dissolve, yes, flow away, there beating upon him & almost
2 exhausting him with its intensity, ~~all that beauty—It was~~
it swept him out the weight of the day, its heat, <its> beauty; ~~the now that the~~ secrecy
& ~~this~~ no one would ever know it. Partly for that reason,
he had <(its ~~complete~~ complete & inviolable)>
found life, like an unknown garden, surprising; yes, really it took
~~takes~~ one's breath away, to pitch into deep deep pools out of
one's
depths; there coming over him now by the pillar box. Opposite
the British Museum ~~this~~ with the ambulance passing &
sense of the city shaking itself free of the grasp of the sun, &
all banners ~~f~~ blowing out & heaven knows what
compassion & mute expression <wild fellowship> of good will
on the faces of the
people walking—all this being burnished, washed over, what
word could one find?, by ~~the~~ bright sparkling air, & at their
feet,—such was his sense of the smallness of this old
& its civilised world—<an ~~old~~ an spread> a yellow Turkey carpet.
exquisite Civilisation, death,
electric ~~cert~~ certainty; ~~a slow~~ —it swept him out of himself, &
activity Heaven knows how, he felt tears collecting, <like [ ],
directly> as from a
very high roof & falling one two three four on ~~his face;~~
~~the tide of life, that the vast~~ sea, which is in one,
~~surging~~ his being, by that rush of emotion; swept
bare, sandy, like some <white-shell sprinkled> old beach. And
~~this is~~ its this, thats life
he meditated; our privacy, our solitude, ~~our~~ Clarissa
once, going on top of an omnibus with him somewhere.
Clarissa always so easily moved, ~~by~~ such a bundle of nerves,
all a ~~quiv~~ a quiver in those days, & spotting
such queer names, sights, shops—indeed they never ended
an expedition with out a bag full of treasures—
~~what became of them?~~ given to <her> old women ~~who~~
with the everlasting bad legs, presumably—

since one never saw them again, Clarissa had a theory about this.
~~She had many theories. So~~ <As> young people have, always
theories
How did it go? ~~That life~~ We are ~~th~~ not ~~this~~ that & ~~the~~ other—
she said, ~~playing her fingers on the back of the seat:~~ not here, here,
here: ~~but~~ (Just because I happen to be talking to you now) I'm
spread all over the place: ~~I'm~~ pervasive. So that to know
any one,
one must seek ~~about~~ <them out> ~~in every quarter~~ <out in>. The
people, <even in places,> who
completed her, perhaps she had never met. Odd affinities
she had
for people she never spoke to. It ended in a mystical
transcendental theory ~~which allowed her to believe as she~~
~~seemed to need to believe, that death was not final,~~
~~but life which was made up of so many lives went on in~~
~~them when the that he would~~ ~~of being~~ & it gave
certainly she was} which got round death, allowed her to
believe, or at any rate to hope, that, since nothing whatever
was known about human personality, it might be
recovered ~~from~~ after death attached to this person & that or
even
haunting certain places. {And then of course, her mind flew ~~to~~
back to Bourton, to the country to ~~her~~ youth; loving it as she
did even then with a passion he had never seen
equalled in any other creature. Pools, trees,
certain views the white house sleeping at dawn
(for they ~~rode~~ missed their train one night & walked}
which was oddly true, of her at least.

no but
She meant—
I'm

eager as she always
was for life to
go on <u>forever</u>
~~we~~
our apparitions,
what we say &
do, is only the
least part in
the <u>rest</u>
this fundamental
[spoken?],

~~This~~ the unknown
what we now
[ ] state
[ ] up,

~~So that to know her—that was her argument, one must seek out all~~
~~& the other people too;~~ the people, & the places, for surely
certainly, looking back over all that long friendship of
~~more than~~
~~&~~ almost thirty years, her theory worked to this extent: brief,
broken, often painful as their actual meetings had been,
what with his absences, & interruptions (this morning, for
instance in came Elizabeth & stood there like a long
haired colt, handsome, dumb, just as he was beginning
to talk to Clarissa) the effect of them on his life was
~~immeasurable immense,~~ immeasurable. There was a
mystery about it: here you were given one sharp, acute
uncomfortable grain: ~~that was~~ the actual ~~m~~ intercourse
<matter>;
horribly painful more often than not; yet in absence, ~~often~~ in
the most unexpected places, ~~Calcutta, bazaars, jungle~~
~~cu that~~ <it> would flower, ~~spread~~, open out & let you wander in,
quick ~~at ease~~, & look & touch & taste & get the whole
feel of ~~her~~ <its & understanding> & meaning months, ~~why~~ even
years, after ~~she <it> had~~
~~the meeting~~ it had happened. ~~He would always think of her~~
~~on a certain peak on the Himalayas~~; in He had
remembered her on board ship, ~~climbing~~ <in> the Himalayas, <&
bazaars,>
in the most unlikely places. (So Sally Seton,
generous enthusiastic goose thought of him ~~when~~ <the connection>
with ~~the~~ <when she saw ~~a~~>
blue hydrangeas) She had influenced him more than
any other person. And always in this way, ~~when she~~
coming before him, ~~often without his wishing it~~ appearing so
damned cool, lady like critical; ~~or~~ <or ravishing, romantic,>
recalling some
~~lane,~~ field, ~~autumn~~ <some> English harvest. ~~The~~ He She
~~thought of her much oftener~~ <~~brought~~ back> ~~in~~ the country,
~~more much more~~
than in London. One scene after another . . . . .
He had reached his hotel, crossed the hall, with its

mounds of chairs & sofas & ~~plan tall palms; The young~~ He
~~got his bedroom key. There were letters for him <which he~~
~~250~~ ~~took, &> & He went upstairs.~~

240

280 ~~The hou~~

1360 The house lying down there white among the trees.

240 ~~Old Breitkopf would sit <strumming> at the piano & then begin~~

37,60 ~~"Ich grolle nicht"~~

~~without any voice.~~

Then <after dinner> old Breitkopf would open the piano, & sing
"Ich grolle nicht";
with<out> a voice, no, but ~~with such~~ <with> immense passion,
<as> he
they would ~~walk that~~ terrace in the starlight. Or he saw
her snipping flowers in yellow gloves; <she was never still.>
in & out of the house all
day long; floating up & down like a wagtail on the
edge of a pond. all movement, ~~lightness,~~ fun.

And here was a letter from her.

He put Clarissa's letter apart from the others on the dressing
table in
~~his bedroom.~~ ~~It worried him that she should have written,~~
~~Thus~~ He would have to read it ~~to face facts.~~ ~~But it worried it~~
~~him.~~ Here was another of those meetings: some thing bound
to be painful, <&> ~~disturbing;~~ upsetting; something new; added,
~~which~~
had to be taken in, <added> made part of the past; oh one
mustn't flinch from it of course; but to see Clarissa, to read
her letter, needed the devil of an effort; ~~& there he brought out~~
~~his~~ but there.

or lie sunk in arm chairs, half asleep, [tangling?] with the arm, making absurd jokes—How they laughed at Breitkopf—singing through the whole of Brahms, poor old man,

He opened it. ~~It was only a scribble.~~ How
heavenly, she said, it had been to see him. She must ~~just~~
tell him so—that was all.

But it put him out of temper. It irritated him.
Coming on top of his ~~dreams~~ thoughts of her, it was like a
nudge in the ribs.

~~Then~~ Why couldn't she let him ~~go~~ <be>? After all, she was
capable of marrying Dalloway; had lived with him in perfect
comfort these twenty years. ~~Fundamentally she was a~~
~~conventional~~

And of course these hotel bedrooms are not consoling
places. Any
number of people hung up their hats on those pegs. Even the
flies are not domestic. ~~It It is not To attain that degree~~
And say what you like, <the> ~~of~~ cleanliness is really forbidding: Some arid matron makes
the rounds at dawn, scouring, or causing to be scoured, for all
the world as if the guest were ~~some~~ a joint of meat to be
served up on a <perfectly> clean platter. For sleep one bed,
for repose <sitting in> one
armchair; & for cleaning one's teeth or shaving one's chin, one
tumbler, one looking glass. The room had suffered a
~~such~~ <the> interference of three or four books, <an open bag,>
slippers, & ~~cas~~ dressing gown
~~bag without~~ but they ~~slipped, they~~ they only rested on a
slippery surface. It was Clarissa's letter that roused him to this
Heavenly to see you. She must say so." He pressed the
paper, so that ~~it he could not poss~~ he could not see the
writing.

To get that letter to him by six o'clock, she must have ~~ran out~~
sat down & written it, ~~sent somebody out with it,~~ directly he
left her,
~~stamped it, & sent somebody to the post~~
~~She felt sorry for him no doubt. She wanted to skim over the~~
It was as people say very like her.

She was upset by his visit. She had felt, ~~for her,~~ a great deal;
had for a
moment, when she kissed his hand, regretted ~~even the past; &~~
~~every~~thing <thing>, had ~~wished to be off,~~ envied him, had ~~recove~~
remembered probably ~~one of~~ some ~~pictu~~ thing he had said—how
they could ~~have~~ change~~d~~ the world if she married him—& then
has defined him, she thought ~~of~~ of Richard:—~~a mediocre man,~~ his ~~good~~
not once ~~good, secondrate, sound,~~ mediocrity: then forced herself,
~~helped by her~~ <with the> indomitable vitality, to put it ~~all in one~~
~~aside; everything~~ aside, there being in her a thread of
life which for toughness, endurance, power to overcome
obstacles & carry her triumphantly though he had never known
the life of. Yes; but there would come a reaction, directly
he had left the room. She would be frightfully ~~frightfully~~
sorry for him.
She would think ~~of anything in the world~~ <what in the world> she
could <she> do to give him a
moments pleasure—(short always of the one thing); & he could see her
with the tears running <racing> down her cheeks, ~~entirely~~
~~walking~~
~~running~~ <going> to her writing table & dashing off that one line
which he was to find directly he came in; ~~& probably even at~~
"Heavenly to see you
~~this moment she was <still> thinking of him.~~ & she meant it.

Peter Walsh had now unlaced his boots.
But it would not have been a success, ~~all the same~~, their
marriage. ~~It was too strong in her—the love of~~
~~respectability. Visit She must have maids & visiting~~
~~cards & days parties.~~

~~Getting up, & making ready to change into evening dress~~

The other thing ~~was~~ after all, ~~so~~ <came so> much more natural.
Now it was a very odd fact that this Civil servant, who had
filled quite meritoriously ~~too~~, positions of responsibility in
India,
~~read, & read, & read. Whatever~~ people might say about him—
~~as~~ that he was cranky, flirtatious, a little hubristic—
though <& gave> ~~giving~~ himself <the> airs of one too good for his
position, ~~there~~ <had> ~~attached~~
~~to him &~~ (especially now that his hair was gone grey) a
~~slightly contemplative, air <or> contented look;~~ <slightly>
humorous or contented
look, which argued that he had ~~a private~~ in reserve

a ~~private~~ cupboard ~~of cut of some sort~~ to which he resorted. ~~in~~
Obviously, ~~his~~ he did not live ~~altogether~~ on the surface. And
~~it was~~ <In a> ~~attractive to women & girls.~~
which made him attractive to women ~~& girls~~, who liked that
the sense ~~it gave them~~ of that he was not altogether manly,
~~&~~ He was a cultivated man, ~~up to a point Seeing books in a room, he~~
~~would at once take a volume out.~~ & seemed to indicate that
he had a private store—a cupboard, so to speak, ~~under~~ a
secret lock, in which he kept a fine old bottle of liqueur.
It might be books. He never came into a room without
walking to the book case & taking a volume out. For example,
he was now reading—Women liked him

Such a perfect gentleman. Then so susceptible; & then so fierce & incorruptible wh. combined with extreme simplicity

~~It was difficult to define it.~~ They liked the sense that he was not
altogether manly. He did not tell the same kind of story at dinner.
& made them feel And then he was fond of books—never came into a room without
a walking to a book case & taking a volume out (He was now
reading, with his bootlaces <hanging down> undone.) And
then he was a
gentleman, ~~in that~~ which showed itself in the way he sat down &
~~got up,~~ & knocked the ashes out of his pipe, & in his
manners of course to women. For it was very charming;—
quite ridiculous, ~~his~~ how easily ~~this he was overcome~~
some girl without a grain of sense could twist him round
her finger, ~~& then he would be her slave, &~~ ~~Any woman
could; but that not coarsely~~; But ~~not~~ at her own risk.
That is to say ~~he was~~ though he might be ~~very~~ <ever so> easy,
~~very~~
& indeed ~~have a kind of gaiety~~ <with his spirits> & good
breeding ~~that made~~ & gentle
~~him~~ fascinating, <to be with> still ~~there was something queer.
People~~
~~who had known him He turned crusty.~~ Lying,
Still ~~or~~ it was <only> up to a point. ~~You could easily get on the
wrong side of him: Some~~ There was something queer.
He would Some ~~<this> quite~~ small thing, ~~a~~ <—a> would put
him in a
rage. ~~And~~ <But> that was ~~very~~ charming. ~~Even Daisy~~
too. He was not, ~~as~~ <a> ~~what~~ a ladies man in type at all.
You could very easily say the wrong thing {And that was
charming. His grumpiness was charming, & the
feeling that however easy it might be to bamboozle
him ~~either by singing his favourite songs, or
wearing some of the sort of clothes,~~ no, no, he
saw through <u>that</u>. He wouldn't stand that. He
could shout & rock & hold his sides together too with
other men in the smoking room. ~~And probably,~~
~~But it was his~~ ~~but never had any intimate friends out there,~~ ~~so~~
so that He <u>was</u> a man. Only, ~~what with~~ liking books,

& having ~~had <made> this mis unfortunate marriage (which he never discussed~~
~~with anyone) he was different somehow; he had this reserve; he~~
~~& now that he was going~~ this—what could one call it?—
being different.

Compared with ~~Major~~ <Martin> Simmons, ~~in such~~ it was obvious. And

In changing, as Peter Walsh, <(shutting his book,)> thought it now about time to begin,
his ~~letters were~~ pocket was emptied of letters & on top of them was
the Kodak snapshot of Daisy Summers on the verandah, ~~looking~~
all in white with her fox terrier on her knee. very, very
charming. In fact it was the best he had ever seen of her.
It did come, after all, so naturally—(he took his boots off)
so much more naturally than Clarissa, ~~after~~ all;
No fuss; no bother; no finnicking fidgeting; no ~~mind~~,
~~noises.~~

And the <adorably pretty> face in the photograph, <with its> adorably pretty & young &
seemed to be saying ~~that is what I<'m> am not clever. I am not~~
Thats right Thats right. I'll give you ~~ab ev~~ absolutely
everything. It said, running across the verandah to wave her hand.
And she was only twenty four. And she had two children.

vision of her
at Highgate
a widow
with a past

Well, well, well,

Well, indeed he had got himself into a mess, at his age. And it came over
him when he woke in the night pretty forcibly. Suppose they did
marry? For him it would be all very well, but what about her?
Mrs. Burgess, a good sort & no chatterbox, in whom he had confided,
~~said~~ thought this absence of his, ostensibly to get lawyers opinions
might serve to ~~end the~~ make Daisy ~~see~~ re-consider; <think ~~to~~ what it meant.> It was a
question ~~what her~~ <of her> position ~~would be~~ in ~~ten years~~ time, Mrs. Burgess said.
~~Other women, English society~~, <the social> barrier, giving up her children.
~~in~~ ~~In ten years time~~ She'd be a widow with a past one of these
days, draggling about in the suburbs, is more likely ~~become~~
~~rather miserably~~ indiscriminate: <you know what women get like> with too much paint.
~~Well~~ ~~But~~ ~~One could~~ But Peter Walsh pooh poohed all that,
~~Risks one had to run.—~~ ~~One h~~ ~~She must settle <decide> for herself.~~
~~He couldn't think now what would happen when he was~~
~~dead~~—he wasn't going to die yet; ~~& in short the thing could be~~
would settle itself, if ~~only everybody <people> kept cool; & he~~
~~disliked scenes; he knew he couldn't made a fool of himself;~~
& ~~But~~ <But> She must settle for herself, ~~which~~ for he
~~couldn't judge &~~ judge for herself; ~~what mattered;~~ & so
padding about the room in his socks he ~~got out~~ <smoothed> his
dress ~~clothes~~ <shirt>, & supposed ~~that~~ he might ~~after all~~ go to
Clarissa's party, or might on the other hand, go to one of the
Halls, where there was certain to be some<thing> amusing on
~~the truth being that he could, at his age, fifty two,~~
~~that he found lots of things to could not sit down & think about~~
~~these crises,~~ or might ~~sit go on~~ read his book, ~~these~~
which indeed ~~had~~ <was> an absorbing work written by a man he used to
know at Oxford; & ~~suppose~~ <if> he did retire, thats what he'd do—
write books. ~~Enormous~~ He would go to Oxford &
poke about in the Bodleian ~~for a year or two~~. He'd

~~And still the~~ Vainly the pugnacious young woman ran to the
end of the verandah waving her hand.

[*pencil*] Peter Walsh padded about the room. That the crises are never real.

but how she ~~would come with~~ him, didn't care a straw what
people said,
~~There was Peter Walsh in his Bloomsbury hotel changing for
dinner, &~~
~~as he padded about the room,~~ There was Peter Walsh padding
about the room, automatically ~~getting ready, &~~ shaving, washing,
~~with those & thinking~~ continuing, as he took up coins, put down
razors, to ~~think of this book, &~~ poke about in the ~~Bodle~~ Bodleian,
~~of making~~ <& get> get~~ting~~ at the truth about one or two little
~~qu~~ questions
which had always intrigued him; & ~~he would go or~~ & ~~have a go
round~~ &
~~chat with whoever it might be; & which since~~
~~have a~~
~~And he would~~ & so ~~occupied, & so content, for h~~ & have a
chat with
whoever it might be, & so ~~lose touch more & more~~
disregard more & more ~~what~~ precise hours for lunch, ~~mi miss~~
<miss> ~~forget~~
~~fail~~ engagements, & ~~as~~ when Daisy asked him, as she would,
~~for to say some thing~~ for a kiss; a scene ~~would he not~~
~~he he might~~ forget momentarily what was expected; for <fail
to come up to the scratch, not that he was not
devoted to her,>
~~is~~ it became ~~more & more <increasingly~~ ever so> difficult
~~to him~~ to concentrate
~~upon <wh> these moments, or to indeed to~~ on moments,
~~to arrive at a clear cut understanding of the importance of
all this curious what people expected did on the importance of
these ceremonies, & agreements social conventions; how women
respectable people liked things <did> done. And more than that.
Its Partly through having lived abroad,~~ Though as life
went on, this interest of one's own observations
& his own interests, his own <susceptibilities> ~~passion for
seemed if anything to increase~~
~~in whatever he was doing~~ <seemed rather to> increase~~d~~—if
any thing, yes,

what things mattered to

~~becoming more & more absorbed in~~
in short it might be happier for her to~~—forget him,~~ <~~that he~~
~~should lose him~~ to> & fulfil~~ling~~ her
duties as the wife of a major in the Indian army, <&> ~~merely to~~
~~have~~
~~a memory, seeing that is how very~~ only to remember him as
he was in the ~~year~~ <August> 1922; ~~a~~ <like> a figure standing ~~at~~
~~the in a~~
at ~~a tur~~ a crossroad, which grows more & more remote as
the dog cart spins ~~along~~ <away>, ~~bearing away with it Daisy~~
~~from under~~ <disappearing, in the whirl of grey dust,>
her away, ~~with it, &~~ though her arms might be outstretched,—
her voice might cry still, to the phantom figure, how she would
do anything in the world— He ~~did not know~~ was
He never knew what people thought. ~~He~~ It became more & more
difficult for him to concentrate. He became absorbed; ~~in~~
he became ~~so~~ busied with his own concerns, & meditative, &
gay, &
in want of female companionship, & absent minded, &
fond of society, & ~~for~~ unsociable, & ~~me~~ grumpy, &
urbane, & less & less able (such ~~was~~ <so it seemed> the upshot
of his
meditations, as ~~she~~ <he> shaved) less & less able to ~~come up to~~
understand why people attached ~~this~~ such importance to
~~cere~~ forms—why couldn't Clarissa <couldn't> find them a
lodging,
& be nice to ~~his~~ Daisy, & then he could ~~enjoy, what he~~
~~had~~ have his home, & his friends & his— But ~~why~~ by what
name could he call this ~~busy~~ haunting & hovering, which
was so essential a part of life; this poise over ~~the~~ —
~~well~~, (at the moment he was actually engaged in sorting out
various keys, papers, — this swooping & tasting, this
power of being ~~altogeth~~ for long stretches of time
quite sufficient to himself; & yet, heaven knows
there was no body more dependent upon
others; he could never keep out of smoking rooms at hotels;
he liked Colonels, ~~he~~ liked golf; ~~as for~~ <above all> women;
& ~~the amusement &~~ society, & the fineness of their

companionship, & their faithfulness, & audacity, & greatness in loving, which though it had its drawbacks, seemed to him —& (there was the dark pugnacious face on the top again) so wholly admirable; so splendid a flower to grow on the crest of human life; & yet he could not come up to the scratch himself, being always apt to see round things, & to tire very early of mute devotion, & to want variety, ~~even~~ in love; though ~~he expected~~ it would make him furious if Daisy loved anybody else: he was jealous; horribly jealous. But where was his white tie now? And his watch; seals; & note case. & Clarissas letter & Daisys photograph; & his book . . & then, to go & so he went down stairs.

28 They were eating
240 Sitting at little tables round vases, dressed or not dressed, with their
280 shawls, & ~~their hair done, their pu stiffness, their isolation,~~
1920 ~~they sat at~~
480 ~~dinner;~~ bags laid beside them, ~~their hair done,~~ <&> ~~an air of~~
65,20 with their air of ~~strangeness, ceremony, unnatural ease~~,
2,80 ~~they~~ pretence, for they were not used to so many courses at
30 dinner, & composure, for they must not let anyone guess, <were
9,400 able to pay for it,>
& ~~discom~~ strain, for they had been running about London
all day, shopping, interviewing, & their natural curiosity
for they looked round or up as Mr Walsh came in, &
their good nature, for they ~~were~~ would have been glad to do
any little service—~~for example~~, as ~~for example~~, lend a timetable
~~Bradshaw or~~ impart <some useful> information, ~~or & more than~~
~~delighted should it turn out that Mr. Walsh or any other~~
~~guest of~~ & their ~~perpetual~~ desire, ~~tugging at~~ <pulsing in> them,
tugging at them, somehow to establish connections
if it were only a common birthplace, ~~or~~ friends ~~who~~
& their ~~odd~~ ~~might have been~~ of the same name, there they sat,
~~furtive~~ <furtive> eating dinner when Mr. Walsh came in & took his seat
glances, <&> odd at ~~h~~ a little table ~~in~~ by the curtain.
silences, & It was not that he said anything, for being solitary, he
sudden withdrawals could only address himself to waiters. <but ~~sat~~> ~~it was~~ his way
into hostility & of looking at his menu, of pointing to ~~the~~ <a particular> wine,
suspicion, of hitching himself up to the table & addressing himself
seriously <yet not gluttonously,> to dinner that won him their
respect, ~~their~~
which, having to remain unexpressed for the greater
part of the meal, flamed up, where the Morrises
sat, when Mr. Walsh was heard to say at the very
end <of the meal> "Bartletts Pears." Why he should have

have spoken so moderately yet firmly, ~~&~~ those two words
neither young
Morris nor old Morris, nor ~~Miss~~ <Mrs> ~~Morris~~, nor Miss ~~Morris~~,
knew. ~~He They~~ But he seemed to be [<~~as~~?>] appealing to them
as fellow diners, to consent in their support ~~in~~ in some
lawful
cause, ~~to & <so that> when the Mr Morris could not help at once some~~
~~so that a glance of went between the tables, &~~
& to be at the same time, so resolute, so unflinching, such a
desirable champion in short that ~~they~~ their eyes met his,
& a little talk, <~~as they~~ when> did become ~~quite~~ inevitable.
Already the
Morrises were very favourably impressed.

when they all reached the smoking room simultaneously

~~they drew together inevitably.~~
a little talk between them became inevitable.
It was not very profound—only to the effect that London was crowded;
had changed in thirty years; ~~for~~ <that> Mr Morris was a man of business in
Sheffield. ~~& Yet in truth,~~ <that> Mrs. Morris had been ~~several times~~ to the
~~play; &~~ & ~~that~~ & they had all seen the Prince of Wales, ~~but~~
yet, thought Peter Walsh, here was ~~the <an>~~ absolutely convincing
proof ~~of the fact, which~~ that ~~nothoth~~ nothing ~~is~~ can compare
~~with the for sheer niceness, & sense,~~ & with the Morrises: no
family in the whole world has that mixture of honesty, & sense; ~~no~~ <&>
& their relations to each other are perfect.} And they don't care a
hang for the upper classes. And the girls are training to go into

[the family]

business. And the boy has won a scholarship at Birmingham.
And the ~~mother has~~ <old lady> (who is his own age about) has three more

[& they have motor-cars, &]

children at home; & they are all going to be a great deal <putting ~~by a very~~ great deal>
~~better educated than~~ Mr. Morris; who still walks about in his
shirt sleeves mending taps, & mending boots on Sundays.
~~Yes,~~ It is absolutely superb, thought Peter Walsh, feeling

[swaying a little backward & forward]

as he stood /among the hairy red chairs & ash trays,
(& this was a very exhilarating feeling) played on in different
~~places~~ parts of him by ~~all~~ these Morrises, & ~~exercising~~
exuding melody. Yes, for they liked a man who had
that way of saying "Bartlett's pears" They liked him, he
felt; ~~it was~~
He would go to Clarissa's party. ~~That was what he wanted, to feel all over He~~ The Morrises moved off;
he moved off. He would go to Clarissa's party, &
in case he could there find someone ~~who~~ to whom
he could say "Stravinsky now—what about him?"
And who's writing ~~anything~~ <anything> ~~worth writing~~? ~~What ought one to see?—pictures, for example? or the~~ What's being
painted."

played?" Oh yes, & ~~all the~~ & mere gossip.

description of the hot night people sitting out on the steps & drinking & on & on

For this is the truth about that inexplicable ~~character creature~~
being ~~that~~ our self; who fish like inhabits deep seas, &
~~lives in a~~ & plies among ~~green~~ obscurities; ~~shadows~~, threading her
way ~~am~~ between the boles of giant weeds, & over sun-flickered
spaces, &/ into gloom, <cold deep> ~~profound~~
<sunk & suffused> sonorities; suddenly she
~~felt startled~~, shoots to the surface, & sports on the
wind wrinkled waves: that is, ~~one~~ its a ~~eras~~
positive need to brush ~~&~~ scrape & kindle the spirit, gossiping
~~asking getting~~ a ~~little first rate inf hand information from~~
~~Richard Dalloway for instance about the~~ What, for
instance, did the government mean—Richard would ~~tell him.~~

to do about

know; ~~& <about>~~ their Indian ~~policy~~;—

reflecting ~~in~~ (already known)

Since it was a very fine hot night, ~~a~~ & the paper
boys went by with placards ~~stating~~ <proclaiming> in ~~red~~ huge red
letters the fact "Heat Wave"; wicker chairs were
placed on the hotel steps, & there detached gentlemen sat,
Peter Walsh sat there. One might fancy that the day
~~One mig~~
was just beginning. Like a woman who has slipped off her
print dress & white apron to array herself in blue & pearls;

evening

~~& with the same little shiver of~~ the day changed, <to ~~night~~> & with the
same sigh of exhilaration ~~which~~ that a woman
breathes, tumbling her stiff petticoats on the floor; ~~&~~
~~[snuffing?]~~ it too shed dust ~~&~~ heat; & colour; the traffic lessened;
motor cars with pale yellow lamps <sparkling, twinkling> succeeded <the> lumber~~ing~~ of
vans; & here & there, among the ~~leaf~~ greenery of the
squares ~~a bright~~ an intense light hung. "I resign.
~~to you~~" the ~~n~~ evening, <seemed to say> as it paled & faded, above the
battlements, ~~of the the rock like~~ <red pointed> prominences & eminences of
hotel, flat, & west end ~~b~~ block of shops; ~~to—as if~~
~~indeed. & then the~~ but London allowed none of it; ~~but~~

in conspiracy she seemed, or partnership with the sky; ~~but~~ as
of the two of them now, she above, the streets below, entered
into
~~some some~~ a compact, she, the sky, presiding over the
dancing revelry of London, ~~with that~~ & ~~sealing a~~ resuming
into her compassionate & ethereal breast all those
splinters, those bayonets of light which, as a ship nears
the shore, or a traveller the town, can be seen
hanging in a glow worm haze; ~~upon the night.~~
streaming up & up. . . But it was far from dark. The
great ~~impre~~ revolution of summer time had taken place
since Peter Walsh's last visit to England.

Then, just as she was vanishing, ~~the~~ she was called forth,
established,
by the lights in the streets; as if London were in conspiracy with her;
to seal the revelry of the night, & resume into her compassionate
& ethereal breast, ~~to arch over &~~ all that flare. For the
great revolution of summer time had taken place since Peter
Walsh's last visit to England; ~~&~~ This prolonged evening
was new to him, & inspiriting rather, for, as the young people
went past, with their despatch boxes, awfully glad to be out, &
proud too, one might imagine, of ~~being~~ stepping this famous
but ~~joy~~ all the same
pavement, joy of a kind—~~in the seemed~~ cheap, tinselly, if you like,
rapture—seemed flushed on their faces. They would have now
two or three hours of this effervescence. ~~And then,~~
(& on the leaves, how strange: ~~like~~ dipped they seemed in ~~lake~~ <sea> water pale, green lurid)
~~sur surely~~ It sharpened, it refined, th~~is~~<e> ~~evening~~ yellow blue
~~evening~~ light; it was wonderful, exquisite. It was encouraging too
for, where the returned voyager sat, by rights, in the
corner of some smoking room, biliously summing up the
ruin of the world, here was this traveller looking forward
optimistically to the future, praising electricity,
really envying young people their summer time &
the rest of it, & suspecting—from a word of a girls, a
housemaids laughter—that ~~very~~ shift ~~of~~ in the whole pyramidal
accumulation~~s of~~ which, in his youth, had seemed immovable.
of
On top of them it had pressed; weighted them down, like
those ~~leaves~~ <flowers> Aunt Helena used to press, between
sheets of
grey blotting paper with Littrés dictionary on top.
She was dead, presumably. ~~And~~ He had heard
~~h of~~ of her losing the sight of one eye, & it seemed to him
~~that~~ fitting; She would have a ~~grey green~~ ~~eye of~~ glass, eye
~~& would st sit~~ She would rigidify. She
~~&~~ She would die like some bird in a frost,
gripping her perch. She belonged to a different
age, ~~&~~ but, being in her way so complete, would

always ~~remain~~ stand up as the horizon, stone white, eminent,
like a
~~statue;~~ a light house, marking ~~a~~ some part stage in the
adventurous, long, long voyage, which seemed an eternity,
~~For oh the length of it, Oh~~ This interminable life; a
And he felt for a coin in his pocket to buy a newspaper, &
read how Surrey was all out, feeling that so he had done
~~there~~ <a> million times, ~~& The same boy would be offering
the same paper;~~ And Surrey was all out, once more;

And Surrey was all out once more;
He was seriously interested in county cricket. He ~~read~~
<turned about the paper>
& read all the scores in the stop press news; & then how it was a hot day—
~~&~~ Having done things millions of times ~~had only~~ enriched them,
though it might be said of course to take the surface off. the
past ~~en~~ enriched; & experience, & having cared for one or two
people; & so having acquired the power, which the young lack, of
of centring on ~~po~~ what matters; & Reading what one likes, meeting
whom one likes, ~~&~~ moving ~~off~~ <on> without any too great
expectations (he ~~moved,~~ left his paper on the table & moved)
which however (& he looked for his hat & coat) was
truer of some than of him, for here he was, starting to
go to a party, at his age, in the belief that there still
might await him some ~~experience there~~
~~new~~ experience. But what?
~~Anyhow~~ Beauty never failed. It was not beauty pure &
simple: Bedford Place leading into Russell Square. ~~was not~~
It was straightness, partly, emptiness; lines of windows lit up;
pianos sounding; a sense of ~~of~~ pleasure making,
hidden, or only now & again emerging when, through the
uncurtained window one saw parties sitting over tables,
or <(once)> young people, (once, slowly dancing, <old [men?]>
people idly looking out,
at top windows; & parrots in cages: & in
the large Square, where the taxis shot so swiftly,
the sense of loitering couples, dallying, embracing couples,
shrunk up ~~stationary~~ against the railings under the
shower of trees; so silent, so absorbed, that one
passed, timidly even, as if in presence of some
deep silent process, to interrupt which would have been
impious. And so on, through the flare & glare,

The light overcoat which Mr. Walsh wore blew aside, ~~revealing~~ <showing> the
trim angular figure; ~~th~~ the indescribably characteristic half
tripping
step; ~~the way~~ how, with his head bent slightly forward, & his brown eyes, ~~faintly~~ well open, still a little hawklike in his stone coloured crinkled face, he took his way, hands behind his back, observing.

~~All through Mayfair, Belgravia, Kensington, front doors were being opened. Here in Portland Place.~~

All through Mayfair, Belgravia, Kensington, front doors were
being
opened. Here in Portland Place by an ~~old~~ athletic ~~young~~
& discreet young man, ~~who~~ supported by an elder in the hall,
~~to~~ so ~~that a to~~ <to> let issue a very fine, high stepping,
~~white~~ <old>
~~haired~~ woman, in buckled shoes, with three purple ostrich
feathers proudly curved in her white hair: ~~<off she swept>
shut in her motorcar.~~
~~She swept here in~~ in Brook Street, <in> Grosvenor Street, in
Charles Street; doors were being opened; ~~rings light pale~~
ladies; wrapped like mummies in shawls with bright flowers
on them—red chrysanthemums or white flying storks—
descended; & the ~~doo~~ motor started; in ~~Kensington~~ in Belgravia
in Kensington, ~~through little~~ down steps, through small
<front> gardens, still
~~doors they descended, all~~ lightly swathed, with combs in their
hair, they came; & gentlemen too, their coats blowing open,
cigars in their lips.
until what with the ~~motors~~ descent, & the start, ~~the
they~~ <it> ~~seemed as if the streets were~~ it seemed as if they
stepped into little boats, moored to the ~~rivers~~ bank. ~~It seemed~~ as if
~~people were~~ <they> embark~~ing~~<ed>, <floated out> ~~or~~ lightly
~~in~~ <for> some carnival.
And as the ~~quick~~ stream is ~~all~~ skated over by spiders, so
Piccadilly seemed; ~~& the~~ with its traffic: ~~midges dancing too, in
ballroom shaped companies; where the light fell;~~ & & its
silver beaten ~~wood~~ pavement. ~~& its~~ Companies of midges
dancing round the lamp. <&> Here ~~out on the pavement~~ in
Chelsea a retired judge, all in white sat at his house door;
& here a shindy went forward of ~~drunken~~ of
brawling women, & here ~~nothing,~~ only a swinging
policeman & looming, ~~impending silent~~ horses.
And then again ~~a street with~~ the river; & then a
~~Br~~ bridge; & then, some ~~faint~~ expectation, took hold of Peter

Walsh, as he ~~turned walked in Westminster,~~ that the ~~taxis people in~~
taxis were going to the same house that he was.
They were going to Clarissa's house; ~~a some of them~~.
And, as they passed him, he faltered. This beauty, in which he
had been swimming, ~~for~~ all the way, this cold stream~~;~~ of
visual impressions, failed him ~~now~~ as if the eye were a
deep cup which ~~craved~~ <soon> ~~to be filled~~ & ~~then~~ overflowed; & now
nothing gave him any pleasure. ~~Again,~~ ~~To speak, to~~
~~be with people~~; He wanted to be rid of himself observing, ~~&~~
~~he wanted~~ to be replenished, or, as the Morrises did, made
vibrate, here & here & here, like a man of gifts & parts.
He ~~took out his pocket knife.~~ He flicked his hand ~~here & there~~ <to his>
tie, coat; He ~~took~~ <half> opened the large blade of his pocket knife.
One must press forward; one must go on.

& ran down the china walls.

Lucy the housemaid had only had just

the Kitchen

Sept. 7th 1924. Lucy, the parlourmaid, straightened, arranged, a chair, a ~~ch~~ chair cover, very expeditiously, ~~as~~ so as to have the drawing room ready, when they came up from dinner; ~~& for~~ <&> she must not be caught. & it must look—~~well~~ as if ~~this~~ <it> was <all> natural,
~~this was~~ <what they> usually had
~~This tidiness being like this:~~ ~~Indeed—well,~~ <& hoping> ~~for~~
one moment, ~~she had~~ a
look, ~~ev~~ not ~~&~~ whoever might come must feel how clean it was; & the beautiful silver, ~~&~~ the ~~fire irons,~~ brass fire irons, the ~~all~~ new chair covers; she appraised each; felt the excitement of life almost excessive: & then ~~there was~~ a roar of voices; ~~the~~ the dining room door being opened; ~~but it shut again.~~ She must
fly.

1923 There was a rumour in the kitchen that the Prime Minister was coming. Not that one Prime Minister more or less could have made much difference to Mrs. Walker, ~~in her present confusion~~ among the innumerable ~~plate~~ plates; ~~the brilliant light, the hurrying, scurrying,~~ saucepans; cullenders, frying pans, ~~relics of~~ chicken in aspic, ice cream freezers, pared crusts of bread, lemons, soup tureens & pudding basins which, however hard they washed up in the scullery seemed to be all about her, on <the bare kitchen> tables on chairs; while the fire
roared, the electric
lights glared & still supper had to be spread in the dining room. There she exaggerated, as was her wont ~~at these~~ <at these [times?]>
in crises. ~~Mr~~
Gunters men always ~~came &~~ saw: to that ~~& the gilt~~ chairs they brought; Rumpelmayers <had> sent ~~cakes & biscuits~~ <[cakes?]>;
but when
Lucy came down & told them about the Prime Minister coming, Mrs Walker felt that ~~one Prime Minister~~ <it didn't matter,>
more or ~~less~~
~~made w~~ it couldn't make much <a scrap of> difference to her; one Prime Minister more or less. ~~There~~ They were, going ~~out of the~~
<up into>
~~dining room,~~ the drawing room, the ladies, Mrs. Dalloway walking last, of course; & almost always & sending some message down to the kitchen of praise. Next morning they would go into the dishes one by one. The soup salmon; ~~not done enough.~~ the fault of the salmon was as usual

"My love to Mrs Walker" that was it one night. The

~~but Mrs. Walker was~~ underdone. ~~Really~~ <for> She was always nervous about
~~salmon- &~~ her pudding, & ~~let the~~ so it happened. But ~~Mrs.~~ some
how ~~Dalloway had said~~ Lady, with fair hair, & something ~~sli~~ silver in it
had said to Mrs. Dalloway ~~what a how~~ <what a> wonderful ~~it was~~ pudding
There she stood <at the table> weighing one thing with another— salmon ~~underdone~~, pudding
~~all right~~—& spinning the plates round, ~~&~~ while now &
again there came a burst of laughter, then a voice speaking, then—
roar of from the dining room ~~which was~~ above the kitchen, <where> & the
laughter gentleman sat. & <then> Mrs Dalloway sent Lucy down for
another bottle of those wines which Lucy ~~was so~~
knew about; ~~to Mrs. Walker they~~ were all ~~much alike;~~ <as like as peas.>
but Mrs. Dalloway had told Lucy that some of them
~~were worth oh ever so much~~— Some had come from the
Emperor of Austria's cellars;

It was borne through the kitchen. Lucy reported that Miss Elizabeth was <she couldn't take her eyes off>
~~looking~~ lovely. Emily the scullery maid ~~was~~ remembered that she must
[margin: in her new dress]
look after that dog—Elizabeths fox terrier which since it bit
~~if <when>~~ excited, had to be shut up; & might <(Miss Elizabeth said)> want something. ~~Yet~~
But ~~the~~ the stairs were impassable. Ladies & gentlemen were
passing up & down. ~~The first of the door bell ring; an early visitor h~~
There was the rush of a motor. The door bell rang. That was the
first to come, & soon they would come so quick that Mrs. Parkinson
would ~~n~~ keep the door ajar, ~~& open instantly~~ &
the hall would be full of gentlemen waiting while the
ladies took their cloaks off, <looked this way & that way in the glass> ran a comb through their hair,
& then, ~~giving~~ <ladies ~~going a~~ going first, gentlemen following, they wd. give> their names to Mr. Wilkin on the first
landing ~~they would be announced~~ & he would announce
them, ~~& Mrs. Dalloway then~~ & Mrs. Dalloway ~~always had~~
~~some thing to say.~~ would smile.

Mrs. Parkinson, & Mr. Wilkins were paid to come, ~~&, as~~
had ~~that~~ <a> sort of <professional> understanding together, a likeness too, of manner,
even of dress. ~~whereas Mrs.~~ But Mrs. Barnet who sat in
the cloak room ~~with~~ rising cumbrously to help the ladies
was of course in the family for thirty years, & came ~~really~~
~~always~~ every summer ~~just to help the ladies, give them~~
~~their cloak tickets, &~~ <to help> & remembered the mothers of girls,
& though very unassuming ~~in her~~ with her white hair &
apron, did shake hands; said 'Milady' very respectfully,—
yet had a humorous way with her, looking at these
girls, & ever so ~~kindly helping~~ <helping tending.> ~~elderly~~ Lady Lovejoy for
example who apprehended some difficulty with her
under bodice. Why she had read about them in the papers,
~~how~~ & so of course she knew about Mrs. John & Miss
Florence, & somehow they felt, Lady Lovejoy & Miss Florence,
that their cloaks were laid more respectfully than

other cloaks upon the chairs & sofas, & the tortoiseshell box of pins more promptly offered them, & some little privilege in the matter of brush & comb awarded them, since Lady Lovejoy had known Mrs. Barnett at Bourton thirty years ago: ~~She remembered her! oh perfectly. And, would make a point of stopping to talk,~~ ~~It was one of the a feature of Clarissa's parties—Mrs Barnett in the cloak room.~~ ~~And~~ & ~~even~~ So, she would sit patting down the furs, & smoothing out the Spanish shawls with their red flowers & their flying storks & deciding which were real ladies, which not. A cup of tea would be brought her later, by Emily, perhaps, if Lucy were still too busy, & ~~the~~ a shawl might be looked at. But how was Emily to get up stairs to look at that dog? And Emily would dash away again to the kitchen. And Mrs. Barnett would be left with all the clothes, ruminating.

Lady Lovejoy

very ~~happy.~~, <~~proud.~~ proud. happy> as Lady Lovejoy felt;
mounting the stairs, &
~~She was~~ But next moment Lady Lovejoy had to draw herself
together, ~~when~~ & ~~say speak~~ give ~~her~~ <their> names to Mr
Wilkins
~~who had an admirable manner~~. He had an admirable
manner; as he bent & straightened himself, bent & straightened
himself, <&> announc~~ing~~<ed> with severe impartiality, Mr. & Mrs.
Thistleton; Mr. Horne & Miss Horne; Major & Mrs.
Ash; Miss Weld; Sir John & Lady Needham; Miss Austwithe
Miss Lady Maddox; Colonel & <& Mrs> Garrod; Lady Cynthia
Henderson, Ellis; Mr. & Mrs. Martin; Mr. & Mrs. Boyton; Mr. Walsh;
Mr. & Mrs. Langley; Mr. & Lady Joan Mitchell; Sir William
& Lady Bradshaw; Mr. Stanmore; ~~Mr. Lady Bruton~~ Mrs. & Miss
Mr. & Mrs. ~~Weld~~; Berryman; Mrs & Miss Chesterton; Mr.
Whitbread Bowley; Miss Runton; Lord ~~Crag~~ Garfield.
Never, ~~one might have~~ <had he> drunk, never gambled; his
bearing in
family life ~~was~~ <must> irreproachable; ~~but &~~ except that it
seemed impossible that such a being, ~~with his clean cut, fac nose~~
clean shaven face, ~~& cold cheeks~~ <& cold cheeks> ~~little eyes~~
could ~~have~~ ever have
~~taken~~ blundered into a ~~roomfull~~ <the nuisance> of children.
He was
of the type of Sir William Bradshaw; something like Sir
John Whats his name, ~~Pe~~ Mr. Walsh reflected. ~~After~~
~~touching~~ Clarissa's ~~hand, & hearing her say, what~~ had just
shaken hands with him; just said what she ~~always~~
said to everybody. "How delightful ~~of you to have come!~~
<to see you>"
He was sorry ~~he had~~ come; very sorry. She was
~~always at~~ her <as> worst at ~~these parties. she was~~
insincere,
~~she was~~ effusive, she was formal. Indeed, it was
foolish to have come

~~He stood by himself.~~ Clarissa had shaken hands with him. She
had said what she said to everybody, apparently—there she was
at it
again—"How delightful to see you!" It was a great
mistake to have come. He knew no one.

She was at her worst
effusive, insincere,
formal.

~~Probably~~ Ten to one the party was going to be a failure, Clarissa
thought as ~~she pressed the hand of~~ dear old Lord Lexham, ~~&~~
<stood there>
~~expla apologised~~ apologising for his wife who had caught cold
at the
Buckingham Palace garden party; ~~&~~ There was Peter, ~~W~~
criticising her; there in that corner, ~~now he was wandering off,~~
alone. Why, after all, did one do these things? Why always
seek these pinnacles & stand drenched in fire! Might it
~~ca~~ consume her anyhow. Better ~~anyhow~~ to brandish one's
torch—
~~then hap then to~~ & go out than taper & dwindle away,
like some Milly Henderson. It was extraordinary how Peter
~~had the~~
put her into these states ~~at once~~ <like this>, ~~just~~ by <just>
coming in. ~~a~~ He
made her see herself, ~~(like a housemaid)~~ dramatically;
he made her exaggerate; ~~It~~ was ~~to~~ that he
~~criticised her~~; & ~~But~~ why come, merely to criticise?

~~There~~

~~It was~~ <why> ~~a lack of generosity~~ <always> ~~about him in~~
taking, &
never ~~giving~~ <give?> ~~And~~ Why not risk one's own little
point of view—there he was wandering off; & she ~~wanted to~~
must speak to him—But now she never would. He had
chosen; she ~~had chosen~~ <too>. Life, ~~somebody said,~~ was a ~~long~~
series of humiliations, <of> revelations. Always, always, one had
~~to let go of this~~ this, to give up to let go, ~~And yet~~ But
~~it was extremely~~ thank heaven, she did ~~like~~ enjoy <love>,
all the same,
~~the thought of that~~ that nice old man telling her how
his wife would not wear her furs at the garden party
because "my dear, you ladies are all the same"—Lady
Lexham being ~~eighty~~ at least eighty five, ~~&~~ She
did, like people. She did think it mattered, ~~anyhow it was~~

~~all she could do. making, these~~ <this> part~~ies~~, in spite of
the awful, appalling
strain, <the suf> which ~~almost~~ made her feel sick—~~that~~ it
was going to be a
failure. ~~Nothing was going to go right.~~ She wouldn't
mind an
explosion; a disaster. What she could not stand was the
~~aimlessness of it pe~~ people wandering about. <aimlessly>
~~Milly Henderson's at every~~
~~corner;~~ standing all in a bunch in a corner like Milly Henderson.
Why not hold herself upright?
Very gently the curtains with all the birds of paradise on it
blew out, & for ~~a moment~~ it seemed as if there were a <~~sudd~~>
flight of
wings, ~~of~~ into the room, <~~at~~ once> drawn back. Was it
draughty?
Milly Henderson wondered, who was subject to chills.
Anyhow

remembers things
to write about
to her sisters

She was subject to chills. But it did not matter that she should
come down sneezing tomorrow; it was ~~for~~ those girls ~~in~~ <with>
their
naked shoulders, she thought of, being trained ~~by a~~ to think
of others,
by an old father, the Vicar of Bourton, but he was dead now;
trained by her face ~~also~~ <too>, for she was plain, or worse,
insignificant,
with her thin hair, ~~pale eyes, & weak yet in~~ &
meagre profile, though there was beginning, as happens
late in life sometimes, to shine through ~~the~~ some ~~fine~~
mild beam, something purified~~, chastened~~ into distinction
by ~~fifty years & years of &~~ years of self abnegation: ~~as~~
but obscured again—that was the ~~disappointing thing~~ pity—
~~about~~ her—by ~~panic,~~ <panic> fear of life, <by> that distressing
gentility which was shared by all the Hendersons,
(& in a much grosser form by ~~the opulent & blooming~~
Rosamond, for example, who had married a country
Squire;) ~~so that~~ But ~~it was scarcely to be wondered at in~~
poor ~~Milly, Her income was so small. Her~~ <but> It made them <all> dull.
~~Milly~~ <She> was dull; ~~ineffective~~, <timid &> & ~~disqualified~~
<Milly was> more & more
disqualified year by year from taking part in
gatherings of well dressed people, who did this sort
of thing every night of the season, their maids just putting
their dresses out ~~for them~~, whereas Milly Henderson
worried & fidgeted & compromised by running out &
buying a dozen pink bows, ~~which she~~ & ~~th~~ then ~~&~~ throwing
a ~~sli~~ silver shawl on top. For her invitation to Clarissa's party
had come at the ~~very~~ last moment. She was not quite
happy about it. She had a feeling that Clarissa Dalloway
had not meant to ask her this year, Why should she?
~~The Dalloways knew all sorts of people,~~ &
There was no reason really, except that they had
always known each other; & Indeed they were cousins:

But naturally she thought much more of Clarissa than Clarissa
did of her. It was an event to her, going to a party.
It was quite a treat just to see the lovely clothes. ~~And~~
~~really;~~ she ~~couldn't be certain~~ wasn't that Elizabeth, quite
grown up, with her hair in the fashionable ~~m~~<b>ob, <in> ~~all~~ in
pink? ~~which~~ Yet she couldn't be more than seventeen
But ~~quite~~ girls when they first came out didn't seem to wear
white as they used. (~~She And~~ She ~~would~~ must ~~notice every~~
remember every thing ~~because~~ <to tell> Edith ~~would want to~~
~~hear~~)
Girls wore ~~quite~~ straight frocks cut rather loose at the hips,
~~&~~ <with> the skirts were quite short; <well above the ankles,>
& they had their hair
bobbed, or <was that girl> shingled ~~was it~~?
And so of course, Milly Henderson did crane rather
standing there quite forward to look; & it wasn't so much she who minded
calm, not having any one to talk to, for she felt that they were all
such interesting people, <to watch> politicians presumably,
Richards
friends; but Richard Dalloway who felt that he must go up
& speak to her ~~he~~ something must be done. ~~And~~ so he said in his
bluff way, "Well Milly, how are you?"
Whereupon Milly ~~started off upon the heat~~ <said that> So many
people
felt <the heat> more than the cold.

"<Yes> They do, ~~they do~~" said Richard dalloway.
Yes. But what did one say next?
<Well Richard some body> Suddenly ~~old Peter Walsh~~ took him
by the elbow.
<~~Well Richard~~> "Hullo Peter!" he cried <out, turning round>
~~turning round in~~
ever so pleased to see him!
yes, really delighted to see him! ~~again.~~ <"You haven't changed
a scrap"> And off they went
together, ~~for it was~~ walking right across the room, ~~talking~~
~~Richard Dalloway~~ giving each other little pats, ~~for~~ as if
they had met after a long time, Milly Henderson thought,
watching
them go, ~~&~~ certain she knew that mans face.—A tall man,
middle aged,
~~with~~ rather fine eyes, <dark> wearing pince-nez, & <with
~~little~~> a look of John Burrows.
Edith would be sure to know.
~~It blew out again.~~ The curtain blew out again, a little
impatiently.
~~It~~ It disturbed a conversation & Clarissa <laughing,> knew
~~at that moment,~~
then, just from seeing Mr. Lyon beat the curtain back rather
impatiently, that it was all right; It had begun. It was going to
be ~~a~~ success.

~~Mr.~~ Yet for some time longer she must stand there.
{Everyone arrived
at the same moment.

{List of names}

She had six or seven words with each, ~~but she knew,~~
~~each~~ Then they went on, & ~~she knew~~, but now ~~it was~~
~~going all right;~~ it was into something that they went—
into another atmosphere.
~~Her rooms were full, of this; they were They~~ They were
meeting; ~~th~~ not standing about.
And yet, for her own part, she wasn't enjoying it;

280 This stage was too much effort. It was too much like being—
300 just anybody
84,000 standing there; & yet this anybody she did a little admire;
couldn't
help feeling that it was an ~~achievement,~~ something, after all,
to have
made ~~them~~ this, ~~whatever it was~~, happen. made them come; that
that this post on top of the stairs (she had <quite> forgotten
what she looked
like) was a signal somehow <stood, ~~for some~~ up, [ ]>.
Ridiculous ideas always came to her
~~everytime she gave a~~ about now, every time she gave a party
she had this feeling of being someone else, & that everyone was
cursed; ~~that is unreal according to one~~ <in one way> standard;
<~~this~~> & much more real,
in another. Partly their clothes & ~~there was this~~ being taken out
of their ordinary ways; & the background. so that it was
sometimes the way to say things you couldn't possibly say
anyhow else; things that needed an effort; ~~& for lots of
people
it was a relief to be not in their own house any more;~~
that couldn't be said just meeting ~~in an office,—or~~ every day
But <this was> not for her: not yet anyhow

{more names}

And what was so odd about it was the extraordinary sense of
time, ~~or~~
passing ~~time. What happened~~ was that ~~people~~ <one's friends> kept
passing one after
as all one's another, (& they were all oddly alike in some way)
friends ~~& she kept wanting to~~ feeling how they ~~had lives~~
came up ~~it was their triumph, their procession,~~ they ~~having~~ being all so
the stair, courageous—going on, going on; ~~& some
so old, &~~ quite old, some of them, & . . .

But who on earth was it?

"Lady Horrocks"
Sally Seton! ~~It was~~ Sally Seton! ~~She had held too~~
She loomed through a mist. For she hadn't looked like <u>that</u>.
Sally Seton, ~~in~~ when she <Clarissa> grasped the hot water can, to think of her, under
this roof, under this ~~roff~~ roof! Not so <ordinary>, like that
All on top of each other in the old way words tumbled out in a
shout ~~shriek~~ of laughter. passing through London—heard from Clara Haydon—
up for the
What a chance! ~~so up~~ <so> ~~I have~~ thrust myself in—without
~~In this~~ invitation.
~~There was no reason One might~~ <She> put the hot water can
down quite composedly. ~~for she was~~ <as ~~she talked~~> The lustre had gone out of her.
~~And~~ Yet it was ~~an~~ extraordinary to see her again. And Clarissa
sparkled, kindled. ~~She caught~~ They kissed each other, there inside
the drawing room door; first one cheek then the other. &
then Clarissa turned, <with Sally, hand ~~in hand,~~ in hers,> & ~~saw the with~~ saw ~~all~~ her rooms
~~qu quite~~ full, ~~& the~~ of people, ~~ro~~ & heard the roar of ~~their~~ voices, &
saw the silver, the blowing curtains, the shade, the colour,
all
as she would have it, ~~& was—oh she~~ was glad that
~~Sally~~ ~~She was glad that Sally should see all that;~~
~~Why hadn't they met? all these years?~~
(she had the simplest egotism, the most open easy of ways)
~~Instantly~~ "I have five enormous boys" said Sally.
But M$^{r.}$ Wilkins was warning, menacing: ~~almost~~,
emitting ~~to a~~ in a voice of commanding authority as if
the whole company must be advised of an ~~important~~ <an>
& the hostess instantly reclaimed
event, ~~& in came~~ about to befall them, <one> ~~a~~ name.
"The Prime Minister" said Peter Walsh.
~~No~~, one couldn't laugh at him, ~~in~~ He looked so ordinary.
You might have stood him behind a grocer's counter &
bought biscuits ~~off him~~. Yet here he was, rigged

up in a gold coat. ~~so And~~ <But> to be fair ~~he there was about him~~
~~by virtue of his office, or~~ as one saw him going round, ~~with~~ first with
Clarissa, then with Richard Dalloway he did it very well.
He was somebody. {The amusing thing was to watch the effect on
the other people there} Nobody looked at him. They just went on
talking; ~~&~~ <yet> it was perfectly plain that this majesty was
passing. Old Lady Bruton, swam up, & they retired
<together> into <a> a into
~~little~~ room, which at once became guarded, spied upon; &
~~then you could hear~~ & there was a sort of stir & rumble all
through the room, ~~because of this~~ <the> Prime Minister!

(she looked very fine, too, very ~~v~~ weather beaten very

Lord, lord! The snobbery of English life! their
passion for dressing up <~~each other~~ themselves> in gold coats, doing homage!
~~There~~ was Hugh Whitbread! ~~that~~ mere lackey! Snuffing
round the precincts of the great~~! as usual, rather~~ grown
rather fuller, rather whiter, ~~more magisterial~~ if possible, &
~~with just the same look of unimpeachable,~~ but Hugh
Whitbread all over!

That must be— by jove it was! Hugh Whitbread

She gets the sense of opposition (from Peter— & Miss Kilman)

He always looked as if he were on duty; a privileged but
secretive being;
~~a~~ hoarding secrets which he would die to defend; ~~though~~
though it would
be only ~~p~~ some little piece of tittle tattle dropped by a court
footman
which would be in all the papers tomorrow night—such were his
rattles, his baubles, in playing with which he ~~had come to~~
the ~~verge of~~ grown white, come to the verge of old ~~de~~ age, &
~~played a respectable part~~ 'enjoyed the respect & affection'
of all who knew him. For inevitably one said things like that about
Hugh; that was his style ~~all over~~; the pompous, the official; the
style of those admirable letters which Peter had ~~see~~ read
thousands of miles across the sea, in the Times, & had thanked
God he was out of the pernicious hubble bubble if
it were only to hear the baboons chatter & the coolies beat their
wives—~~it was better than the~~ Hugh Whitbread had a companion—
an olive skinned youth from one of the ~~Legations~~ <universities>.
Him he would
patronise, initiate, inoculate, one might suppose, with the
poison. For he liked nothing better than doing kindnesses,
~~h remembering birthdays~~, making the hearts of old ladies
palpitate with the divine joy of being thought of in their
age, their affliction, alone, & thinking themselves quite
forgotten; yet here was dear Hugh, ~~kind, faithful Hugh,~~
driving up & spending ~~quite~~ an hour ~~gon~~ talking of the
~~old~~ <past> days, ~~& stopping to~~ remembering the <[grateful?]>
servant, & praising
the cake, though ~~he~~ Hugh might eat cake with a
duchess any day of his life; &, to look at him, probably
~~spent a~~ <did spend> a good deal ~~of his~~ time in that agreeable
occupation. He ~~was always~~ <handed cakes.> an adept at ~~handing~~
~~cake~~. <~~Re~~ That was his epitaph.>
~~He~~ ~~His~~ tea parties. The all judging, the all
merciful, ~~he,~~ might ~~see~~ excuse. Peter Walsh
had no mercy. Villains there must be; ~~in~~ & God knows

Rodmell to Lewes.
~~2. 3.45 6-15~~

[page 67 *verso*, *pencil*]

[*pencil*]
~~fr.~~
Lewes fr Rd.
~~3.40~~
6-10. 6.2
[ ]
from 6.56.
~~8.31~~
~~7.5.6.~~

The ~~horr~~ rascals who get hanged for battering the brains of a girl
out in ~~the~~ train, ~~are often superior, &~~ do <have done> less harm on
the whole ~~that~~ than <the> Hugh Whitbreads~~, who have been to~~
~~Eton & Balliol & who are~~ & his kindness.
~~There he was~~ <Look at him now>—for the Prime Minister & Lady
Bruton ~~now~~ emerged <were coming>—
scraping & ~~f~~ bowing & intimating ~~that he~~ for all the
world to see, that he had some <thing to say> ~~communication~~
~~to make~~ to
Lady Bruton. ~~He was con &~~ She stopped. ~~She n~~
She wagged her fine old head. She was thanking him
presumably for some piece of servility. ~~She should~~
~~have known better.~~ She had her toadies; ~~always some~~
minor official in one of the government offices, <for she must> who
ran about putting through little jobs on her behalf, &
~~lunching with her getting~~ a luncheon, in return, ~~&~~ <for> they had
to lunch somewhere; ~~but herself she was~~ Probably
she had forgotten him.

But she derived from the eighteenth century. She was all right.

NP

{And now Clarissa escorted her Prime Minister down the room.
prancing, sparkling, with ~~that~~ the stateliness of her grey hair. She
wore earrings & a silver green mermaids dress; lolloping on
the waves, & braiding her tresses —~~wasn't~~ <she seemed,> there
~~some~~ old
~~fragment of poetry; he had u used of her?~~ ~~But~~
~~for she still had the her~~ having that gift still; to be; to exist; in
the <to sum>
to ~~sum up, just as she caught her scarf on her~~ arm,

it all up in her

moment; as she stopped, or turned, caught her scarf in some old
other woman's dress, unhitched it, smiled, laughed, all with

& the flush of gaiety enjoying, about in its element

the ~~greatest~~ most perfect ease & the air of a creature breathing
<the sea> ~~rath~~
in ~~the~~ ~~And~~ <But> age had just ~~sudd~~ brushed her; as ~~an~~ even a
mermaid might mirror in her little glass the setting sun on
some very clear evening, going down. {There was a breath of
tenderness;} her severity, her prudery, her wooden dulness,
~~all crisped, as were ran~~ were ~~sunned~~ <warmed> now, & she had
about her,
as she ~~stood~~ said good bye to the ~~fine the~~ thick, ~~[old?]~~
gold laced man, who was doing his best, ~~& with some success,~~
<(good luck to him)>

to seem important

to embody a whole ~~pack of~~ men, <herd of human beings>
~~she seemed, in view of her~~
~~illness, to be in view of her illness perhaps, some~~
~~strange air of waking going to~~ ~~the look of a~~ ~~some~~

All seemed kindled with some exquisite cordiality

~~final,~~ ~~some the air of a~~ an ~~unexpli~~ unexpressible
~~human a sort of dignity, & the air of & one waving her <th~~
~~pressing>~~
~~hand to with inexpressible cordiality, & yet to all this~~
~~crowd, & stepping, as indeed Clarissa would die, with~~

true

~~dignity, as if she said wished them <him> all well, &~~
must now, being on the very verge of existence, take her
leave.
So she always made him think.

The Prime minister had been good to come. And walking down the
room with him, ~~Sally~~ with Sally there, & Peter there, ~~&~~ Richard, ~~too,~~ <very ~~mo~~ pleased>
with all those people ~~no doubt~~ <rather> inclined <perhaps> to envy, she had
~~had~~ felt that intoxication of the moment, that dilation of the nerves;
~~with that~~ yes, but after all, ~~was it not not only other peoples~~
~~feelings,~~ it was what other people felt ~~about her~~, that; & so,
though love it she did & feel it tingle & sting as she walked, still,
these semblances, these triumphs, ~~with~~ dear old Peter for example,

thinking her so brilliant,

had ~~an emptiness;~~ a hollowness, ~~at heart~~; & it might be that she
was growing old, but they ~~was~~ satisfied her no longer as they
used ~~to do~~; ~~when an~~ & suddenly as she saw the Prime Minister

go down,

~~disappear,~~ the rim of the Sir Joshua picture of the little
girl in a hood brought back Kilman with a rush; ~~welcome~~:
~~drastic, satisfying that in a strange way~~—Kilman, her
enemy. ~~And the~~ <u>That</u> was satisfying. ~~To~~ Ah! how she
hated her! Hot, hypocritical, ~~devout~~; corrupt; ~~the~~
Elizabeth's seducer; the woman who had crept in, ~~in~~ &
~~among them,~~ to steal <to> ~~&~~ defile; ~~really,~~ she loved her.

It was

~~Her~~ enemy<ies> ~~is much more~~ one wanted, not ~~a~~ friends.
But ~~as if the~~ They made ~~out~~ <one> emerge out of this nebulous

befriended one, by their hatred, much more truly than ones friends—

haze. ~~had,~~ ~~But what did she mean about loving?~~
~~Certainly not was not Kilman, the but—for who could?—~~
~~It was <but> Kilman's hatred of her, & contempt for her; that~~
~~made ennobled Kilman, & for Mystically that odious woman~~
~~had befriended her;~~ more truly befriended one than friends—
than M^r. & M^rs. Marston, ~~Sir~~ Miss Truelock, Sir
Edwin & Miss Parslow, <(she saw coming up the stairs,)> who must ~~&~~ now
find her if ~~she~~ <they> wanted her, for she could not stand shaking

hands ~~at~~ <on> one

at the door all the evening.
~~She must~~ Which should she talk to? <[*pencil*] Now for the party!>

A general view of the world.
The different groups:
All sketched in.
She makes her way gradually to the
Bradshaw group.
She is livid about Septimus.   She visualises what happened.
Goes into the little room.   The clock striking her whole life
Sees the old lady put her light out.
Transition to Richard & Elizabeth, (They didn't enjoy themselves
Then to   Peter & Sally   on the stairs
Sally loved plants: a mother.
But we havent seen Clarissa.

[page 70 *verso*]

She was for the party.

Sir John was holding forth at a prodigious rate.
This fine old fellow had produced more bad pictures in his
day than any ~~of two other~~ <two> academicians in <the whole of>
St Johns Wood.
They were always of cattle drinking; innocent animals;
agriculturally speaking perfect; & <but> ~~the merely a profitable~~
~~by a~~ <foundation> ~~product~~ of Sir John's activities in other spheres—
~~the the source of~~ his racing, ~~drink~~ drinking, entertaining
~~collecting~~ collecting ~~oak ca~~ furniture, buying tapestries—
all his hobbies & activities—moreover he never missed a
first night—<all> were founded upon ~~cattle drinking; &~~
~~his~~ These cattle, standing in sunset pools, tarns, &
lochs, absorbing moisture, or signifying, for he had a
certain range of attitudes, by the ~~erectness of their [—]~~
four legs & the proud turn of their heads
raising of their <[their?]> ~~fr~~ horns, the approach of a stranger.
~~of~~ His art, however, was not a thing one mentioned. Dealers
took the pictures to the midlands. Sir John dined out
every night of his life, & was famous for the
splendour of his appearance, the roar of his laughter, & the
gusto with which he had ~~tasted every~~ <dined in> garret & alley, &
~~gilt chamber & in width of his range, which, though it~~
~~had touched the highest pinnacles once, was now lapsing~~
~~more & more congenial~~
with which he recounted, even in these upper middle class
drawing rooms (for though he deplored her circumstances
he loved Clarissa) stories of the music hall stage.
Such was he telling now~~; & old~~ to young men of
fashion; elongated young men in white waistcoats;
though Eddie ~~P~~ Sitcomb, to be sure, was on the
wrong side of forty, & had heard most of the stories
before, & ~~missed a~~ was a little apprehensive, when the story of

~~400~~ of the late Duke came up, ~~h~~ as to the effect the point of it
~~26~~ might
300 have upon Mrs. Hilbery.—that wandering will o' the wisp,
~~200~~ that vagulous phosphoresence, for in her old age she had
~~24~~ become witch like, fairy like, ~~shrunken, white haired, at once~~
~~280~~ a float a little vaguely & whimsically upon these old
~~3~~ waters. ~~of life~~; this dear ~~w~~ sun-warmed ~~ocean~~ <life>; &
~~840,0~~ stretching her hands to the blaze she came towards Sir
John's laughter, which seemed to reassure her on a
point which sometimes bothered her, if she woke early in
the morning, & didn't like to call her maid for a cup of tea;
how we must die; So there she stood, drinking it in, ~~this~~
~~how~~ <that> the duke loved the lady; ~~like an with her~~
poised like a bee on the last red flower; until the sweet
~~began to tingled~~ <ran> in her blood, & she boomed off again,
~~laughing~~ hither, thither;

There was literature; Professor Briarly; scrupulous guardian
of the
past; a strange man, for though one would have thought,
he had barricades enough, degrees, honours, lectureships,
between
him & the accidents <risks> of life, still there he ~~was~~ <stood>,
balancing the
end of his chin on the point of his collar, so that he looked
like some supercilious yet suspicious stork; ~~&~~
taking his bearings with the susceptibility of a schoolgirl, in an
atmosphere which might not be favourable to his queer
~~mixture of~~ blend; ~~of his~~ <his> prodigious learning & ~~his~~ timidity;
his wintry charm ~~crossed~~ without cordiality; his innocence, <blent> ~~yet he~~
was a
with snobbery his serene & lofty indifference, ~~& let~~ which yet
failed to protect him when ~~some~~ <a> scribbler, <(Hutton)>
grateful if an
editor tossed him a novel to review, & ~~n~~ unable ~~even~~
~~to c~~ even for such a party as this to collect <compass> the
~~right~~ <both> waistcoats & ties or ~~make f~~ & ~~his hair~~
~~stood erect by nature~~ make his hair lie flat,
old— truculently ~~countered his~~ <contradicted.> flared. ~~It was~~ There was
danger abroad: ~~there was~~ youth, <there was> rawness; &
though the
learned man whose scales swung so delicately &
registered so perfectly every grain of ~~dust~~ <gold or dust> he
weighed in them—
Sophocles, ~~Vo~~ Virgil, Voltaire—vailed his crest
punctiliously to genius, & made a point of ascertaining
by reading the weekly journals if there was any of that
that [some?] article about (he did not pretend to possess it
himself—he was scoffing, cynical, exquisitely urbane in
manner, & never took anything seriously) still
~~he was~~ he did ~~his best, to deflate~~ instinctively
withdraw, recoil, quiver, if made aware, by a ladies
~~woman's~~ hair, a ~~m~~ youths boots, of an
underworld, very creditable, doubtless, ~~& full of~~ of

of rebels; of ardent young people; ~~though~~ it was desirable
 that they
should have their outlets: ~~but for himself,~~ & ~~withdraw~~ intimate
with politeness, with good breeding with tact, ~~into~~ with some
slight sniff, ~~into the veiled chamber, whose, removed~~
~~from these shocks & tended~~ ~~he could indulge that~~
~~his penchant for a world without the values of moderation.~~
~~Crestfallen, for he tugged his hair, the untidy youth felt well~~
~~snubbed. He felt, the sturdy by no means, well,~~
~~come over him~~ ~~He knew no Greek.~~ ~~With the gait of a crane,~~
~~he moved off; deftly, to the side of~~
Hutton was snubbed; Hutton was rebellious;
As for Hutton, with his hair & his red socks, & his
reams of poetry: ~~with~~ his passion for nature; who could
recite most of Wordsworth by heart; he was ~~instantly~~
confirmed rather unfortunately by this little incident, ~~in~~
~~the~~ first in the sanctity <divinity> of his own genius; ~~which~~
next in the tyrannical ~~injustice of~~ English society;
but it was seeing life, this, ~~mixing with~~ & for
~~the~~ two or three weeks to come he would enact
this encounter with the Professor in select circles,
where he could practise his divine gift of song. He could
play, he could sing.

Lord Gayton & Miss Nancy Blow were not perceptively adding
to that
ferocious attack, ~~as with now lapsing, now what went forward~~
~~take an~~
of ~~ton~~ tongues. They were not talking, actually, as they stood
side by side; but smiling; ~~intimating not merely their content, but~~
~~their fitness, their~~ balancing ~~like~~ on their bough; for they would
off very soon, together, elsewhere; & had just looked in; &
never had very much to say, in any circumstances. ~~But the young~~
~~Lord~~ They looked, after all, so ~~perfectly~~ clean; a ~~down~~ <bloom>
of powder &
paint might have alighted on her, ~~but so that~~ such as
peaches wear in the sun; but he ~~had~~ was hard; ~~he was firm;~~
he was scrubbed; he was rinsed; ~~the~~ his grey green eyes even
~~having~~ the brightness of polished marbles, the quickness
~~the &~~ alertness of a birds; ~~&~~ No ball could escape him, or
danger surprise him; he hit, he struck, he leapt, he pounced
always with the same spring & featness; & he had his humours—
his duties; his ~~ambition & his career~~; & his tenants, & his
farms; & his mother & his sisters; & had been all day at
Lords, & that was what they were talking about, more or
less; cricket, cousins, the ~~pictures~~ <movies>; <the movies &>
~~&~~ dances, ~~people, the movies;~~
for Miss Blow was just as ~~fond of the~~ fitted to life, apparently
as he was; had no doubts; ~~had~~ no secrets; was
~~plain as a~~ turned twenty one, & standing, or moving,
drinking, or smoking, was always like ~~that~~—poised,
alighted, unruffled, & clothed ~~so perfectly that~~
~~though at such with~~ <at> such enormous expense that it
seemed as if her body had merely put forth of its own
accord ~~a green sheath; a transparency;~~ a <green> veil.
~~This green dress was~~ So why talk? shout, embrace,
swing; be up at dawn, & running through the dew
of the park in bare feet; carry sugar to ponies;
kiss the snouts of lovely chows; & then all

tingling & streaming plunge & swim; but the enormous
resources of the English language, ~~were~~ & the power ~~what~~
<which> it ~~her~~
~~put~~ bestows of illuminating even the hour of breakfast with
argument, with discourse, with **f** facts drawn from the
four corners of the world to lie glittering & sparkling upon the
plainest of boards; that recourse was denied them;
~~silence reigned:~~ & ~~They The Earl & Countess in the~~ when
they did without it: They ~~often~~ ate in solitude; they
were infinitely good to ~~their people;~~ the people on the estate;
but, unfortunately, they were dull. ~~But not for ten years to come.~~
~~Not however for ten years to come.~~

~~But~~ it was angelic, it was delicious, of youth & rank to
have come. (She
~~was had of course~~ loved Lords: she ~~could not help it~~ <loved
youth.>) But the
room was packed. There was ~~dear her~~ dear old Aunt—Aunt
Helena—
For Miss Helena Parry was ~~alive~~ after a fashion alive. She
was past eighty. She ascended staircases slowly with a stick. She
was placed in a chair. She was all white shawl, & white
head dress.
People who had known Burma in the seventies were always led
up to her. For at the mention of India, or even Ceylon, her
eyes, ~~(one was gre glass) v~~ (they were glazed ~~but~~ not glass)
slowly deepened, & beheld, not human beings, she had no tender
memories or proud illusions about [~~fighters,~~?] Viceroys,
generals & mutinies: it was flowers <orchids> she saw; &
mountain
passes: herself, perhaps, carried in the sixties, over
solitary peaks, ~~poking the~~ or descending & <or> poking:
~~with~~ scientific ~~exaltation in~~ this adding to her collection;
so riding on; an indomitable Englishwoman; ~~grim~~
~~grim; gr curt~~ taciturn, a lover of views, which she painted,
an explorer; ~~for whom this~~ basking now in the lethargy of the
very old; fretful if disturbed, by a war, say, or bomb
dropped at her very door, from that deep meditation over
~~the sunny passes of Burma in the sixties;~~ those ~~little~~
in her sixties roses; those orchids; & all India glowed, & her
own solitary figure journeying— That was recalled,
directly Peter Walsh spoke to her of Burma & ~~Ceylon~~.
But this? ~~What was~~ this! She looked around her;
there were people; ~~she was very noisy: very ugly.~~ <very
noisy:> She
She knew nobody. Yet she could not resist, if

he pressed he ~~Peter Walsh~~ did her the honour to ask her, recalling what M[r]
Darwin
had said in a letter to a friend—he had not meant her to see it
so ~~that~~ the compliment was sincere—about her little book on
orchids. No doubt it was forgotten now. But not by Miss
impervious to Parry, who impervious ~~it seemed~~ <[stood?]> ~~to the tumult~~
sorrow <[grief?]> of the age,
rambled hour after hour through drawers, & cupboards,
(her ~~poor~~ companion attending) ~~with &~~ held up, put down,
scented relics; attached <bequeathed> ~~cards to the legs~~ of
sofas & chairs to
hither & thither; ~~different relations~~; ~~& lived~~ disposed her affairs; & was,
M[r.] Walsh thought, as he sat by her; scarcely changed at all from
the Aunt Helena ~~he had known at Bourton~~; had ~~hurt~~ <left>, he
remembered with shame, that night Clarissa asked him to come
in ~~without~~ a ~~boat~~ boating.
word, in the
drawing
room

Millicent Bruton ~~who~~ approached; ~~humorous, brushing~~ <sailing> past Clarissa with her
usual laugh—they had nothing to say, ever—~~but~~ to welcome that
agreeable sinner, that very able fellow who had ~~some how~~ should have made
~~hang~~ draped in black,
a name for himself, <but hadn't> ~~but~~ & of course, old Miss Parry.
Wonderful old lady! So she stood, ~~like~~ a spectral grenadier,
inviting Peter Walsh to lunch; ~~to meet~~ gratified; cordial; but
without small talk, & remembering after all nothing whatever ~~of the~~ <about>
flora or fauna of India; ~~which she had visited~~ She had been the
guest of the Governor General; had inspected troops; thought some of those
Indian civilians ~~the very finest types of men of their class;~~
uncommonly fine fellows; & what a tragedy it was, then—
~~cere~~ ~~The~~ Really it was ~~rather~~ a tragedy to her, ~~that India~~
~~which her family & if it came to that Peter Walsh's family had~~
should ~~be~~ cost to her family; ~~fine fellow, the salt of the earth;~~
~~who had been given it absolutely the pick of~~ the state of India; &
she would like <likeing> Peter's opinion, ~~on the state~~ he having landed,
only the other day, so she heard; & ~~bring~~ she would get Sir Sampson
~~Michael~~ to meet him; ~~for if anything could be done~~ to
patch ~~things up, to~~ ~~for her convictions were~~ for if anything could
be done to patch up a state of things; which ~~she felt to be~~
~~lamentable & fraught with the gravest consequence,~~
~~not merely for our generation but for the future,~~
really prevented her from sleeping at nights—the folly of it—
the criminal folly!—~~of course,~~ There she was; an old woman;
not good for much nowadays; but her house, ~~&~~ her
servants, her table, ~~her~~ <her> good friend, did he remember her?—
~~Mill Mar~~ Molly Brush—they ~~were~~ asked nothing better

were all at the service

~~than to help. For this~~ <after> Empire, ~~this~~ This isle of Kings, this
good <dear dear land,>
Shakespeares England, was in her blood; & if ever a woman ~~did believe that~~ could have worn the helmet & shot the arrow, could have guarded sleeping camps by night, led ~~fo ba~~ battalions, driven hard roads through inhospitable morasses, & quelled beneath her perfectly honest yet singularly barbarian hordes; that woman was the ~~fine old~~ Lady Bruton;
who,

& lain under a shield, noseless ~~wording in~~ the ~~a~~ on some ~~sites~~ grassy <barrow> hillside,

debarred by her sex, {& some odd truancy of logic~~al fr~~ when it came to putting things down in black & white,} from being altogether effective, ~~had~~ yet had the thought of the Empire always at hand, & ~~a~~ had ~~aq~~ acquired from her pre-occupation upon her that ram-rod bearing, that indescribable robustness of habit & demeanour which seem to reflect an ideal of such pomp & ponderosity; march, <&> masculinity; ~~in so~~ that one could not figure her even in death parted from ~~her English fiel fields,~~ or the earth, or roaming territories over which, in some spiritual
shape,
the Union Jack had ceased to fly. Peeping behind her, was

Sally Seton, Lady Ross.

~~beaing~~ not quite sure whether it was Lady Bruton, & ~~whether~~
almost
~~the tall that~~ was Peter Walsh ~~by her~~ side—~~but~~ <quite quite>
certain,
suddenly ~~overcome~~ that she remembered old Miss Parry—
~~was Sally Seton; Lady~~ upon whom she pounced.

And Clarissa! And Clarissa! She caught ~~t~~ at ~~her~~ Clarissa;
But Clarissa could not ~~wait~~ <stay>; ~~could not~~ would come later,
(for they
~~must all stay) when they~~ They must ~~stay~~ <wait>—her old
friends, her
dear Peter, her dear Sally; ~~for now with one a moments~~ <who>
looking at each other quickly, ~~with embarrassment,~~
looking up, looking down, remembering presumably what Clarissa
~~bl~~ tingled to remember—oh they had all said such things!—felt
such things!—~~cl~~ shook hands; Sally laughing; ~~Sally's~~ but
~~indescribably changed,~~ <her> voice ~~being~~ <was> wrung of its old
richness; ~~as but hers still;~~ & her eyes,~~—how without that~~
~~somehow questing no longer, as they used; <when they>~~
~~looking<ed> earnes gravely~~
~~passionate, now <out> of the window, as Clarissa remembered;~~
~~then~~
~~sparkled. For she was passionate if sympathetic~~
when) ~~her~~ big <dark> eyes, ~~her eyes~~ <not> all aglow <as they used
to be> with sympathy, with laughter,
for she was forever flashing & changing, the most ~~remarkable~~
~~picturesque,~~ the most coloured, <picturesque> ~~flaunting~~
flamboyant
creature in the whole world—~~She had only to~~ changing
from this to that all in a second; violent too; denouncing
poor ~~de~~ Hugh Whitbread; trouncing Peter; ~~in~~ unable
to tolerate what she was forever calling "Richard Dalloways
mediocrity," & pointing to Clarissa the effects of their
compromise: marriage: She was for remaining virgin <single>,
~~& instilling for what did she want with for the idea of~~
~~single~~ ~~& writing, or painting, or~~ leading some Crusade ~~into~~
~~the he heart of Whitechapel; flying a~~ ~~against this~~
~~world; endowing~~ They were to abolish poverty; they were to found
an order; Oh they had sat up to all hours ~~<to> together, &~~
~~seen the dawn;~~ of the night together! ~~But~~ & then,
slipping on her clothes, Sally had ~~rambled~~ <rushed> off into the
woods, stealing once, a whole chicken, & upsetting thereby

The entire household, who complained of her cigarettes, & her
untidiness;
~~but loved her too, & even Papa did that, though she almost~~
~~killed him by leaving his Shakespeare in the rain; &~~
~~her poetry seemed She would~~ but yielded as everyone did
to her
vitality; And she would recite poetry; & she would write; & she
would ~~bear down~~ <appearing in a twisting cottage> upon some
cottager wearing her red cloak;
& she would weep <cry>: & she would accuse—what nobody
who knew
them both could believe for a moment—Hugh Whitbread of
kissing her (hand or lips, Clarissa cd. not remember which)
behind the dining room door one evening: ~~It was~~
to punish her, she said, for her ~~views about~~ <regarding>
women; ~~that~~
~~they~~ should have votes. Commonplace men, she said, did <do>
that:
& Clarissa had to hear the whole story of it, hour after hour;—
~~run messages & take notes;~~ to persuade her not to
repudiate him in some public fashion, ~~from f~~ in the
presence of the household <butler>, perhaps— ~~She was~~ <wh.>
capable ~~of it, da~~
~~She~~ was <with> daring; ~~she was was~~ <her> courageous; &
destined <as she> they
felt for some great career, to be famous, to be
ill fated; to die perhaps, of starving, ~~or in some of~~
~~crusade for women;~~ & nothing ~~could~~ ever ~~quite~~ instead of
which she ~~explain~~ her marriage to a bald man, with a large
married buttonhole, who owned mills in ~~Durham.~~ ~~Nobody~~
~~had he knew of him;~~ ~~she met him;~~ ~~they~~ How
They said in Durham. But never mind;
~~The sight of them both Peter Walsh, Sally Seton—& their~~
~~brought back,~~ All the same, she was perfectly enchanting.
They both were beloved, familiar. ~~Guardians~~ of her past:
she thought, ~~seeing p~~ <putting Sally hand aside> going on, &
seeing them ~~there together—with~~
Old Aunt Helena, guardians of her past; if older, well, so
was she; if less romantic, ~~come to terms~~ with life, less
dashing,—daring
hints ~~foolish & effervescent,~~ so was she; & with them, ~~the~~ the two

of them, the three of them, she shared all ~~that~~ her early days,
her dreams, her
first rights of self ~~miraculous beginnings;~~ her trees, her sunsets; ~~for~~ her dark nights;
her evening flowers; her stars dancing; & old Joseph Breitkopf
singing Ich grolle Nicht; her father too; & the pale
drawing room paper; the smell of the mat; ~~Chough's shaggy coat:~~
~~mys~~ a part of all this; Sally must always be; Peter must
always be;
~~the for all~~ guardians, ~~as she felt, of~~ & sharers, ~~& so, come
back to~~
her but she must go on

But she went on. There were the Bradshaws, ~~talking to Richard.~~ <(Sir William & Lady)>
whom she disliked. ~~<They> talking to Richard. talking to Richard.~~

But why? she wondered. Why ~~had~~ <did> ~~she that cant~~
the sight of them, ~~he so~~ standing there, at the end of the room, talking to
curl up?
~~Richard, he chill, constrict,~~—at Richard, ~~put~~ <make> her at once uncomfortable? <all of a shiver>
He was rather handsome than otherwise. ~~She looked~~ A very
~~fine~~ distinguished man he looked; with his fine head <~~very~~ like;> blue eyes,
~~grizzled~~ hair; ~~but there was something ram like about him;~~
& ~~the~~ air of patient ~~obv~~ observation, consideration, which even as
he stood talking; ~~seemed to~~ showed that ~~he~~ what he was—a
great doctor, ~~perhaps the greatest nerve~~ specialist in England;
accustomed to decide <questions> cases of appalling difficulty: ~~to~~
to ~~advise hear combine the doctor & priest?—for that was what it came to.~~ for think of the cases that came before him,
day after day, people in the utter most extreme of misery,
think of having to tell him to have to express one's feelings let that man see one unhappy.
people on the verge of insanity, & their wives & husbands. And he
~~helped them.~~ ~~Well,~~ One wouldn't like to <~~be at the mercy of~~> helped by Sir
William Bradshaw in ~~her opinion~~. Not that she had
ever ~~been in~~ had the least reason to complain herself. <ever consulted him herself,> Only
once ~~for a~~ she had gone with some one ~~whose son was wounded~~ to ask his advice; & ~~he had been te very helpful. And then Richard had come across him about a Bill for that he wanted to get through~~ & he had been very kind; most
sensible: ~~But heavens, what a~~—But Heavens, how
what a relief it was to get out into the street—partly because
of the atmosphere, ~~the~~ & there was some poor wretch sobbing
she remembered in the waiting room among the ghastly
plants & old novels, & the pictures wh. were even
worse, for Sir William or his wife collected,—
~~one always had to praise some~~ either pictures or
silver, she couldn't remember which, like all doctors,
~~poor creat~~ thinking it necessary, to be broadminded &

humane, when as a matter of fact if only they'd stick to their
job. But he did that after all. He was a great swell, Richard
said, who had met him over some Bill; <said> very able indeed;
but Richard agreed but Richard <said> ~~too~~ "didn't like his taste"; ~~which~~
with her: ~~what~~ didn't like his smell~~?~~ What was the phrase?
And Lady Bradshaw. ~~Lady Bradshaw was~~
~~rather superbly dressed, enti in grey:~~ There was no
harm in ~~the~~ her:
~~poor woman. Only look at her!~~ She was ~~a~~ <the> typical wife,
<successful man> ~~no~~
in her solid doubt, of a ~~successful barrister,~~ man; rather overdressed,
beaded shoe ~~prosperous:~~
~~& very very solid; everything was~~ Oh but the pair of them
standing there, ~~what~~ it needed an effort to go up & say, as
she must, how she was delighted
But Lady Bradshaw cut her short,
~~Oh~~ They were so late: ~~for~~ & (withdrawing into the
They must shelter of a common femininity she whispered murmured, that
apologise just as they were starting a patient—~~& the men who~~ <Sir
They were William had heard . . . &>
disgracefully late ~~were talking~~ a poor young man had killed himself.
(Richard & Sir William were discussing this Bill; & this
wh. can case ~~h~~ (of ~~a~~ shell shock not revealing itself for some years
after
~~had come up.~~ ~~It was private)~~ <much> was to the point, &
could be mentioned, in secure privacy, to Mr. Dalloway.
And mentioned it was: & instantly dropped.

And Clarissa, left them talking, to see who it was in the little room,
that she must speak to.

But there was nobody. The arm chairs still kept <amusingly> the impress of the
Prime Minister & Lady Bruton. She had been turned towards him, <deferentially> it ~~seemed~~ <looked>.
expounding, <he> ~~one of her doctrines. This was Clarissa's little room.~~
The parties splendour fell to the floor; so strange it seemed
to be <in> here <~~in~~> alone in all her finery, lips still tingling, ~~these~~ words, ~~half formed.~~
emotions, <shaping,> about to break: ~~now~~ <& as she ~~sh~~ alone ascended;> all of a sudden congealed in
<about> a figure of
formidable & loathsome significance: the Bradshaws; death.
~~He had killed himself. That couple, the Bradshaws, had dropped it out~~
~~as tribute to themselves: some young mans death.~~ But how had he
killed himself—there coming to her, as always in such violent events,
a sense of her body's ~~suffering~~ too; if it was a motor accident, she was
hurled into the telegraph post; if a fire she was ablaze; if ~~a~~ drowning,
under she went, before she could think or pity: He had thrown himself
from a window; up had flashed the ground; through him the spikes had gone; &
there he lay with a <great> thudding in his ears, which ceased. ~~Then his wife had come;~~
The police had come; his wife; the Bradshaws. Yes. ~~But~~ Why had he
done it? Why ~~exchange~~ <~~leave~~ exchange> this ~~adorable~~ world? Why ~~have the~~
pluck your flower, like that? In this dumb colloquy
he was ~~all that~~ <the> youth she <had> dreamt of: he ~~was~~ the argument, the
& the dawn; ~~&~~ the ~~fair~~ hill top with Peter chattering: home &
the evening, & ~~the stars on the terrace:~~ This he was, & he had
done what they had~~n't not done:~~ none of them dared ~~to~~
thrown it, out of the window. ~~Wise Brave he was; but~~
~~perhaps wise~~ with some foresight, presumably, of the
intolerable accumulations ~~of middle age~~; seriously accepting
what had been his faith once, beauty, goodness; ~~ex~~
discerning, ~~for~~ with ~~that~~ unmitigated ~~eye~~<in>sight, the
Bradshaws, the Kilmans; he had ~~torn the whole thing up;~~
jumped; escaped them. For ~~heaven~~ after all, one might

attentive, he
sedentary
had sat for
[ ]

arrested by the
emptiness; &
in that
suspension
congealed above
her in one
formal &
loathsome
crested
[ ]:

leaving
rusty
holes.

their rust
splintering his
bones;

beat ~~up~~ the water up; tread this life, lightly & make the waves
sparkle,
but the soul was rotten, its timbers ~~rotten~~ water logged, &
the last nails loosening: ~~she would go under; she had~~

~~He was dead;~~ & <but> they went on ~~living~~ {~~acu~~ accumulating,
chattering, ~~fixing~~ lodging themselves more & more securely;
~~shaped,~~
~~intoxicated,~~ imbibing ~~life,}~~ this intoxication of living.
Thousands of
young men had broken off ~~obsequiously~~ <obediently> most of
them, but some of them
freely, in the war; ~~had said,~~ how there were better things
than growing old.
~~Precisely. Something more~~ A thing there was too;
not necessarily youth, a thing wreathed about with chatter, ~~&~~
defaced, obscured; ~~& as for her self, she was all~~ in her own life; let
drop every day ~~of her life~~ in corruption, dust, straw; her lies, her
levities; ~~her came about her; & all this effort. All~~
~~His That he had escaped.~~ He had determined that there should be
at least a testimony—was that it? An attempt to—was that it
communicate~~—was that it?~~—feeling. ~~That is,~~ The
impossibility, ~~here~~, as things are, of reaching the centre
which, mystically yet indubitably, all sorts of people ~~one~~
~~wouldn't~~
~~expect it of, yet~~ feel evading them: the ~~unsatisfactoriness~~
of life;
its the distance; ~~the disturbance; this~~ how always, always,
closeness draws apart; rapture flies; ~~solitude intervenes,~~
~~save for those, at last too soon~~ one is alone~~. too~~ yet
~~too soon alone, &~~ That he may have meant. ~~or again~~
~~that~~ & ~~so, feeling, as she could understand, some~~
there was ~~death giving <taking> him anyhow peace, & suffering at any~~
an embrace ~~rate ending this~~
in death. ~~contamination.~~ Or was it nothing of the sort; was he,
as she could understand, so filled, so enforced, so
ecstatic~~—everyone has~~ <there are> such moments ~~after all~~—that
he, at least, made sure, plunged, hording his treasure? ~~into the~~
~~depths. or were there <there> for some here & there~~ some
~~young~~ or ~~weren't there people who~~ <again.> ~~who~~ mathematicians,
~~they might be,~~ or poets, thinkers; Shelley, for example:
~~they weren't the most~~ <[ ] [ ] the> amenable ~~of men to~~
~~this~~
~~dispensation~~ of ours, & if he had ~~that~~ had that violence,

& Sir William Bradshaw ~~had as one felt he did in private, let~~
had come—
~~just let had~~— but <u>what is</u> it <as to> that one human being ~~can~~
do to
another? ~~How Hateful in some obscure way he might be to her,~~
Hateful he was to her; obscurely evil; ~~like a menacing;~~
~~sharklike; monster of impun<e>ity (absolutely without~~
~~sexuality~~
nothing [with?] lust ~~feelings,—she didn't mean that) & if he had~~
~~been there, when one was ill,~~
~~Could the sense of evil so master & overcome that this faced~~
~~with it,~~
~~m~~ impure. ~~Sex~~ Without sex; ~~without~~ <or> lust ~~of any kind;~~
~~he~~ was
~~to her the type of~~ impurity. And ~~so,~~ then being a doctor,
having
power—& ~~then being~~ ill, & having to fight, & then ~~being~~ losing
crushed & then perceiving evil, & then ~~saying~~ & nothing ~~able to~~
free — capable of that indescribable outrage; of
Kilman's outrage: the Odd, that the things one hates in
people one can't express!

have ~~thoug~~ escaped? Or was it ~~that~~ <the> dread, ~~that horror~~
<the terror>;
she felt it too; horror filling her sometimes at the ~~mere~~
thought of what
~~they did, ones parents, setting did setting affect this or~~
~~alight, sending~~
~~affect a capacity so~~ ~~so interminable~~ <this> ~~a~~ flame; ~~& all~~
she felt it too; <this> ~~how incapable of holding~~ holding on to ~~this~~
overwhelming the incapacity to withstand, the ~~hollowness~~; ~~the~~ <ones> ~~ove~~
over whelming
~~hostility of the race; incompetency <littleness> against the~~
~~hostility of the~~
~~pressure of the life; & against &~~ other <the> people always
triumphing;
~~its vast~~ loneliness, its entire feebleness, flashed on it, as she had
sometimes felt, walking ~~d~~ in the street, so that ~~if~~ Richard had not
its escape been there, ~~merely~~ to read the Times aloud; so that listening
basked in one could recoup ~~those flying~~ could hear him breathing in
the room;
could wait like a crouched bird under a leaf; could gradually
recover that insolence & levity, ~~life & whatever the~~ life
maybe; could recover, ~~she meant,~~ her beauty; not in in
Gods & power, but only in the breath, in the Times, in the
fire; & so fanning this little flame, could feel rise within
& feel risen once more the imperious thing. But he had not recovered;
more ~~daring, sealing~~ more stricken had fled, with a
~~clearness of light which laughed at; dispersed~~ his death a
trinket which the Bradshaws ~~tinkled~~ <jingled> among their
chains.

~~Ah but~~ But ~~still,~~ With a

[*pencil*]

send [racing?] up that immeasurable delight:
ones parents giving <one> it, here, into ones hands; & one
couldn't drop it;
must walk holding it; ~~in spite & the~~ the incapacity
to withstand the onslaught;

~~had left them,~~ This being her disaster, her disgrace: not only
the ~~Bradshaws; but~~
so ~~complex being the soul; so~~
For who could say?

But it was her disaster, her disgrace; ~~that he~~ a punishment
inflicted—~~Not to be near at hand; to have to guess; never~~
to see sink & disappear in this profound obscurity, here a man,
here a
woman; ~~whom who~~ unknown, for knowledge was denied, & so
their smiles, their set
{down they went, ~~with~~ in ~~that~~ <their> pitiable yet heroic
dumbness,
she ~~forbidden to~~ forced to stand here, in her evening dress,
guessing—that was}

—He ~~had a wife~~ <was married>. ~~He was~~ ~~He~~ had a wife.
She was now, at this
~~very moment,~~ led by kind women in white aprons to look
~~her last; but at~~ <on> what face? It was unknown <She did
not know>, ~~for~~
~~li~~ knowledge was denied, ~~&~~ so down they went
in their pitiable yet heroic dumbness, with their
smiles, & their ~~fero~~ savagery, & their hands raised to ~~cover~~
(it was ~~another~~ the women [ ] it that moved humans)
~~their faces,~~ imploring, beseeching only one thing ~~to be left~~
~~alone~~ <solitude>,
<&> She ~~being~~ forced to stand, here, ~~meanwhile,~~ in her evening
dress;
which ~~seemed to her~~ <was> an outrage; a ~~thing~~ to be shouted
down. in
streets;! ~~or~~ seized & slain wherever one chanced to find it—in
shifting sounds of her ~~own~~ [figure?]
her drawing room now, in the ~~persons of~~ Bradshaws; in
herself; yet in her ~~own~~ callous & cruel ways; her
her defecting from that sublimity known once, years ago,
~~Fo~~ For it seem~~ing~~<ed> ~~now,~~ so long stretched, & <so> laden, the
~~fifty two years~~
~~she had lived~~ her fifty two years; spun from that
high & airy pinnacle; ~~& then,~~ that moving sparkling

~~dal~~	~~Exit~~, out of doors; it being like a fresh swim ~~just~~ to take the air on the
& then all day to	terrace ~~after breakfast~~; & then ~~the London:~~ it ~~thickened, it~~
~~swim~~ to	clipped it
splash about	thickened; it ~~imbued~~ imbued itself in soil; ~~became~~: &
pale-air,	She wanted ~~things; & she~~ schemed & pilfered; was never wholly
[ ]	admirable; hadn't minded excessively anything, ~~but let~~ things
~~Air~~; & Aunt Helena;	take their
her father; air;	way; ~~had been possessed, for example, by that~~ & wanted success;
[ ]	~~wanted old~~ Lady ~~May~~<Bex>borough ~~to call~~; quite enormously;
that she should	for years
call;	~~everything~~ had been done for Lady Bexborough: her first first thought in waking;
	her last; to ~~be~~ succeed; And then, had other women her entire
	emptiness? ~~a~~ mind, heart, empty?; ~~a~~ only to be re-filled, (&
	that was half humbug too) by seeing her husband, whom
	she had married from an extraordinary deep instinct; his roses today
	~~being~~ almost shocking her, since their bond wanted no decoration, &
	they never gave each other a thing—& ~~never spoke.~~
	~~but he her [ ] by making that [ ] p &~~
~~how~~	~~perfectly healthy m normal man, a Prime Minister!~~
Richard,	~~And~~ ~~do it~~ off in the morning; ~~come~~ welcoming him home;
	~~asking him <about how> how his committee went.~~ His committees & his
	Armenian; his histories & his speech making; his

Then she afterwards

I must admit that no one could
ever find enough work to do to
keep her busy:
      happily this was found to be the case
      though not till very long afterwards
      people free [*scribble*]

[page 93 *verso*]

His committees & his speeches & his
~~It was her doing his~~ Albanians & Armenians—it ~~it~~ was
~~her command; laid on him to~~ were

There was no doubt   There was nothing much to be said
for this.

[*scribbles*]

There was

[*scribbles*]

It seemed ~~so~~ long, <&> ~~so~~ laden, her fifty two years;
beginning up there, on the terrace, in the fresh air; then it
dipped, imbued itself in soil; she schemed & anguished
~~that is to say;~~ was never wholly admirable; wanted
success, Lady Bexborough ~~& the rest of it, Lady Bexborough~~
her first thought on waking, <&> her last, which led to an
~~odd~~ <an> emptiness, only to be re-filled by sending Richard to
his
Albanians & Armenians; not that he wanted it—he
he would have liked best ~~to~~ horses & dogs, <&> his campaigns
of General
Bargoyne, <&>; ~~but she must have him out in the open, making~~
~~speeches; & it was good in her, on the whole;~~ this
but she liked to send him out & welcome him in; & ~~did~~
got some extraordinary joy when, on a platform, some
his effort— whiskered old man praised him. Indeed, his roses today, his
~~gift gift, &~~ his attempt, <at speech> ~~but~~ he had said nothing, &
to say something
had almost shocked her, since their bond wanted no
decoration: ~~& they never gave each other a~~ thing.
was an instinct; he

Such was his goodness; ~~such was~~ his character; ~~& though & in the~~
shadow ~~of~~ <in> which she lived~~;~~ was after all his making, & the
dew & the
rain & all those softnesses & severities which ~~foster the growth~~
~~& prevent her what wild~~ forbid these wild leaps; make the
& make, so she felt, ~~putting her~~ straightening ~~the~~ Lady Bruton's
chair, & ~~just glancing down the~~ <pushing in one book on the>
single shelf ~~of books,~~ make
the ~~interest, <paramount> & the importance, & the small things~~ a
~~& make a dark descend~~, ~~make~~—But how could she ~~proceed~~
define ~~any farther~~ it?—or attribute to him or to herself this
~~quality this superb~~ reality <the quality> of ~~the~~ chair; &
book; this
the sense she had of being, alive though she was, a light
cast upon the surface; no more than that—the veil through
which ~~the~~ truth showed, beauty showed; she having done
with personality—now, & shed the triumphs of youth,
lost her self, it seemed & in this ~~pro~~ process of living
& existing now, here & here & here, ~~an~~ as the sun rose—
brought the rocks & fields to ~~beauty,~~ colour, or sank, &
~~left~~ filled them with the blue of night— ~~Ah~~ And
that she was; & ~~And she was~~ Many a time~~,~~ <as a girl> had she
~~stopped~~ <seen>, ~~as a girl~~ having lighted both the candles on
either side of the
looking glass to see <look on> her little pink face with the
lips pursed as she always pursed them to give her face point,—
~~She had often~~ ~~she had looked <stopped> at the sky looked~~
~~at the~~
~~seen~~ stopped, & seen the sky; ~~its black~~ <or> risen & seen the
sky;
thought it (& she parted the ~~yellow curtain now) a~~
seen it between peoples shoulders at dinner; seen it here in
London (& she parted the curtain) when unable to
sleep—

[Left margin:]
& the
others' private
life
& leg flies out
each slow
moment.
sparkled with whiter
it light the—the
birds of
paradise, on the
blinds;
the veils through
wh.
Wed. Thurs:
Fri:

This was one of the greatest
things that had eve

This was one of the
most remarkable of all
her ideas & the one
which gave the greatest
pleasure to her friends.
Happily [ ]

[ ]
This
This was
one

[page 96 *verso*]

It held something of her, ~~or~~, foolish as ~~this~~ <the> idea was;
~~had~~ was known to her;
this sky, this sky above Westminster. She parted
the curtains
~~for one look;~~ & And ~~there~~ at once, {the remarkable & the
indifferent nature of that familiar sight}—the sky <sky> above the
houses of Parliament on a hot June night surprised her.
~~Peaceful & she had~~ ~~Why~~ For, she had thought, it will be
~~high & pure~~ solemn & dark; it will be that august sky which
so often had seemed to ~~her, & Peter perhaps to her to observe~~
~~without any~~ not indeed to ~~rebuke her, but to display~~
~~such careless whether anyone looked at it such an~~
exist, ~~beautifully,~~ in its beauty, independent; but here it was.
pale; & with vast clouds; & these clouds went sailing by,
fast, black clouds, ~~tapering~~ sweeping through a pale sky.
And it was~~nt~~ <not> still; it was ~~a~~ new to her then, she had
never seen it
before. Not that extraordinary movement & wildness; for
the wind must have ~~been rising~~ <risen>. What are they after,
she
could not help asking?—~~for they,~~ so stately, so tremendous,
<in their> sweeping in procession?
And then, there was the old lady opposite.
($M^{rs.}$ What ever her name might be) ~~was~~ going to bed.
~~&~~ There was, that is to say, somebody in that room,
for ~~the~~ a hand moved ~~the brush on the~~ across the
dressing table; & ~~then~~ <a hand> drew down the blind; & then
there was a shadow passing; & then ~~whoever it was put out~~ the
light. went out
~~But~~ <And yes>, she thought, as ~~the~~ Big Ben began <with>
his usual
solemnity to ~~announce the fact that~~ strike
twelve times;

to turn away its beautiful cheek; to rebuke her

But whose fault ~~is~~ <was> it? she asked ~~herself~~, stricken
~~with rage~~ & despair:
as Big Ben ~~halfed, cut~~ off. <as> ~~But~~ Big Ben began striking, & ~~how could~~
began striking ~~she~~
~~& how could she wait, & how could she convey to the~~
& what did it ~~all~~ mean, & why was she so happy,—
~~how did she know as~~ & why did she feel no pity, no not a
but for him of a scrap for the young man who had killed himself, but
herself meant ~~only for~~ & ~~no one~~ <for it was> should tell her that this was not
nothing but joy, enough,
nothing but ~~even~~ to have lived <even> for a moment, & f it had been
pride; beautiful . . . it had been strange, ~~& it~~ the voice of Big Ben
of ~~Big B~~ striking four five six, while everybody in
her drawing room ~~cried~~ roared & laughed, while
rejoiced her, the clouds swept by; ~~& then seemed to her <enthralled her> all~~
~~one could~~
ask, & she would go back & she would fight Sir
William Bradshaw; & she would take that rose,
~~& she would~~ Richards rose — she would be
& she would never, ~~submit~~ <submit>, never for an ~~a~~ instant!
~~give up!~~

[*pencil*]

Eight, ~~said~~ Big Ben, nine; ten; eleven; &
then with a sort of finality the ~~pes~~ presumably
the strokes were accurately placed, &
the last was no more emphatic than the
first. Twelve.

Eight said Big Ben, nine, ten eleven; & then with a sort
of finality, though presumably the strokes were accurately
spaced, ~~&~~ the last no more emphatic than the first
Twelve.

Always that—always that mystery, that fascination, that
glimpse withdrawn. But whose fault was it, she asked,
as Big Ben began striking. One, Two, Three; &
~~she felt~~ she was extraordinarily happy: she felt no
pity for the young man who had killed himself; nor for his
wife; nor for herself; nothing but pride; nothing but
joy; for to hear Big Ben strike Three, Four,
five, six, seven, was profound & tremendous, hearing
too ~~the~~ as she stood there, motor hoot & bus pant, & then
some sudden strange cry; while ~~at her~~ behind her in
the drawing room, people chattered, shouted, laughed;
She must go back; ~~she must~~ breast her enemy; she,
~~must~~ take her rose, Never would she submit—
never, never!

Eight, Big Ben struck, nine, ten, eleven; &

But Clarissa was gone.

Where was that woman?
Peter Walsh asked Sally ~~Seton~~, for after all these years,
~~he couldn't~~ <how could he ~~ca~~>
call her Lady Rosseter? Where was Clarissa? Sally
supposed—
well she supposed, & so did Peter for the matter of that, that
there were important people, politicians; whom neither of them
knew
unless by sight in the illustrated papers; ~~&~~ whom Clarissa
had to be nice
~~talking~~ to them. Yet there was Richard, not in the
Cabinet;
~~he never would be in the~~ He had not ~~really~~ been a success,?
Sally supposed; ~~not~~ For herself, she scarcely read the
papers, ~~or~~ She sometimes saw his name mentioned. But
in the wilds, then — well, she lived an extraordinary <a very solitary> life;
Clarissa would say; in the heart of
solitude; ~~she sometimes felt, but~~ among ~~people whom Clarissa~~
~~The pe cotton millers of Manchester am business men;~~ great
manufacturers & people who ~~after all~~ did things <after all>,
~~& she~~
She, ~~in her way, did things.~~ <too—she did things:> She had
five sons!
Lord, lord! what a change had come over her!
Last time they met, Peter thought, had been among the
cauliflowers in the moonlight—(The great leaves ~~all~~ curved
like rough, ~~in he remembered,~~ like bronze.) She had
& Sally marched him up & down; ~~& he had~~ that night ~~before he~~
catching at roses ~~left; after that scene by the fountain; the most painful—~~
as she ~~he had to get through it some how.~~ he was to catch the
early train. He had wept. ~~Oh~~ heavens! ~~oh~~ heavens!
That was his big knife <old trick—opening his pocket>
the again! ~~And~~ They had been
once very intimate—she & Peter Walsh—~~about that~~ when he was
in love with Clarissa, & there had been that dreadful scene
~~with~~ <over> Richard Dalloway at lunch, ~~when~~ she had
called Richard "Wickham" ~~And~~ why not call
Richard "Wickham"? ~~Richard was~~ And Clarissa

was furious with her! Indeed, ~~after~~ they had never seen each
other ~~since~~—not intimately, ~~not in the old way, for Clarissa~~
~~had~~
~~her life,~~ And Peter Walsh had gone off to India; & she had
only heard ~~quite~~ vaguely that he had made an unhappy
marriage, & she didn't know whether he had any children—
& she couldn't ask him—& he was changed too, rather
shrivelled up, but she felt all the same a ~~great~~ real
affection for him, for he was connected with her youth,
~~She could remember~~ & she had still a little Emily Brontë
~~which~~ he had given her, for they had been great friends,
& ~~shared~~ <&> ~~they~~ had talked & talked about every thing,—
he was to write, surely? In those days he was to write:
~~Have And~~ had he written?

She asked him, ~~putting~~ <spreading> her hand ~~out~~; her firm
& shapely
hand, on her knee, in a way he recalled. She was
~~a~~ still attractive; ~~she was a~~ Still a personage, Sally Seton.
But who was this Rosseter? ~~A~~ He wore a
cammellia ~~in his buttonhole~~ when he married—that was
about all Peter knew. "~~He has~~ They have men servants &
conservatories" Clarissa had said. And Sally owned
it with a shout of laughter. She had ten thousand a
year! Whether ~~it was~~ before the tax was taken off or after,
she couldn't remember!

300 And Sally used to be ~~a more~~ a ragamuffin ~~of a girl~~ <girl>; Sally
280 had pawned her
2400 brooch. <to come> Oh yes, Sally remembered it. She
600 never had a
8400 penny to her name; & going to Bourton had been ~~a kind of~~
it had been a the only thing that kept her sane. ~~Clarissa had saved her life,~~ she
(~~heaven~~ what a believed, so unhappy had she been; at home. And M[r.]
shock to Peter!) Parry was dead; & Aunt ~~A~~ Helena was, ~~indeed it had been a~~
~~great shock to Peter:~~—alive: & ~~Cl~~ the ~~Dalloways~~
marriage had been, Sally supposed, a success?—& that
very handsome, self possessed young woman <in red> was
Elizabeth;
(& they watched her, standing very upright against the ~~wall;~~
~~with a young~~ <some young man beside her>
both ~~silent~~ man); & <but> Clarissa: <I>—~~Yes;~~ For what Sally felt was
simply
~~yes~~, Clarissa this: ~~if she had been,~~ ~~She had been one of the~~ she had
herself. owed Clarissa an enormous ammount. They had been friends.
not ~~just~~ acquaintances; ~~not but~~ friends; ~~& it was the only~~
~~the one night~~ she still saw Clarissa: in ~~a lovely green~~
all in white ~~among th her~~ going about the house with her
hands full of flowers <to this day> (~~the~~ tobacco plants
always reminded
her of Bourton); ~~& the~~ ~~The & then~~ She remembered ~~long~~ <long>
talks. ~~Then, odd though it seemed, Clarissa had seemed~~
<been> ~~could~~
Peter understand?—~~at once very~~ <both very> old & <very>
young—<very> mature & <very> childish.
~~Such a~~ ~~She had been~~ ~~Well the truth of it was that~~
(very unhappy ~~Sally herself, coming from very unhappy surroundings~~
as she) was ~~had seen~~ in ~~Clarissa~~ everything she needed: ~~rest & peace &~~
~~goodness &~~ Clarissa had been rest & peace & goodness.
But always lacking: ~~Otherwise how did she marry~~
~~Richard Dalloway? For~~ Lacking what?
For ~~example~~, to be frank—(& she felt that Peter was an ~~very~~
old friend—did absence matter? did ~~di~~ place
matter? & she had often wanted to write to him,
only ~~she had felt~~ shy, torn it up—~~wished~~ but

So one learns as one learns every thing growing old) "I have been to see my son at Eton" Sally said. He has the mumps—to be quite frank ~~But~~ our Clarissa

~~The it isn't accidents that matter:~~ but ~~having~~ but these
things don't matter)
~~were they happy? had it been a success? Didn't~~
~~Wasn't it)~~ how could she marry a mere sportsman who
cared only for dogs? ~~How could she had be merely this?~~ <And
then all this?>
~~And indeed Hugh It was~~ Hugh Whitbread—it was
strolling past them; ~~with his his eyes fixed, with a curious~~
~~happily resting with~~
Oh ~~but~~ Hugh ~~Whitbread~~ <who> used to be so handsome!
~~And had he kissed her, in the di smoking room?~~
And Hugh ~~who~~ had kissed her; or was that a figment of her
imagination, Hugh's kiss in the smoking room, & the
~~Sally~~ ~~That man~~ ~~The admirable Hugh!~~ His kisses
seemed remote~~—could he kiss?~~ ~~Where Really he looked~~
Was he married? ~~W~~ He wasn't going to recognise them.
He ~~kept~~ blacked shoes or counted bottles at Windsor—
~~Life was~~ But Sally must be frank: that kiss.
On the lips, she could assure him; in the lobby
one day; & she had gone to Clarissa in a rage, &
Clarissa said <wouldn't> ~~she~~ hear <of it.> a word ~~against~~ ~~him~~
<of it.>
Simply laughed. Clarissa was in her own way the most
Hughes socks were without exception the most beautiful
she had ever seen. And had he children?
Everybody in the room, ~~H~~ Peter told her, had six sons
at Eton, except himself; & he, thank God, had none.
no sons, no daughters; & no wife. Well, he didn't
seem to mind. He looked younger, Sally thought, than any of
them
~~He was as~~ there.
It had been a great mistake

[*pencil*]
Oct 1924
4th

[End of Notebook Three]

Appendix One

[Following part of a review of *Figures in Modern Literature* by J. B. Priestley. ("Appreciations." *Nation & Athenaeum*, 27 September 1924)]]

He ~~was standing by himself~~ <stood alone>. ~~He watched Clarissa receiving her guests.~~

How delightful to see you!" She was at her worst.

~~She appeared to him at he~~ Clarissa had shaken hands with him, She had said what she said to everybody. /It was a great mistake to have come. After five years, Mr. Walsh, one

--~~as~~ he saw her most often at Bourton, in the late summer, when he
~~was generally~~ <stayed> there, for a week, a fortnight even;
<in> those ~~were the~~
days ~~of long visits.~~ one stayed, settled in. ~~She~~ They walked.
The first ~~to reach~~ <on> the top of some <the> hill. ~~he saw her~~
<There she stood> standing there, ~~her~~
hands clapped to her hair, her cloak blowing out, pointing to
~~some~~ the Severn down below. Or <in a wood> making the kettle
boil—very
ineffective. The smoke going up & curtseying, blowing in their
faces.; begging water, from an old woman in a cottage,
a lonely old woman. She of course would ~~br~~ paint a
tree, a barn, some ~~ordinary dwell~~ meadow, with three trees in a
ring, ~~or~~ so passionately she loved it all; ~~She~~ <They> walked
<always> ~~for miles.~~ The
other people drove. She was bored driving, disliked all
animals; (except ~~her~~ that dog)
sport, <of course> ~~all country things & having about her~~ a
& sport of course.

The old woman
~~coming~~
<standing>
to look after them
all smiles.

~~They argued hour after hour, as they walked; they argued;~~
They tramped miles along road; She would break off to get her
bearings. pilot him back across country, & the
& so they would drop down on Bourton in the dark.
{Eating sandwiches in tweeds on the hall table; ~~was one memory;~~
snipping flowers in yellow gloves; learning poetry by heart as she
walked the terrace; but sticking at nothing long; ~~off~~ in & out,
darting, that was his memory of her, flirting up & down like—
waylaid at the edge of a pond,} all the time they
~~h~~ argued, <he> hardly saw the country, covered miles <of green
fields in a kind of dream
talking. They discussed poetry; <they discussed> politics;
they had their bouts of
what they said heaven knows; but he could see her in the stubblefield
walking ~~quick firm swift like a born walker~~ ahead.
[switching?] things, with a flower for her aunt, some ~~beaut~~
~~s un tr~~ walking firmly, swiftly, ~~a born a born~~
never tired for all her delicacy. He saw her
snipping flowers in yellow globes; walking the terrace
learning poetry—in & out of the house

fields all
[ ] a
sort of blur,
until she
stopped him,
cried out, a view;
~~at~~ a tree; or
the house lying
beneath

And here was a letter
from her.

[142 R] [154]

Appendix Two

[The following outline appears in the third notebook in the Berg Collection of the New York Public Library given over to the holograph version of Jacob's Room. The notebook is dated 12 March 1922 and is labelled "Book of scraps of J's R. & first version of The Hours." The page numbering follows that originally assigned by the Berg's curator.]

October 6th 1922.

Thoughts upon beginning a book to be called, perhaps, At Home: or The Party:

This is to be a short book consisting of six or
seven chapters, each complete separately,
yet there must be some sort of fusion.
And all must converge upon the party at the end
My idea is to have some ~~very [ ]~~ characters,
like Mrs Dalloway much in relief: then to have
interludes of thought, or reflection, or short digressions
(which must be related, logically, to the rest)
all compact, yet not jerked.

The Chapters might be,

1. Mrs. Dalloway in Bond Street.
2. The Prime Minister.
3. Ancestors.
4. A dialogue.
5. The old ladies
6. Country house?
7. Cut flowers.
8. The Party.

5,000 One, roughly, to be done in a month: but this
8 plan is to allow of some very short ~~pages~~:
48,000 intervals, not whole chapters.

There should be some fun--

> a possible revision of this book <

Oct. 16th 1922.

Suppose it to be connected in this way:
Sanity & insanity.
Mrs D. seeing the truth. S.S. seeing the insane truth.
The book to have the impression of a play: only in
narrative. Some revision therefore needed.
At any rate, very careful composition.
The contrast must be arranged.
Therefore how much detail--& digression?

The pace is to be given by the gradual increase of S's insanity. on the one side; by the approach of the party on the other.

The design is extremely complicated.
The balance must be very finely considered.
Character must be indicated.
All to take place in one day?
There must be excitement to draw one on.
Also humour.
The Question is whether the inside of the mind is
both M$^{rs.}$ D. & S.S. can be made luminous--
that is to say the stuff of the book--lights on it
coming from external sources.

[Holograph notes dated from November 9, 1922 to August 2, 1923. Found at the back of a small book containing Woolf's reading notes and partial translation of the Choephori of Aeschylus, as edited by A.W. Verrall. The book is in the Berg Collection of the New York Public Library. The pages are unnumbered.]

M$^{rs.}$ Dalloway. Nov: 9th 1922
So far M^{rs} D in Bond Street &
the P.M. are written.

too jerky & minute. some
general style must be found, or one's
attention is too broken.

Suppose the idea of the book is
the contrast between life & death.
All inner feelings to be lit up.
The two minds. Mrs D. & Septimus.
And the design is something like
this--

M$^{rs.}$ D: ~~ent~~ comes on alone.
(as in past Chapter:)

We then go on to a general
statement, introducing Septimus.

They are linked together by
the aeroplane.

We then return to M$^{rs.}$ D.
alone in her drawing room
& settle into her.

My feeling is that Chapter 2 should be
calm & well written:
It is to be psychology.
Gradually increasing in tension all
through the day.
    But the continuous style?
    Must have the effect of being incessant.
    texture unbroken.

All must bear finally upon the party
at the end; which expresses life, in
every variety & full of conviction:
while S. dies.
How far are breaks in the texture
allowed? One must give the
surroundings--time & space--as
well as the individuals.
  Can one admit rhapsodies?

This (of course) will be an advance upon
Jacob. The human soul will be
treated more seriously: one must
emphasise character.

Septimus (?) must be seen by
some one. His wife? She to be
founded on L? Simple, instinctive,
childless.

They sit in Regents Park for example.
But the interview with specialist
must be in the middle.
She is to be a <u>real</u> character.
He only real insofar as she sees
him. Otherwise to exist in
his view of things: which is always
to be contrasting with Mrs.
Dalloways.

<u>Fuller plan.</u>

Hours: 10. 11. 12. 1. 2. 3. 4
5. 6. 7. 8. 9. 10. 11. 12. 1. 2.

Eleven o'clock strikes.
This is the aeroplane hour. wh.
covers both Septimus and Rezia in Regents
Park. & Clarrissas reflections. ~~& Cla~~
which lead to 12 o'clock: interview
with specialist.

19th Nov.

That Septimus should pass through all
extremes of feeling & happiness &
unhappiness—intensity.
should always remain out side human
affairs.
No chapters. Possible choruses.
Of course the style must change.
Some long dialogue.
Regents Park is to be one whole
Chapter.
    Starts with aeroplane; happiness—
or rather intense feeling & seeing.
The waving of the boughs: lights &
shadows: voices. {real} He sits.
Rezia goes off to play with squirrels.
Their happiness. This is to mean that
~~happ~~ there is no reason in their
happiness; or unhappiness: since
the same things cause both. But
how is the transition to come from
one to the other? R's character
should be shown. Her passionateness.
Southerness. instinctiveness: yet
of an old civilisation. Question of

S's character. founded on R.?
His face. eyes far apart—not degenerate.
not wholly an intellectual. Had
been in the war. or founded on me?
~~or on C?~~
    She must see him to begin with.
as a woman sees him.
    feels him alternately far & near.
    ~~wears a~~ (<u>June</u>)

might be left vague—as a mad
person is—not so much
character as an idea—this is
what is painful to her—
becomes generalised—universalised.
so can be partly R.; partly me;
    The statue to Ready money.
The long slope of grass. tables where
people have tea.
He must be logical enough to
make the comparison between the
two worlds.

Why not have something of G.B. in him?
The young man who has gone into
business after the war: takes life to
heart: seeks truth—revelations—some
reason; yet of course it is insanity.
His insensibility to other people's
feelings—that is to say he must
have the masculine feelings.
selfishness: egoism; but has also
an extreme insight, & humility.

Why not have an observer in the
street at each critical point who
acts the part of chorus—some
nameless person?

That everything should sing to
Septimus

Feb. 26th. Mrs. D. must be seen by
other people. As she sits in her drawing room.
But there must be a general idea—one
must not get lost in detail: her
chapter must correspond with his.
Question of choruses. That is to say of
links between chapters: also, could
the scenes be divided like acts of a
play into five, say, or six?

May 7th.

The choruses are not 'convincing' yet.
The reality is better. The psychology
should be done very realistically. .
No doubt dialogue will help.
One wants the effect of real life.
There ~~w~~ shd. now be a long talk
between Mrs. D. & some old
buck. Hurry over. His view of her.
Her substitutions of feeling about
death youth the past: with
her anxiety about Dick ~~as surf~~
threading it together.

Story to be provided by Elizabeth.
must all be kept an uproar; in
extreme of feeling.

18th.: The talk between Mrs D. and P.W.
might now go on to a confession
by him.

June 18th. too thin & unreal somehow.
Must now go on to make Peter walk
away through the Green Park with
the sound of the roar in his ear.
The merit of this book so far lies in its
design, wh. is original—very difficult.
~~Really the truth is that~~

P.W. should now walk in a great state
of excitement to Green Park, as if
on the waves of the sound:
which should die out & leave him
somewhere in the Green Park:
He should dislike the thought of
Clarissa: yet be excited by her:

should all the time be on the
defensive against people who
think him old. That was
why he ran away from Elizabeth.
But he must think: not merely
see.
Every scene should build up the idea
of C's character. That will
give unity, as well as add to
the final effect.

July 22nd

Seems as far as I can judge, rather
good. There should now be a
chorus, half of calm & security, the
nursemaid & the ~~f~~ sleeping baby;
half of fear & apprehension—
the little girl who sees Peter
W. asleep. ~~The~~ There is
something helpless & ridiculous—

about him as well as terrifying. His
abandonment to sleep. The child
runs away frightened ~~in~~ towards
Rezia & ~~This~~ These feelings should be
treated however generally: as poetry,
not psychology.
However, R & S. (or whatever they are
called) must be reached.

He is still exalted.
She is bored, yet apprehensive.
They must go to the dr.
As they meet people, S. is outraged.
Begins to be disillusioned.
The Barrel organ? Beauty
of an impersonal kind is still
real. Most human beings
betray each other. That one
passes beyond them. They cant

Possible development of story

The dr.
Other guests? Some comic relief
something about the country.
Someone fishing?

[*verso*]

help finally. Then what remains.
This is what he thinks at the drs.
Who goes on saying that he must
weigh 11 stones. His cowardice
is insisted upon. The sense that
other people are engaged in living but
that he is not. ~~His resolution~~
He must somehow see through
human nature--see its hypocrisy,
& insincerity, its power to recover
from every wound, incapable of
taking any final impression.
His sense that this is not worth
having. That only the best is
worth while.

Aug. 2nd There must be a reality which is
not in human beings at all. What about
death for instance? But what is death?
Strange if that were the reality—but in

what sense could this be so?
Same of falling through into discoveries—
like a trap door opening. But
this is not at all apparent to Dr.
There shd. be a ~~far~~ fairly logical transition
in S's mind. beauty of natural things.
This disappears on seeing people.
His sense of their demand, upon him:
What is his relation to them?
inability to identify himself with them.
Exasperation shd. be the dominant theme
at the drs: This will leave the
final stages to be worked out before
death. They must, in some form, precede
death.

[The following 18 folio pages come from the third notebook in the Berg Collection of the New York Public Library given over to the holograph version of *Jacob's Room*. Woolf labelled the notebook, "Book of scraps of J's R. & first version of The Hours," and dated it 12 March 1922. The page numbering follows that originally assigned by the Berg's curator.]

[*pencil*] p.58

in the body, which lies on the beach, says <too> that is all. Fear
no more

the heart subsides
& remits to the
body the
charge of life.
The consciousness
of the bee
passing,

says the heart. ~~&~~ Fear no more. <The> ~~And the heart subsides,~~
&
~~remits to the body.~~ ~~Only~~ the ~~gr~~ bee passes; the grass waves; &
right at the other end of the beach ~~whi~~ a dog, which is
fetching a
stick out of the water, barks, <&> barks; <barks> ~~barks~~ &
<barks> comes nearer & nearer

“Heavens, the front door bell!” exclaimed Clarissa,
staying her needle ~~to listen~~.

~~“Lucy will have <must have> the sense to keep people~~
~~out <say not at home>.”~~

~~And~~ Staying her needle, <~~anxious,~~ sound> she listened;
~~anxious; then indignant:~~
~~for~~ ~~There is a <one> courage which faces the cannon ball;~~
~~<&> another~~
~~which dares to at the command of something much more~~
~~pressing than love of country, <or> desire for glory, to press~~
~~past pass the parlourmaid with a bunch of flowers.~~

“Mrs. Dalloway ~~won't~~ will see me” said old
Oh yes, she will see me, he repeated. putting his hat down.
Yes, yes, ~~h~~ yes, he said ~~three times under his~~
~~breath, & began to mount the stairs.~~
~~He had to hold the bannisters with one hand, while~~
beginning to mount the stairs
But he doubted it: he was anxious; ~~he was~~ about it;
he was superannuated; <he was> a failure.

which thus sighs collectively for all sorrows; & yet
[~~sugg~~?] renews, begins,
~~again~~ [ ] <[ ]> & of all

says the heart, committing its burden to ~~a~~ some great sea
And the body alone, listens; the bee passes; the wave breaks; far,
far away the dog barks; barks; & barks.
"Who can—what can—exclaimed Mrs Dalloway, hearing ~~his~~
~~footsteps. She~~ a step on the stairs. She made as if to hide
her dress; as if virginity protected chastity. ~~And the door~~
~~opened, & in came old Peter Walsh!~~
~~"Dear Peter! Now she heard a hand upon~~
the door. <She saw the ~~hand china~~ brass knob move.> Now
the door opened; & ~~The grey smiling sardonic~~
~~unexpected~~ head of ~~dear Peter, old Peter,--appeared.~~
~~Peter Walsh appeared. Dear Peter, old Peter How~~
~~astonishingly~~
~~unexpected!~~
For a single second she ~~h~~ could not remember what
he was called. ~~Peter Walsh of course!~~ She knew him
so well! was so glad, so surprised, <embarrassed> so happy to
see him!
~~Peter Walsh~~! Old Peter! & stepping ~~absolutely~~ over
her dress she ~~took both~~ held out ~~both~~ her hands.
A strange meeting!
For it was a question what each had done in the past year.
~~a summing up made necessary by the fact that she~~
~~had refused him.~~ For she had refused ~~to marry him~~
~~twenty years ago.~~
~~He has failed, thought Clarissa,~~
& they met~~; &~~ now & then, like this. He came to her.
He wanted her. And if they had married, what
would have happened?
Its an abominable hour to call, said
~~Mr~~ Peter Walsh, sitting down, ~~rather~~
~~Clarissa~~, <She> ~~he the~~ has grown older he thought.
I shant go in to the whole matter, he thought, for poor dear,

She's grown older And instinctively his hand went into his
trouser pocket, & he took out a large pen knife, & half
opened the big blade.

Exactly ~~The~~ same, ~~check suit~~, thought Clarissa. The same
check suit. ~~&~~
that old ~~compass~~, <knife--> ~~& she looked at his face.~~
~~I remember from~~
~~the first. She looked at him She saw~~ Affectionately,
intimately she looked at him, ~~sitting in his check suit near her;~~
<in the face,>
~~How extraordinarily fond of him~~ she was! ~~as of a young~~
~~brother,~~
<which> Sensitive, queer, <in wh. the> ~~a~~ little, ~~obstinate, with~~
~~curiously <those> bright~~ ~~eyes~~ <were still very bright:> ~~in a~~
face that ~~face that just somehow ye always looking<ed> a little on one side,~~
~~& clever &~~ ~~a clever face, a weak face, a~~ ~~Surely she had~~
~~done right not to marry him: yet who could be~~
~~Peter always looked a little on one side; still clever,~~
bright pugnacious obstinate [ ] a little on one side;
She ~~always~~ was <always> charmed, ~~by~~ always refreshed,
always
felt it was the face of an extraordinarily nice ~~sensitive~~
human being ~~man but a failure!~~ That knife! <But> Always that knife!
When he proposed to her, he had that knife! He was
~~such an oddity!~~

~~"Are you just back?" she~~ asked him, thinking as he
How delightful it is to see you again! she said,
~~was~~ irritated by his knife, ~~&~~ for there was something—
how could she define it?—egotistical about Peter which
made him do things like opening & shutting a knife
without noticing how ~~they~~ <it> got on people's nerves.

~~We~~ <I> ~~only~~ arrived on Monday; said Peter ~~Daisy~~
~~went to her people~~ to day; ~~Tomorrow I~~ I have one
or two matters to see to in town. Then I shall go
down to the country. Now I wanted to hear
everything that has happened. All the news. How ~~are~~ is
Elizabeth? How is Dick? What preparations are
there?"

~~It had a~~

Bright eyed, brown, pugnacious, <face,> what could you
say of it <his face,>
except that it <was> Peter's face, ~~the fact of that mobile,~~
~~delightful~~
en ~~sensitive, unsatisfactory absolutely unsatisfactory man,~~
~~whom one had on~~ <&> seeing <it> ~~whom~~ something in one
exploded?

"How perfectly heavenly it is to see you again!"
she exclaimed.

~~And~~ <But> he opened his knife, & that irritated her, for
there was something—how could she define it?—
egotistical about Peter which made him do a thing like
opening & shutting a knife without noticing how it
got on people's nerves.

"I arrived on Monday" said Peter. "There are one or
two matters to see to in town. Then I shall go down to the
country. Now I want to hear all the news. How is
Elizabeth? How is Dick? And what preparations are
there?" he indicated her dress, with his horn handled knife.
~~Clarissa looked instinctively~~ <His> at his grey ~~tw~~ check suit.
~~It was~~ <is> shabby, but it was <is> well cut. <thought
Clarissa.> ~~But he always~~
~~made her feel frivolous.~~ Yet he thought <thinks> her
frivolous.
~~He always had. He always lectured her;~~ He
disapproved of her. He ~~had always~~ lectured her.
~~And the heavy knife~~ ~~And~~ He shut his knife.
~~It is a pity to~~ This visit is a ~~mistake, he thought.~~
~~going to be are going <a complete> failure, he thought.~~
Here is
Clarissa doing precisely the same things she was doing
two years ago, he thought. ~~A thousand pities!~~

Pro. Con.

Doyle Wells.

[Walkley?]

[page 189 *verso*]

She goes to a hospital. ~~And that, she thinks, justifies her in~~
~~is a perfect an excuse for idling away her time among~~
~~absolute frivolities. She married Dick Dalloway.~~
The rest of it— her hospital as usual, & then comes back &
thinks she can sit about in her drawing room all day
long, playing with bits of silk, & having people in to gossip,
& then going down to the House in the afternoon. & then
calling on the right people, & so on & so on, he went on,
growing more & more annoyed, ~~with She~~ <for he> thought,
    ~~that how~~ she
Clarissa had sat like this for two years while ~~he~~ was in
    <I've been in>
India, ~~not wanting him, not thinking of him~~, After all, she
married that ~~good creature~~, <awful ass> ~~Richard~~ Dick,
    he thought, &
there's nothing perhaps so tragic as the effect of marriage—
It makes women dull. Here's Clarissa, might have
been a decent human being; ~~took~~ read books; talked sense;
had ideas of her own, or what one took for such, & then she
marries Dalloway, & ~~after that~~ its all up, its all up! he
thought shutting the blade with a little snap.
    ~~"We're~~ Dick's very well, said Clarissa. He's at the House.
She ~~took up her~~ <opened> scissors, ~~as~~ nervously. The knife,
    <the obstruction,> made her
nervous. ~~The obstruction between them depressed her.~~ It
had always been the same. When he had asked her to
marry him the ~~same~~ sort of repulsion had ~~suddenly~~
come over her! No thank Heaven she had
never married him!
    "~~This~~ You don't mind me ~~doing this little bit of sewing?~~
    <just finishing this?">
she ~~said~~ asked. "I shan't ask you to our party!"
she said, beginning to sew—"our party tonight,
because ~~you~~" her scissors had fallen. He picked them up.
"~~You give~~ Why won't you ask me to your party?" he said.

Well Peter, she said,
It's so delicious to hear her say that, he thought. And
relaxing his body he lay back in his chair, Its all so
delicious he thought.
~~Why won't you ask me to your party, he repeated.~~
"~~I should~~ <But I shd.> ~~enjoy a~~ <your> party . . .
There again thought Clarissa. ~~At one moment~~ he's odious;
<one moment>
the next, perfectly enchanting: Now I remember how
frightfully difficult it was—how for months I
couldn't make up my mind— At one moment,
I'd ~~said~~ felt no no no.—& the next well after all he's
~~Well its been a very long time~~ since we met" he
<~~Its an age.~~ It all seems as if I'd left it yesterday>
he said; & he thought that though it would be quite
impossible to tell her everything, some things he would
tell her.
~~He would tell~~ her But he would wait; he would observe
he was <not> by ~~no~~ <any> means sure.
And yet I suppose all sorts of things have
happened. Tell me about yourself Clarissa!"
Its so extraordinary to see you! she exclaimed.
There are days when everything reminds one of something
<the past.>
that happened before. Do you remember how the blind
used to flap? at Bourton." she said looking out of the
window.
They used, said Peter. I cant help f wishing I
got on better with your father, he said. I ~~was an~~
~~unusually boy, I suppose.~~ I should. have now. I have
He never liked our—well friends, said Clarissa.
ah! Peter thought, I proposed to her of course. <so I did—I
proposed to her.> Yes. & ~~its~~ she
still has an extraordinary ~~power~~ romance over me.

& then could have bitten her tongue for reminding Peter
~~in~~ thus that he had ~~proposed to her. <been in love with>~~
wanted to marry her.
Ah, Peter thought, so I did. I proposed to her. And then
~~one of those moon feelings~~ he was overcome with his own
past grief. ~~&~~ only now, ~~like~~ it was like the moon, which
one looks at from a terrace, so ghostly beautiful with
~~the white~~ light from a sunken day. But ~~now it cant scorch~~ me,
I was more unhappy he thought; it makes me feel ~~only~~ very ~~very~~ old, & very lonely
than I have ever ~~sorry for what I missed, myself; &~~ And, ~~then as if~~
been since, he thought, he were sitting on a terrace in the moonlight,
he began to edge a little nearer to Clarissa, as
if he wanted ~~somebo~~ company. ~~But~~ There it hung above
them, this moon. She seemed, too, ~~to~~ to be sitting in the
darkness. ~~looking up at it.~~
"I can't bear to go back there now" she said
~~though~~ Who has it ~~now~~? he asked.
~~It went to~~ Herbert ~~Parry, Uncle~~ she replied.
Uncle Andrew's son.
And then, just as ~~it~~ happens on a terrace, in the moonlight,
first one ~~& then as~~ person feels ashamed that he is
already bored; & yet as the other still seems to be
very quiet, he begins to ~~notice shadows~~ move his
foot, & to notice some iron scroll; <or> some leaf:
~~he~~ & clears his throat, but says nothing.
So ~~Peter~~ Walsh did, now. For ~~he~~ I'm not old at
fifty he thought. ~~I'm~~ My gracious I'm not old.

Clarissa doesnt think me old, he thought. Still he did not
like to look at her, because she sat looking at the moon,
which had begun to bore him.
Do you remember the mill? she said, ~~with a catch~~
280 ~~in her~~ <in an abrupt>
50 voice, ~~because she felt~~ that ~~she was about~~ to burst into
14,000 ~~tears, it with~~ <under> the ~~violence of this~~ pressure of an
3 emotion
15,000 which first caught ~~at~~ her heart & then made the muscles
3 of her
45,000 throat stiff. & ~~as she said the word "mill"~~ contracted
as she said her lips / in a spasm. She was a grown woman
mill who could see herself throwing bread to the ducks between her
parents. ~~That exquisite happiness day pure blue day,~~
~~that absolute contentment, had escaped destruction in~~
like a bubble wh. ~~the grind of the hours, & like suddenly, like a feather which is~~
~~frail but flawless, or one suddenly filled the room. And here~~
~~she was, a woman of fifty, & which remains floats~~
~~quite round on the holding the sky~~
She was a grown woman coming to her parents with her
life & saying to them, ~~now here I am with all this~~
~~load of suffering on my back, which I bore for your sake.~~
~~This is what I made of it.~~

~~It was like a little bubble which has survived, full of air & light.~~
And at the same time she was a grown woman, coming to
her parents with her life & saying this is what I have
done with it. ~~She thought that she had borne an enormous~~
What had she done? She looked at Peter Walsh,
through the peaceful day by the mill. & her look
had thus something so ~~grave~~ strange, so ironical, & so
in it, as if it had passed through waters to reach him, ~~that~~
~~Peter Walsh~~ & had become a little strange, a little
vague;

~~"I've got the a secret to tell you" he said.~~
~~"I want to ask you to advise me," he said.~~
~~She began to sew again.~~
~~Yes, said Peter, I have been a damned fool.~~
~~"I can't grow old," said Peter. I can't, he said, &~~
~~there he had his knife again, clenched in his hand. Yet he was~~
~~grey, his round head was grey.~~ ~~She felt for her sciss dress.~~
~~And Peter thought to himself, I can go on, or I can stop.~~
~~I can make a clean breast of the whole thing. or,~~

~~All in a moment~~
There he

She looked at Peter, through the peaceful day by the mill,
~~where she had put down her~~ & her look passing through
that bubble of time which had remained unbroken
reached him ~~questioningly, hesitatingly,~~ <doubtfully> &
settled on
him like a bird which touches the branch, &
rises ~~fluttering~~ <& flutters> before it settles again.

Yes, said Peter, yes, yes, yes, as if she drew <up> ~~from~~ to the
surface some thing which he had wanted to ~~conceal, He~~
~~could remember too.~~ forget. {"But you know, I can't
grow old, he said. I can't, I can't. He}
clenched his knife.

~~Why should you? said Clarissa.~~
I can go on, or I can stop, he thought to himself. I can
make a clean breast of the whole thing, or--tell her
~~The question is whether her damnable sophistication~~
~~allows one to speak—her finery, her furs, her her—~~
~~he looked at her to see what it was--her frigidity! <coldness>~~
~~Oh cold! cold! <its her coldness> that is what she is,~~
~~he thought,~~
~~she was always cold to me, & compared it with the~~
~~warmth of the beautiful voluble girl about Daisy.~~

She is too cold, he thought; ~~&~~ too pure, & beside her, Daisy
would
seem a vulgar pretty ~~foolish~~ little flirt. & she'd ~~rather~~
~~despise me,~~ & think me a failure too—which I am, in a
sense, he thought, compared with this sort of thing; (he
meant the inlaid table & the mounted paper knife) which
I detest ~~the sort of thing I detest!, Yet, yet, he thought, how can I~~
I detest the smugness of it, (for Lucy came into the room,
carrying silver) & ~~just think,~~ <&> ~~he thought, of~~ this
<has been> going on he thought
week after week, while I . . . . There rushed ~~into him~~
<over him>
~~overpoweringly & a sense of all his powers, all his interests, all~~
a sense of himself, so strong, so quick, so lively, involved in
every sort of adventure, ~~& now,~~ that he clasped his
knife, & Clarissa thought ~~that he~~ What a habit that is!
& she felt him at once, charming & irritating—
~~somehow~~ criticising her, as usual she thought, for
being the sort of person to marry a member of
Parliament—what was the phrase that ~~had~~ made
~~her~~ <me> so furious?—oh never mind, she thought, he' ~~is~~ s
real; ~~yes,~~ he's himself, & there she thought, I
too, & taking up her needle she ~~said~~ <[seemed?],> like a
Queen whose
guards have all fallen asleep, & left her ~~deserted~~
unprotected in her palace, ~~which has its~~
~~gates open, so that any one has been strolling in &~~
~~looking at her, doing anything, unconsciously,~~
~~her fortitude, her love, <her children> her atheism, all now to~~
~~come about her & beat off the enemy.~~

And what's happened to you all this time? she said,
~~Now~~ Just before a battle begins, the horses paw the ground,
toss their heads, & the light shines on their flanks. So with
Peter when Clarissa challenged him. ~~to tell her what he was,~~
~~what he had done, & why. all~~ All his powers chafed &
tossed. He assembled from different quarters his ~~power to~~
career at Oxford; ~~sent down, he had then~~ <his> travel~~led.~~
~~He had seen everything.~~ his marriage, divorce; & now
at fifty, passionate love.

"I've fallen love!" he ~~said~~ <exclaimed>. ~~And then~~
~~urged by~~
~~all these hot powers he clasped his hands & walked to the~~
~~window.~~ by the assembly of powers, ~~swarming,~~
& ~~suddenly got out of control~~ within him ~~so that~~
~~he did not care what he did & was borne forward~~
which were now ~~broken loose & had possession of him,~~
breaking loose, ~~streaming~~ charging in different directions, &
giving him the feeling at once delicious & frightening &
~~yet~~ extremely exhilarating of being rushed through the air
on the shoulders of people whom he could not see he
raised his hands ~~as if to control them &~~ to his forehead as if to
control them.

[203]

"Ah" ~~said s sa~~ sighed Clarissa with ~~that~~ <&> look of
apprehension, yet of exultation,

~~Oh Clarissa I'm happier than I've ever been in~~
~~my life! he exclaimed.~~ I'm in love! he exclaimed.
~~but~~ not to her, ~~more~~ to himself, ~~more speaking~~ <or rather> that
is to
~~say, into some a darkness <private> which returns no~~
~~answer as if~~
~~he looked beyond what was present, towards something~~
~~extremely to someone not there, wh~~ to some one, at a distance,
~~not there, as if one could far away~~ someone <presence>
~~of such~~ so [ ]
beautiful that you could not ~~approach~~ to touch ~~her~~<er>, but in
must lay your garland down ~~there~~ a few feet away on the
grass <in the dark>

"~~Yes~~ I'm in love" he said, <to Clarissa> having
deposited his garland.
~~so & now speaking to Clarissa.~~

~~Clarissa said was silent, all for All~~
And Clarissa, ~~he thought~~, will think me old! he thought
instantly,

In love? said Clarissa, ~~with a & the edge of her~~
~~voice~~ <that he, at his age, shd.> ~~Why should~~ he ~~be~~
sucked under ~~at his age~~ in his little
bow tie by the monster? Why, there was no flesh in
his ~~wrinkles~~ neck--& his hands were red: ~~she thought,~~
his eye flashed back to her; but in her heart she felt ~~He~~
All the same, he is in love.

& the power which is deeper still;

And those powers—love, ~~at children, atheism, wh~~—which have
their seat in the nerves of ~~the physical~~ heart, beliefs & desires; &
something deeper than they, the indomitable egotism which
~~like some surly seneschal has charge of~~ mounts guard
over the ~~central~~ treasure of personality & ~~the~~ forever
rides down the hosts opposed to it clears the way, &
~~charges~~ bears the soul to its destiny, & seems
acquainted with ~~its goal~~ <its goal>, this indomitable seneschal,
~~ri~~ aroused ~~in Clarissa~~ by Peters words now
made Clarissa's heart expand & contract, contract &
expand, ~~while & her~~ & ~~she looked more pointed,~~
~~more definite than ever, as she sat in her arm~~
~~chair by the mantelpiece, with her green dress over her~~
~~knees, & her cheeks pink, & her eyes bright, & her~~
~~& charged her cheeks with colour, her eyes with fire.~~ She
sat by the mantelpiece with her green dress over her knees:
she could not thread her needle. He was in love!
Not with her, with some younger woman. And ~~she~~
~~it enraged her.~~ And the wound gaped. And she
would heal it.

~~And~~ who ~~with~~? <~~And in~~ love with whom?> she asked.

~~She listened to his story.~~ And

Now this statue must be brought ~~into~~ from its height
& set down between them as

"She is a married woman,~~" he~~ <he said,—> the wife of a
soldier.

~~he went on,~~ & with <an> extreme sweetness he smiled as he
placed her, in this ridiculous way, before Clarissa.

All the same, he is in love, thought Clarissa.

She's just twenty five, he said. She has two little
children—And now, he thought, do what you
like with them Clarissa—There they are! &

~~& what with pride, & feeling so extraordinarily young,~~
& he ~~smiled with~~ looked tremulous & flushed &
extraordinarily proud, as if second by second Clarissa
too saw how the exquisite vision & it kindled
between them into the rosy flower—
as if he had put down a grey pellet on a plate & it had
risen in a ~~beautiful~~ column ~~of between them.~~ of
~~crimson smoke between them. in a tree, between them.~~
~~For in the atmosphere had suddenly <suddenly> become,~~
~~when so~~
~~now that Clarissa knew had become so warm, that~~
~~everything he was put into it flowered.~~
~~as if here~~ ~~in a tree, through the warmth of~~
~~Clarissa's which came from Clarissa, <herself> now that~~
~~he had told her.~~
~~& he was of course, he thought, & himself as they looked~~
~~together at this wonderful apparition.~~
in the warm sticky air,
~~You are utterly ridiculous, thought Clarissa.~~
She turned him ~~round her finger~~ & ~~laughe mad~~ <she
laughed> at
him ridiculous, thought Clarissa, shaping the woman
in three strokes with a knife. What a waste!
What a folly! ~~Why must Peter always~~

[209]

2,800
10
___

[page 209 *verso*]

And she was indignant. All his life Peter had been a fool!
Ever since he was a boy, getting sent down from Oxford! ~~for some~~ ~~Thank Heaven~~ She had not married him! She might have married him.
Yet he was in love.
~~He got up f & walked to the window, an overcome with the complexities of his position, feeling stirred with a~~
~~"What will you--<do>" she said. Will you marry her.~~
~~Well I don't know, said Peter, looking at the tree, very vaguely, Really,~~ ~~looking flushed, excited,~~
~~And perhaps that <there> is of course, thought Clarissa, after all,~~
~~something upsetting about that, even to me, <even> at my age in that~~
~~age.~~ ~~And she~~ ~~in that particular sort, &~~
~~& she sighed, thinking that~~
And what <then> are you going to do? she asked.
I ~~shall~~ <am go> ~~make her~~ <she is going to> marry me." he replied.
And leave her husband.
~~He's a brute! cried~~
~~And her children!~~ I shall get a divorce.
And her husband, & her children?
She is going to marry me, he repeated.
For Heavens sake leave your knife alone, Clarissa cried to herself, more irritated than she could account for,
But ~~How~~ can you marry her <get a divorce>? ~~Shall~~ ~~you divorce Peter you mean you'll make her live with you?~~
Obviously not, she thought. ~~Oh the obstinacy! The Peter again knocking his head, against setting his teeth--ruining himself at his age. & she thought he is my age, & how here she was, settled, married,~~
Its all nonsense she thought; folly & ~~idiocy on his part,~~ its folly & idiocy, she thought.

Thats his obstinate look, she thought; ~~he'll~~ for it was all perfectly true, what Clarissa was thinking: ~~he~~ <I> kne<o>w

that, ~~He~~ I

Peter thought. I knew what I'm up against. But I ~~was~~ 'll ~~Ever a fighter he~~ thought ~~ra~~ opening his knife, & I'll show Clarissa, & Dalloway, & all ~~these proper~~, the rest of them,

~~Oh Peter Peter exclaimed Clarissa.~~

Oh Clarissa! he cried, & burst into tears, which he was not ashamed of. They ran straight down his face, & he did not wipe them. He sat smiling & crying. & holding Clarissa's hands, & miraculously the

~~or rather the pressure of these forces in him first he was rushed forward by~~ for so he was thrown

by ~~his pas~~ those uncontrollable forces ~~within~~ had thrown him, thrown her up into the air, through the air--had thrown him. He sobbed, without wiping his tears.

[213]

Cha

60
4
~~2400~~
6
280
60
16,800
17,000
4
68,000

[page 213 *verso*]

~~Chariot Cream Laid~~

And ~~actuall~~ she ~~had~~ leant forward, & taking his hand &
kissed him—
actually she had felt his face <on hers> ~~to her after~~
~~all these years.~~
~~swept away too.~~ before she could stay the tumult, the
brandishing of silver flashing plumes tossing like pampas
grass in some tropic gale, up & down in her heart,
which subsiding, left her holding his hand; <~~th~~> patting
his knee; then she
~~taking~~ <took> her handkerchief, dabb~~ing~~<ed> her eyes; &
feeling, as she
sat back ~~in her ch~~ against her cushions, extraordinarily at her
ease with him. ~~Indeed she felt an intoxication of~~
~~friendship & merriment & youth & merriment,~~
~~strangely enough;~~ & young & merry & light hearted; &
~~then,~~ all in a clap, it came over her If I had married him!
~~how~~ this gaiety would have been ~~her daily life.~~ mine all day.
~~Only here was Peter in love with a girl. And where was~~
~~But he was in love. For her~~ It was <all> over for her. The
sheet was stretched & the bed narrow. She had gone up into
the tower alone & ~~left~~ them <left him> picking blackberries
in the sun.
The door had shut, ~~& the~~ suddenly, & there in the dust of
fallen plunder, birds nests, ~~it was~~ how distant the view
had looked &
the sounds ~~coming from so <very> far,~~ <came [ ]> & ~~then~~
it was chill—~~some~~ (~~it~~
~~tower on Leith Hill~~ <on> Leith Hill, she thought,) ~~But~~
where's Dick? ~~she~~ Where's Dick, ~~as if he~~ she asked
shuddering, as half waking ~~in a nightmare~~ a sleeper
starts in bed & stretches <a hand> for help, ~~from another~~,
lunching with Lady Bruton, it came back to her;

I can't sleep, said Peter. I ~~can't~~ <even> think of anything
else.
~~I'm in such a state of mind~~--I'm going mad.

She rose from the sofa, & went to Peter,

~~The queer old creature had mastered his tears, & was actually laughing!~~

~~It is <quite> over, she thought,~~

~~Why didn't you marry me? he said peevishly like a child at the end of a day asking something quite irrational.~~

~~But then~~

How strange it is thought Peter, that ~~even now, after all as if she for really as she came that this horrible romantic feeling for a~~ that she should still have this power,
as she comes tinkling, rustling—should have the power to
~~revive~~
~~all that [ ] thought decent in myself that~~
he thought, & became sad, as if the moon, slowly
mounted the
sky; & they must watch it.

Why didn't you marry me? he said peevishly
like a child at the end of a day asking something quite
irrational—~~why, for instance, they can't~~

~~Have you~~ <Are you> been happy Clarissa, he said ~~quite~~
roughly, with annoyance, with irritation.

~~Absolutely, said Clarissa,~~
~~& both of them dear me,~~ <for> ~~he thought,~~ darned fool though
you were to ~~go with~~ <marry> Dalloway, I don't want
it to have
been a failure, ~~But she can't speak the truth, he thought,~~

And the door opened.

~~This~~ Here is Elizabeth said Clarissa,
At the same moment, [sh?]

[*pencil*]
<u>p. 71</u>

[The following 5 folio pages come from a notebook dated 7 January 1924 and labelled "Reviews 1924" in the Berg Collection of the New York Public Library. The page numbering follows that originally assigned by the Berg's curator.]

w wh he had but surely she had been sprigh<t>lier then, had had some dash
agreed with to— & fire about her, for otherwise how could she have been, as
she was, such a figure ~~to come into~~ <the> a room, such a
termagant? Still she had, however, something he liked.
some Gener~~ous~~<sity>, ~~she was; truthful; & if~~ & ~~after~~ what had
happened was inevitable--~~that~~ the inevitable result <effect> upon
almost every woman with out exception & having children;
~~for it~~
~~was the very devil; that~~ it made them dull~~; & cowlike;~~
made them give up caring for things: for in the old days,
~~with~~ you couldn't deny, Sally had cared ~~for her all right;~~
had gone her own way. He had a Shelley she had given
him, with all her notes & underlinings, & some where a
whole sheaf of poems. Bad, bad; all very bad. But
better than sitting surrounded by children, & what was the
other thing?--~~oh yes,~~ plants. ~~For~~ Clarissa might ~~very~~
~~well~~ be ~~a~~ something of a snob. (But probably this man
Rosseter was ~~such a bore~~ <a wholesale> bore—that was why
she didn't
stay with ~~visit~~ them) Clarissa was a snob he admitted; ~~but he~~
~~said~~, But when he had seen her <come into the room,> this
morning, what had he
felt? ~~She had kept going~~. She was alive. Older,
almost white.

~~Clarissa~~
~~Clarissa~~—was she a snob? Yes, she was in many ways.
Also, ~~she~~ superficial, ~~in many <many> ways, somehow, because~~

because

obviously she ~~was~~ liked to please; ~~&~~ said things she didn't mean;
& how emotional, (but that was mostly on the surface)
~~wh~~ But said Sally when I heard she was giving a party,

& I was actually staying in Victoria Street— I had to come, I couldnt not come (& I'm staying in Victoria Street)

~~I felt~~ I ~~had to come--There are She was A~~ for she ~~felt~~ asked,
~~there Where is she? I came to see her; I humbled my pride, she felt (<she> loving<ed> phrases as she did) I couldn't~~
~~be in London pass her door without going in; &~~
~~it might be all~~
She ~~had~~ I humbled my pride <(so she loved phrases)> —But where is she?" And
~~And~~ That face—how well I know ~~to~~ it—who is she?
Mrs. Hilbery, it was, seeking a door. For how late it
was getting! But as the night grew later, & people
went, one found old friends, & little quiet nooks; ~~where~~
& chairs, ~~for~~ & the loveliest, loveliest views? ~~Had~~
Did they know there was an enchanted park outside?
Lights & trees & wonderful <gleaming> ~~pon~~ lakes? ~~& the~~ And ~~a~~ <the> sky?—
Why not have fairy lamps every night in the back garden; &
& who were they, ~~&~~ she was talking to? Friend,
she ~~kne~~ knew; ~~&~~ friends, she said ~~need~~ <without> no names; &
there were so many doors—in this room—such unexpected
places! ~~And she strayed~~ <Off she> rambled, to find "my hostess,
my dear kind hostess" & ~~so~~ thats ~~old~~ Mrs. Hilbery
said Sally, & ~~thats~~ that? But they couldn't
for the life of them ~~put a name;~~ remember; ~~They both~~
knew her. ~~Somehow~~ Connected with Bourton, they thought;
somebody they both knew quite well; a

~~talking to no one;~~
& couldn't think who she was. Connected with Bourton,
they thought;
she used to ~~come &~~ help surely; <[ ]> to cut up underclothes at
a large table
in the window: ~~where, or why, they could not think; but~~
<&> both
~~connected~~ her with some scene: ~~when Clarissa how she was~~
~~&~~ running out of the drawing room to escape her; & ~~yet~~ being
ashamed; because she was so good; & thinking Clarissa
hard on her;
~~for It was her colourlessness, that Clarissa~~ for ~~so~~ she would
wh he loved have been, they agreed; Yet, said Sally in her
tho he dreaded ~~emo~~ emotional way with ~~that~~ <a> sudden revival of
it, generosity, ~~candour,~~
which Peter used to ~~find in~~ <love> her, for (~~she had been How~~
faithful ~~she is! Here we are both of us,~~ how faithful to her
old friends Clarissa was, & what a quality that was, &
how sometimes at night when she ~~was~~ counted up the blessings
of her life, she ~~had to~~ count that friendship first— ~~For its~~
~~when one's young But he would think her terribly~~
He ~~terribly sentimental. No said Peter, no~~
<He wd think her> ~~But she was afraid of being~~ sentimental;
~~& Peter~~ yet it was
not sentimental at all, ~~Peter told~~ her, ~~but the silly~~
~~timid & cold, &~~ to ~~say what one felt,~~ & ~~growing old~~
~~But~~ she sometimes wondered ~~if anything else was much worth~~
Yet ~~doing. Being clever, being having: was clever saying~~
whether to say what one felt was not the only thing worth
saying.
~~People might be brilliant;~~ ~~One grew tired of every thing~~
~~else, &~~ as one grew old; ~~& why an effort though it was,~~
~~&~~ Why ~~be clever, wh~~ try to be clever; ~~why try to be anything~~?
~~Why not simply~~ Why not say ~~simply w~~ the truth? what
<ever> one first
feels ~~in one's~~ heart. But, he said he did not know
what he felt~~? never~~ ~~And she thought he was~~
Poor man, poor Peter, she thought; & why did Clarissa

<where was Clarissa> ~~have~~ them, for he ~~wanted~~ had come
there, she felt, only to see
Clarissa: all the time she talked he was thinking of
Clarissa; he would not talk of anything else; he was
~~fidgetting with his knife again. And it was getting~~
~~late, & people were going; & who was never was~~
~~there any daughter so Elizabeth took after the Dalloways;~~
~~had~~
fidgetting with his knife again.
~~We~~ <But> His had not been a simple relationship, Peter
said.
In some ways it had spoilt his life, he said; ~~that affair~~.
for perhaps <so> ~~One~~ is never in love more than once, he said. & ~~she~~
what could she say? That life was a tragedy.
That it was better to have loved, ~~than not. That~~
~~on the whole~~. That he must stay with them for a least a
month in Manchester. All of which ~~she said & it was~~
was ~~all~~ true; all very true; ~~& she loved her, as one lover, they~~
~~said, old~~ had ~~wild~~
~~But~~ And ~~she~~ Clarissa <had> loved him; ~~had cared for him~~
~~in some way more~~ truly than she had ever ~~cared for~~ <loved>
Richard.
~~And there was Richard in~~ But <But> ~~no~~. No, no, no, said
Peter. That good fellow—there he was.
There he was, at the end of the room, holding forth; ~~in~~
his ~~usual way~~, &

52 Tavistock Sqre.
Oct 5th
A ~~haf~~ half [_]

<But it had been> A silly thing to do, ~~though~~; in many ways,
Peter said; to marry that;
& yet, he said, "I've had a splendid time"; but ~~h~~ how could
that be,
Sally wondered; what did he mean, & how odd it was {to
meet like this &} know a person & yet not know a ~~thing of~~
<thing> what
had happened to them. ~~He had been in India.~~
And did he say it out of pride? ~~Probably he~~ for after all

Where did he stay?

it must be lonely at his age to have no home; ~~& probably~~
~~he was not very well off; but successful; & rich;~~
~~be not fam he was not famous, she supposed;~~
~~She asked him down to stay with them, &~~ And that it

He must come
to them; for
weeks;
for a real visit

came out was the ~~dreadful~~ thing ~~Sl~~ Sally couldn't get
over in Clarissa—Time after time they had asked her.
She would not come. ~~And it was simply this—said~~
~~Sally~~. For, said Sally, Clarissa ~~would not~~ was at
heart, ~~in spite of her charm~~ (one had to admit it) a snob.

~~after all~~
And she could not
get over the fact

~~Look, she said why give these parties? And her~~
~~husband. Sally's husband—was not She had married~~
~~(Sally that is) had married a Her husband--Sally's~~
~~husband--was not an ordinary working man's son.~~
And it was simply that—she had married, Clarissa thought
beneath her, ~~Clarissa~~ thought, married out of this after all
rather artificial, & agreeable, but surely very
heartless world? ~~The Prime Minister, for instance;~~
~~had he done more for England than her husband did?~~
her husband being, she was proud to say, a miners son.
And so she would go on, Peter felt, for ~~ever~~ hour
after hour; a miner's son, ~~was~~ one topic; wealth
another; as she used years ago to rate them all
for slothfulness, & such like sins, & cry out in
particular upon the injustice of the ~~men to wom~~ <male view.>

[The following 29 folio pages come from a notebook in the Berg Collection of the New York Public Library dated 22 November 1924. The front cover is labelled "Reviews 1924." The page numbering follows that originally assigned by the Berg's curator.]

Mrs. Dalloway (corrections)

She laughed & laughed. He always made her laugh.
But this question of love, of falling in love—what else could
one call it?—with women. Take Sally Seton; her relation, in the old days with Sally Seton. Had not that, after all, been love?

She sat on the floor, that was his first recollection of Sally—she sat on the floor, with her arms round her knees, smoking a cigarette.

5[ ]>

Yet after all, how much she had owed to Peter later. She had owed him words: 'sentimental'; 'decent'; words that even now, when she was fifty two, would ~~come~~ start up in her mind, as if Peter were there saying them; that is, he had ~~been an~~ influenced ~~in~~ her life. A book was sentimental, a person sentimental; a sentimental attitude to life; sentimental she was, perhaps, to be thinking of the past; oh & certainly these parties were all rot—except of course that ~~her~~ she could not have loved him as she had done—still did, if he had not ~~been as capricious as changeable, as easy to~~ enjoyed himself ever so much more than she did at parties. And fallen in love with that silly woman: & ~~a very~~ been altogether a person who, trying as he was, exasperating, exacting, ridiculous, made one always wonder, what will he say?

That he had grown older? He would be coming back soon, & would say, ~~in that~~ outright, & she would see him thinking, she had grown older. It was true, since her illness; she had grown older.

Strange, she thought, pausing on the landing; how a mistress knows the moment, the temper, of her house! Strange she

collecting her self upright for the — thought, the effort;

[*pencil*]

64

60 Dec. 1st — & instantly <with a little firm> [ ] into her diamond shape

124 — she thought she often felt she was [ ],

60 Dec 8th

184

60 15th

244

60 22

304

had always annoyed her; & now at his age, how silly!

& then to her utter surprise, being thrown by those uncontrollable forces, thrown through the air he burst ~~into~~ tears; he wept; he wept, without the least shame, ~~there~~ sitting on the sofa. The tears running down his cheeks.

Remember my party, remember my party, said Peter Walsh, as he started down the street.

But other people got between them in the street, blotting
her out; ~~giving~~
He pursued; she changed. There was colour in her cheeks;
mockery in her eyes; he was an adventurer, reckless, he
thought
of all these damned proprieties; yellow dressing gowns,
pipes, fishing rods; & respectability & evening parties, &
all the rest. On & on she she went up.
And

Well, I've had my fun, he thought,
And ~~are~~ how ridiculous, he thought, to expect any one to share
it; ~~considering that~~ to share ~~the~~ what is after all, so inextricably
mixed up
with us; ~~which is our~~ this ~~making up~~ diversion, & allowing
oneself to
through invent<ing>, <things> not only ~~what one sees,~~ some girl
like that, but oneself
too for he knew very well that this little escapade, this
delightful passage in the day, had been made up,
was a ~~game, a diversion, which~~ & he had made himself up:
for he was not, he knew very well, quite like that;
except for fun—
He started off up the street~~—where?~~ to sit. somewhere,
til it was time for the solicitor; where? No matter. And his

[*pencil*]

So she knitted over the sleeping baby,
in Regents Park

[7]

Such are the visions.
Clarissa had wound herself into his dreams, not as a
person, exactly; he was not dreaming of her; but she
pressed upon him, ~~almost~~
until one is — as a fellow passenger, ~~who has~~ fallen asleep, presses closer
jolted ~~wid~~ awake — & closer.
It was her presence he felt as he woke with extreme suddenness,
saying to himself 'The death of the soul': ~~it was~~ her
~~he felt~~, This it was, he thought, ~~to like~~ to be in love: a
disagreeable pressure, an inconvenient pressure, which,
Lord! Lord!
he cried, stretching himself & opening his eyes, one can't
avoid. But
the death of the soul? ~~What was it~~? <The words recalled>
some scene; some room;
people talking; ~~& a~~ some atmosphere of pleasure & pain, all
mixed up. It became clearer & clearer—the death of the soul,
oh yes, he began to remember.
[*pencil*]
And he had her way of rubbing it in.
[*pencil ends*]
It was awful, he cried, awful, awful!
Still, the sun was hot. Still one got over things.
Still life had a
way of adding ~~on~~ day to ~~an~~ day. Still, he thought, yawning,
& ~~noticing~~ beginning to take notice,—Regents Park had
changed very little since he was a boy—still ~~there were~~ no
it is very— — ~~one goes~~ on—upon which, little Elsie Mitchell, who
tolerance — had been collecting pebbles ~~to join the~~ for the ~~collection of~~
pebbles <[ ]> which she & her brother were making on the
nursery
mantelpiece—the round pebbles having an infinitely
higher value than the ~~ob any irregular~~, oblong—plumped
her handful on the nurses knee, & scudded off again
full tilt into a ladies legs.
Its wicked, ~~I won't stand it,~~ why should I
suffer, Lucrezia Warren Smith was saying to herself: No
I can't stand it, she was saying, having left her husband,
on the seat, to talk to himself, to say cruel wicked hard
things, when the little girl ran into her; fell, burst into a

howl.

She stood her upright, dusted her down, kissed her.
As for herself, she had done nothing wrong; she loved Septimus;
she had been happy; she had had a beautiful home, &
there her sister lived still, making hats. Why should she
suffer?

The child ran straight back again to its nurse.
~~Rezia~~ She was received; she was scolded; she was comforted.
Rezia thought, ~~but why should I be~~ exposed, (looking at the
perambulator, the nurse, <putting down her knitting> the
~~nice~~ kind looking ~~grey~~ man, who
tortured was letting the little girl blow his watch open, to comfort her)
Why why should <u>she</u> be exposed? Why not live in Milan? Why?

Slightly waved by tears, ~~like~~ the ~~pa~~ broad path
lifted itself before her eyes like a flawed glass: ~~But~~ To be
locked by the malignant tortures was her lot; ~~But why~~
The enormous trees, vast clouds of this indifferent world
surrounded shook her; she was like a bird sheltering under the thin
hollow of a leaf, bewildered by the sun when the leaf
moves, cowering at the crack of a dry twig. Why should
she suffer? She frowned, she stamped her foot; ~~sh~~
She must now go back again to Septimus, since it was almost
time for them to be going. ~~The~~ There he was, sitting
on the green chair under the tree, talking to himself, or
talking to that dead man Evans, whom she had ~~scarce~~ only seen
once.
He was a nice gentleman; ~~who had been~~ a friend, in the same
regiment, who had been killed. But such things
happen to everyone.

[Dog pawprints go across this page.]
[*pencil*]
She reached him, she sat down by him,
[*pencil ends*]
She ~~could see~~ <was close to> him now; could see him, staring;
at the sky;—muttering.
Yet Dr. Holmes said there was nothing the matter with him,
What then had happened; ~~to make~~ him? When she sat down
by him,
he started, & from at her, & move away, & mutter something—
what, she could not
hear. There was ~~a no husband in him; & he stared~~. & then
stared & stared at her hand, as if he saw something that
terrified him.

There was no
husband in him;

the thing she knew
~~in~~ him by had
gone—

Where was her wedding ring, he said suddenly. She
had taken <her wedding> it off, she said, because her ~~hand fing~~
hand had
grown so thin. She had put it in her purse.

Our marriage is over, he thought, with extreme relief, as if a rope
had been cut, & he was free ~~now; free~~ to mount into the
cloud. She had thrown away her ring: she had left him.

In chorus, the ~~leav~~ voices rustled of course of course: the
supreme secret must be told to the Prime Minister.
first, that trees are alive; ~~th~~ next, there is no crime; next, love,
universal love, he muttered, painfully receiving these profound
revelations; & grasping them with an incredible effort,
for ~~they~~
the world was <[already?]> changed by them: he was called
forth in
front of the mass to ~~receive the~~ <give> to hear the truth, to
learn the meaning when
No crime: love, he repeated.
And started prodigiously at ~~the~~ a dog, a
Skye terrier, which was looking at him, which was
wrinkling up its cheeks, becoming a man! It was too
~~horrible~~ terrible to see ~~there~~ a dog change before his eyes!
The dog trotted away. (Heaven was divinely merciful.)
But what was the explanation—the [sanity?] explanation

of the obvious fact that with his own eyes he was now capable of
~~p~~ seeing through solid bodies? The heat of the sun, operating
upon a human brain, ~~senti~~ sensitized by evolution
as ~~kod~~ photographic films are sensitized.—
~~Evidently~~, Scientifically speaking, it was a very hot day,
what they called on the placards a heat wave; one of the
hottest days of the years, & the flesh was melted off the
world. His body was macerated till only the
nerve fibres were left. He was spread like a
veil upon a rock.

Exhausted, ~~by~~ but upheld in his extreme fatigue, he lay
very high on the back of the world, resting, waiting, before he
took up his terrific burden once more.

100 And that is being young, Peter Walsh thought as he passed them.
125 To be having an awful scene,—for <the poor girl> ~~they~~
225 he ~~both certainly look as if they~~ <she> were
250 in the middle of morning. But what was it about, he
25 wondered, ~~looking~~ giving them a ~~quick~~ look, ~~out of the~~
5 ~~eyes which~~
125 ~~a~~ quickly, lightly, sympathetically, as he passed; for since he had
not succeeded, had not achieved the art of imposing his
views, ~~his~~
mind. ~~his~~ temperament upon any class, was, indeed, as
Clarissa
still some how felt him that morning, though so exacting & critical still an ~~dea~~
in the [ ], <[impetuous?]> old fool,
~~not~~ <a> ~~a~~ <but> ~~rather~~ a vagabond, he did sympathise, not ~~in the~~
(with a sense of his sentimentally but shrewdly rather, ~~saying~~ thinking that
own likeness to them,) though they might be having the devil of a time, better be them
than
lots of other people. Better be them than the Archbishop of
Canterbury. Hugh Whitbread too—Heaven be praised that ~~w~~
one was not Hugh.

But the ~~strange~~ amazing thing about living in India,
& coming back to London like this, after five years, was
the way it made, anyhow the first days, everything stand
out by itself.
Lovers squabbling under a tree; ~~&~~ the look of things. ~~He was~~
~~absolutely determined~~ Never ~~to~~ had he seen London look more
enchanting. True this susceptibility
He only felt ~~come over~~ that kind of closeness, which

He only felt, after seeing her that morning, ~~unable to get away~~
~~from the thought of her.~~ among her scissors & silks, making ready for
the party, <that> ~~he was unable to get away~~ from the thought of; she
came back & back <to him>, ~~like a sleeper in a subway carriage, jolting~~
~~against his mind; which was always the case to some extent; he~~
~~forgot her for months; suddenly, out in the most incongruous places, she~~
~~came back to him;~~ making him think of her, criticise her, try,
after thirty years, to explain her. ~~People~~ The ~~obiv~~
obvious thing to say of her was that she was worldly,

Oh poor old wretch!
Suppose it was a wet night? Suppose one's father, or somebody
like that happened to pass, & saw one standing there in the
gutter? And where did she sleep?—
Cheerfully, almost gaily, the invincible thread of sound wound
up into the air like the smoke from a cottage chimney
winding up clean beech trees, & ~~pass~~ issuing in a tuft of blue
smoke among the ~~highest~~ <top most> leaves. "And if some one should
see, what matter they?"
Since she was so unhappy for many days now, Rezia had
been ~~aware~~ giving meaning to things that happened, almost
feeling capable sometimes of stopping people in the street,
if they looked good, kind, people; <just> to say to them 'I am unhappy'
& this ~~w~~ old woman, singing, made her quite sure; because she seemed cheerful,
that everything was going to be all right. They were
going to that great doctor, Sir William Bradshaw: he wd. cure Septimus.
And then there was ~~like~~ a brewers cart; & grey horses with
upright bristles of straw in their tails, & school children.
~~It was going to be all right,~~ It was only a silly, silly dream.

So they crossed, M[r] & M[rs.] Septimus Warren Smith, &
was there, after all, anything to draw attention to them,
anything to make one think there is a young man, who after
debating the question to the best of his ability, thinks death
better than life? Perhaps they walked more slowly than
other people, & there was something hesitating, trailing, in
the man's walk; but ~~after all~~, what more natural on a
~~fine summer morning; when~~ what more natural for a
~~clerk~~ who has not been in the West End on a week day
at this hour for years, than to keep looking at the sky, to
look at this that & the other, as if ~~Lord~~ Portland
Place were a room he had come into by mistake, at
the wrong hour; the chandeliers being hung in holland
bags; & the caretaker letting in long shafts of dusty
light upon deserted, queer looking armchairs, when she
lifts one corner of the long blinds to show the
visitors ~~how~~ what a wonderful place it is (the family
being in Scotland)

Certainly Septimus might have been a clerk; but of the
better sort; for he wore brown boots; & his hands were the
his sensitive, hands of an educated man; so too his profile; but not his
intelligent profile, lips altogether, (they were ~~so~~ loose); ~~so~~ that presumably he
was a border case, neither one thing nor the other;
~~equally likely to be send his sons to Eton, or to~~ might end
with a house at Purley & a motor car, or merely continue
renting furnished rooms all his life: one of those self educated
men, whose education is all ~~book~~ learning; <in> books read in
the evening after the days work; from books borrowed from
public libraries, read by the advice of well known authors,
whom he has consulted by letter.

He had, however, gone through other experiences—
the experiences people ~~very much~~ had left home, very young, because of his
go through alone—.

mother chiefly: <(~~her~~ she was [ ])> because of his coming
down to tea, not for the first
time by any means, unwashed; because he could ~~not~~ see no future for himself ~~at~~ in Stroud; & so, making a confidant of his small sister, had gone to London, leaving an absurd note behind, such as great men have written, & the world has read later when the story of their struggles has become famous.

And London has swallowed up millions of young men called
Smith; has thought nothing.

Septimus volunteered. He went to France to save an England which consisted almost entirely of Shakespeare's plays, & Miss Isabel Pole ~~in a green dress~~ walking in a square. There in the trenches the change which Mr Brewer desired, ~~that he should from boyhood to manhood,~~ came over him; manliness [ ] <developed> him. ~~Unsuspected qualities~~ He showed courage, intiative, ~~forethought~~, forethought & the other values of a soldier; X{won the attention, & then the affection of his superior, Evans by name;} & was decorated & promoted;

~~when he remarked~~ ~~to Mr Brewer~~ He ~~that he~~ ~~when he advised~~ football was provided almost instantly.

It was a case of

So there was no excuse; nothing the matter, except
that central
fault ~~when~~ for which ~~it became more & more obvious~~, human
nature would condemn him to death; not feeling. His
chief crime was
that he had not cared when Evans was killed; but all the others
raised their heads, pale & ghastly, shook their fingers at him over
the ~~edge of the~~ rail of the bed in the early hours of the morning:
how he had married Rezia without caring for her—had lied to her;
had outraged Miss Isabel Pole; & was rightly detested even
by people who only saw him in the street; There was some
horror in his face. He would have to kill himself at the
command of human nature.

Dr. Holmes came again. Large, breezy, good looking, he
brushed it all aside. headache & sleeplessness; fears; dreams;
& all the
rest of it. The truth is, said Dr. Holmes, health is largely in our own
control.

[*blue crayon*]

———

———————

———————

[*end of blue crayon*]

But Rezia could not understand him. ~~Human nature~~—
Dr. Holmes—
was such a kind man. He ~~said~~ was so interested in Septimus.
He only wanted to help them he said.

He was deserted. He was absolutely alone. The whole
world was clamouring kill yourself, kill yourself, for our sake.
But ~~he did not in the least wish~~ <why should he> to kill
himself; Food was pleasant;
the sun was hot; & ~~then~~ how does one kill onself, uglily with
floods of blood or by sucking a gaspipe?—he was so weak
X that he could hardly raise his hand.X He was deserted. He
lying on the shore of the world, a drowned sailor. And at
that moment, the greatest revelation ~~of them~~ happened.
A vision
spoke from behind the screen. The dead were with him:
It was Evans who was with him.
"Speak

The leaden circles dissolved in the air. It was precisely twelve
o'clock—twelve by Big Ben, whose stroke, the wind
being favourable,
was wafted over the Northern parts of London; blent with other
clocks, & mixed in ~~its~~ a their aetherial way with the
clouds, ~~the~~ & wisps of smoke; ~~& dying out finally; in th~~ but
& died up there among the sea gulls. Twelve o'clock
struck as the Warren Smiths walked down Harley Street.
Probably, Rezia thought, that was Sir William Bradshaws house
with the grey motor car in front of it.

Indeed it was, Sir William's motor car; low, powerful, grey;
with plain initials interlocked on the panel, as if
the pomp of heraldry were incongruous, this man being
the ghostly
helper, ~~the who~~ the ~~m~~ priest of science; &, as the motor car
was grey, so to match its sober suavity, grey furs, grey
~~gre~~ rugs were heaped in it; to keep her Ladyship warm
when she waited for Sir William as she often did. <For> Often
Sir William ~~was~~ would travel sixty miles ~~or~~ more
through country lanes to visit the rich, the afflicted, who
could afford the very large fee which Sir William very
properly ~~demanded~~ <charged>, being at the head of his
profession
& that profession ~~in~~ <one> in which the strongest age
prematurely.
for his advice. Her ladyship waited with the rugs about
her knees, ~~over~~ an hour or more, leaning back,
thinking sometimes of the patient perhaps, sometimes,
excusably too of all that gold, mounting minute by
minute; that wall of gold which was mounting
~~as the m~~ between them & all shifts & anxieties
(she had borne them bravely; they had had their struggles)

until she felt wedged on a calm ocean, where only spice winds
blow; respected, admired, envied, with scarcely anything left
to wish for, though she regretted her stoutness; large
dinner parties every Friday night to the profession; an
occasional bazaar to be opened; Royalty ~~present to~~ <greeted>
~~her~~
~~presented~~ with bouquets; too little time, alas, with
her husband, whose work grew & grew; a boy
doing well at Eton; she would have liked a
daughter too; interests she had however in
plenty, child welfare, ~~photography~~, the after care of the
~~discharged prisoner~~, <epileptic> & photography, so that if
there was a church building ~~in the neighbour hood~~, or
a church decaying, she bribed the sexton, got the
key & took a photograph while she waited.

Sir William himself was not young. He had
worked very hard: he had won his position by sheer ability
(being the son of a ~~bricklay~~ shop keeper) loved his profession;
made a fine figure head at ceremonies, & spoke well;
~~being often asked to~~ all of which had by the time he was
knighted, given him a fixed look, a heavy look, which,
together with his grey hair, increased the extraordinary
distinction of his presence, & ~~in~~ gave him the reputation
(which is of the utmost importance in dealing with nerve
cases) not merely of lightning skill & almost infallible
accuracy in diagnosis, but of sympathy, tact, &
understanding of the human point of view.

From the first moment, ~~that he saw~~ <as they>
~~them came~~ came in the room, he could tell: it was an

extremely serious case. The patient ought not to have been
allowed out at all. It was a case, ~~he~~ of complete nervous
break down—absolutely complete, he ascertained in two or
three
minutes, (writing answers to questions on a pink card):
How long had Dr Holmes been attending him? Six weeks. yes.
Prescribed a little bromide: said there was nothing
the matter—
Oh yes. (~~This was~~ the fifth time this week <he had> ~~that the~~
~~general practitioner had driven a patient such was hi~~ such
~~examples~~ cases had come before him. Not merely ~~is the~~
was the ~~gravity of the~~ case allowed to reach a stage where cure
was doubtful; the patient suspected the medical profession.)
If Mr. Warren Smith would wait a few minutes—do not
~~move, allow~~ he would speak to Mrs. Warren Smith in the
next room.

He was afraid he must tell her that her husbands case was one
~~of compl~~ extreme gravity. Recovery was certain. But
~~very~~ it would be slow.
~~They must~~ Did he have delusions, hear voices, alternate
between
exaltation & depression? Did he threaten to kill himself?
She was on no account to <should not> hurry
herself. They would
make him perfectly well. <Did> He often threatened to kill
himself? ~~No, My dear young lady, said Sir William,~~
~~It is merely a question of physical rest, he assured her. He could~~
~~see for himself that her husband was one of those morbidly~~
~~conscientious finely~~ strung highly organised men ~~who~~
these very highly organised [ ] are the ones that require most
care, he told her. She could see all that—how good, how
brilliant, how charming, how cheerful, Septimus used to be.

For, at least, Rezia ~~felt that she could say everything.~~
~~He was~~ must tell him—her husband, they ~~were~~ had been
the happiest couple in the world. It was

~~We know~~ It is merely a question of rest, Sir William
repeated. Food rest, & in six months—

His suggestion was, in fact the only possible course
was to send him at once,—there is not

moment to be lost—to a home, kept by some very charming
    people
friends of his, in the country, in beautiful grounds, where he
would be well looked after, perfectly safe. The other
alternative being by no means so pleasant. For
~~if a man says that he is going to kill himself, we~~
10 Shortly, kindly, clearly he explained to her ~~how~~ the state of the
20 case.
200 And with great generosity he intimated that ~~rather than~~
140 if Mrs Warren Smith wd. abide absolutely by his
200 [decree?]—as to nurses & so forth—~~all that~~ what was
absolutely necessary for her husband's recovery—he
would take the responsibility. ~~of~~
    Is
    He is not mad? Rezia asked.
~~But~~ Sir William said he never spoke of madness; he
spoke of a sense of proportion; ~~owing to~~
And now if she understood, if she had no more questions to
ask, if she agreed with him that her husband should
be ~~fetched~~ go that night to the home where he ~~would~~
arrange for him to receive every comfort from refined
& cultivated people—they would return to the patient.

[33]

~~still~~

Suddenly ~~with the force of a cloud,~~ <like a cloud, like a leaden coloured> cloud, as Sir William,
already arranging the look of the very busy man, who must, directly the door
shuts, summons his secretary, dictate a few important letters, snatch a
meal, & jump into his car, disillusionment, ~~despair~~ had come
upon him as William said goodbye.

[*pencil*]
140
280
280
140
19
20
5
100
39,200
280
150
130
150
300
13
1305

~~Shrea~~ Shredding & slicing, dividing & subdividing the
clocks of Harley Street nibbled at the June day indefatigably
accurately, ~~until the authoritatively~~ & with
uniformity, upholding authority, connections submissions
& whispering that life, to be successful, must be
~~orderly~~, <lived with a sense of> until the mound of time was so
far diminished
that a commercial clock, suspended in Oxford Street,
announced, genially & fraternally, as if were a
~~reply~~ to plea.

[37]

And Lady Bruton went ponderously, majestically, up to her room; lay, one arm extended, on the sofa. She sighed, she snored

---

[The rest of the page contains part of an essay on Russian ballet.]

For he would say it when he came into the room. Because it is
a thousand pities, ~~he thought its let peop~~ never to say what one
feels; he thought, crossing the Green Park, & observing
with <&> pleasure how in the shade of the trees ~~&~~ whole
families
~~with paper bags, bottles of milk,~~ were ~~taking their~~ sprawling~~;~~
with bottles of milk, & paper bags; which could easily be
(if people picked up by one of those fat gentlemen in livery; for he
complained) was of opinion that every <park & every> square, during the
summer
months ought to be open to ~~the~~ children; ~~& What could~~ (the
grass of the park flushed & faded, as if a yellow
~~lamp~~ light were moved beneath). <But> What could be done
for female vagrants, like that poor creature, stretched in
abandonment, (as if she had flung herself ~~impudently~~ on
the earth, rid of all ties; staring impudently, ~~debauched~~
~~indifferent;~~ loose lipped, humorous) he did not know.
Bearing ~~Carrying~~ his flowers like a weapon ~~in damp tissue~~
~~paper~~ Richard Dalloway ~~passed~~ <approached her>; intent he
passed her;
still there was time for a spark; she laughed at the
sight of him; he smiled good humouredly; considering
the problem of the female vagrant; not that they would
ever speak. But he would tell Clarissa that he
loved her. He had, once upon a time, been jealous
of Peter Walsh; jealous of his having some sort of influence
upon Clarissa; But she had often said to him, how
right she had been, not to marry him; which, knowing
Clarissa; was ~~perfectly~~ obvious. She wanted support.
As for Buckingham Palace, (like an old prima donna
facing the audience all in white) you can't deny it a
certain dignity, he considered, nor despise what does

after all stand to millions of people (a little crowd was ~~ga~~
waiting at
the gates to see the King drive out) for a symbol; absurd
though it is, he thought; a ~~boy~~ <child> with a box of bricks
could have
done better, he thought, looking at the ~~Vi~~ memorial to Queen
Victoria; its white mound, its billowing motherliness; but
~~for~~ he liked being ruled by the descendant of Horsa:
~~continuity~~; he liked continuity; & the sense of
handing on ~~unbroken~~ <~~the~~ the> traditions ~~in of~~ <of the [ ]
race.> & being
English; Indeed, his life ~~had been~~ <was> a miracle; ~~for~~
let him ~~be~~ make no mistake about it <that>; here he was, in the
prime of life, walking to his house in Westminster, to
tell Clarissa that he loved her; Happiness is this.

It is this, he said, as ~~the~~ he entered Dean's Yard,
Big Ben was beginning to strike the first warning prelude.
~~How Go~~ How lunching out wastes ~~the~~ afternoon, <Luncheon
parties waste the whole> he
thought; approaching his door. The sound of the bell
flooded Clarissa's drawing room; where she ~~stood~~, sat
ever so annoyed, at her writing table; worried; annoyed.

It was perfectly true that she had not asked
~~Milly~~ <Ellie> Henderson to her party; but she had done it
on purpose.
Now Mrs. Marsham wrote "she had told ~~Mi~~ Ellie
Henderson that she would ask Clarissa—Ellie Henderson
so much wanted to come."

But why should she invite all the dull
women in London to her parties? Why should
Mrs. Marsham thrust herself in? And there was
Elizabeth closeted with Doris Kilman. Anything
more nauseating she could not conceive. Prayer
at this hour with that woman.

[*pencil*]

And people would say "Clarissa Dalloway
is spoilt"

(she had heard Richard talk about them ~~say all this~~ a thousand times)

And people would say "Clarissa Dalloway is spoilt";
She ~~did not~~ cared so much more for her roses than for the
Armenians. Hunted out of existence, maimed, frozen in their
mountains, the victims of unjust laws; no, she could feel
nothing
for the Armenians, except in some mysterious way, that
~~it was~~ the only way to help people <was>—~~hers~~—to ~~love~~
<like> roses—
roses being the only flowers that she could bear to see cut; But
Richard ~~had~~ was already at the House of Commons, having
settled all her difficulties. But no: that was not true;

He came in very quietly. She stood perfectly still. Suppose some
Mongol wrecked on the coast of Norfolk had insinuated
himself into
Dalloway family, perhaps a hundred years ago, ~~he~~
that would account for Elizabeth; the Dalloways being
fair & blue eyed; she, on the contrary ~~with a~~ having
dark Chinese eyes in a pale face; ~~& the~~ <an> Oriental calm, &
mystery; <~~the~~> added to the ~~inscrutable~~ perfect manners of the
British upper classes; <manners:> ~~their gentleness, their
stillness, their~~
gentle, considerate, still; ~~with a~~ <& as a child she had
had> ~~perfect sense of humour as a
child~~, but an ~~a~~ extraordinary change had come over her:
as if she stood ~~cased~~ <sheathed> in green glossy leaves;
hard, fresh;
just tinted, like the hyacinth, to which Clarissa compared
her; a hyacinth which has had no sun.

[45]

Miss Kilman was not going to make herself agreeable;
she had always earned her living. Her ~~grasp~~ <knowledge>
upon modern
History was ~~thorough~~, extremely thorough; ~~moreover~~ she
did, out of her meagre income, ~~give away always so~~ <set aside>
~~much to the~~ a ~~certain sum annually for the~~
so much for ~~the poor~~ causes she believed in;
whereas, this woman, did ~~absolutely~~ nothing,
believed nothing; brought her daughter up—~~but~~ & here was
Elizabeth, rather out of breath; the beautiful girl.

So they were going to the Stores. ~~But~~ Second by second,
~~hatred crumb~~ as she stood there, & how Miss Kilman could
stand, heavy, shapeless, but with the power, the taciturnity
of some pre-historic hippopotamus, who armoured for
primeval warfare remains obdurate & monolithic
~~confronting the mod in~~ there on the stairs; how hatred
crumbled, Clarissa thought; second by second Miss Kilman
lost her malignity her size; became an ordinary
woman, hot heavy, somehow pathetic. ~~But~~ <And> what was it
she gave Elizabeth.

Clarissa laughed; at the dwindling of monsters, when
~~you see them in the flesh.~~

She laughed. And off they went.

Volubly, troublously the late clock sounded, coming in on the
wake of Big Ben with its lap full of trifles. Beaten up
broken up by the assault of carriages the brutality of
vans, ~~the cries & clamour of the~~ street. & the eager advance
of myriads of angular men, of flaunting women, ~~who
appeared to be after some~~ the pell mell of ~~churches &~~
business offices & hospitals, the last relics of this lap full of
odds & ends seemed to be dispersed on the body of
Miss Kilman, standing still for a moment, & ~~saying~~
muttering ~~(so that Elizabeth could hear)~~ she always
talked ~~a~~ aloud to herself) "It is the flesh."
She must control the flesh. Mrs. Dalloway had insulted her.
That she expected. But

And Elizabeth waited in the street for an omnibus.
~~Oh~~ it was nice to be out of doors. And she thought perhaps she
need not
go home just yet. ~~So she stood opposite the stores. Already
waiting, she loved being in~~ the air. <was so nice.> Perhaps she
could get on to an
omnibus.
~~And~~ already men & women were saying ~~to each other
what a~~ how
~~beautiful girl? It was beginning. Compared to poplar
trees, lilies,~~
~~Poplar trees & lilies,~~ she was; the comparisons were beginning,
which were to make her life a burden, to poplar trees, early
dawn, running ~~str~~ water, & garden lilies; for Elizabeth
so much preferred being allowed just to do what she liked
in the country; but they would compare her to lilies &
~~things like~~ that; & she had to go to parties; & London was so
dreary ~~so silly~~ compared with being alone in the country
with her
father & her ~~dear old~~ dogs.

[*pencil*]

---

which has its effects forever, & then down it went again.

She ~~fa~~ looked up Fleet Street; she walked just a
little way. like someone penetrating on tiptoe, like

fairys coming, beckoning signalling, beneficent &
entirely

~~Nothing could be more exact. Gathering courage, he looked at the sideboard, at the bananas at the engraving of the farmyard~~
with that weight on <her> ~~shoulders,~~ Holmes & Bradshaw, the
the men who never weighed less than eleven stone six,
collected pictures, & sent their wives to court ~~the lawgivers~~
the judges who differed so strangely <in their verdicts> for

had pointing to them

~~Holmes cont~~
~~Bradshaw contradicted Holmes; He~~ who
for Holmes said one thing, Bradshaw another; the
men who made ten thousand a year & talked of
proportion; who mixed the [ ] & the side board
saw nothing clear; <yet> ~~the~~ [ ] ~~the tyrants~~. <yet
~~imposed~~ inflicted.>
~~To live~~ ~~She would have~~ to live with them. <over them she
triumphed.>

"There" she said. The horrid things were tied up:
she would <put> them away.

She was composed; she ~~seemed fearless.~~ <was gay;>
She seemed confident that she could do it—make them
respect her will. She was free. she was happy.
She went about the room, making it tidy. She said
she must go now & pack their things. She sat down
beside him, & called him by the name of that hawk
or crow, which being malicious & a great destroyer of
crops was precisely like him. And she said
it was nearly six & no one would separate them.

Then she got up to pack his clothes, but

[*pencil*]

There is a moment
in late summer is
the hour for a

The ~~triump~~ triumph of civilisation Peter Walsh thought
the light, high bell of the ambulance sounded! <the ~~vans~~
traffic let it pass;> swiftly with a
beautiful clean efficiency the ambulance sped to hospital
having picked up, intently, humanely, some poor devil;
<some one> hit
~~Civilisation~~ ~~Nothing in India~~ That was ~~the sense he~~
civilisation. It struck him, coming back from the East. ~~And~~
~~together with~~ the efficiency ~~the wh. removed these cases~~
~~instantly,~~
~~there went he thought~~, the sense, <organisation> the ~~co-~~
~~operation of~~ <communal> spirit of
London. ~~The traffic~~ Every cart or carriage of its own
accord let the
~~va~~ ambulance pass.

[*pencil*]
it is the privilege of loneliness to indulge in
sentimentality. One wept tears that were [ ]
seen. It had been his undoing--it had [ ] him
for Anglo Indian society—that & his
cynicism: ~~<wh.> wh into the bargain~~ for if you cry you laugh.

An Anglo Indian, presumably; And here a

The hollow misty cry. But it was her street, this, Clarissa's; & the cabs were sailing round the corners, like water round the piers of a bridge; ~~going~~ quickening, it seemed to him, because they bore people going to the party, going to Clarissa's house. The cold stream of visual impressions
The brain must awake. The body must contract, entering this house, Clarissas. house, where the ~~st~~ door stood, open, where the motors were standing & ~~shawled~~ bright women descending; the soul must brace itself to endure. He half opened his pocket knife.

Lucy came running full tilt down stairs;

[*pencil*]

He should have stayed at home & read his book thought Peter Walsh.

[57]

Behind her, people were still laughing & shouting. She must go
back to them. ~~But th~~ But that young man who
had killed himself, the Bradshaws said; (The clock began
striking; it was time to go back to them); he was free;
Fear no more, ~~she said~~, (the words had been running in her
    head all
day. Fear no more the heat o the sun". ~~With all~~
~~She did~~ ~~Fear no more~~, she said. But, ~~she~~ <heavens!
    she didn't pity him!> why should she
pity him? Why pity anyone with all this going on, she
thought, the clock ~~one two three; the~~ striking one
    two three four;
There! The old lady had put out her light; the house
was dark now. & with all this going on, she thought feeling
~~perfectly~~ happy, ~~as she & mysteriously~~ all the more
    ~~so~~ because
the young man had killed himself, thrown it ~~all~~ away;
so ~~that~~ proved, what she never doubted, the importance
    of <it> all
this; ~~&~~ <she [ ]> the clock striking five six seven eight; ~~the~~
reality of it all, ~~&~~ its tremendous meaning, ~~its;~~ <~~mih~~ might;> a
motor hooted, a woman cried in the street; & its
solemnity, & its beauty; <this adorable world, she
    thought,> some one had made a
very good joke in the drawing room, & she must go back
to ~~them;~~ ~~had proved all this, she thought, & felt~~
~~but~~ it; to the Bradshaws & the rest; to the
must collect from here & there all her scattered parts, &
assemble together the different parts of her, no one knew
how strange, how widely scattered, which for a moment
now standing alone came together, & must be
composed, combined, made whole in order to breast &
confront the world there. Twelve! It was twelve.
And she came in, from the little room.

[*pencil*]

But Elizabeth was silent. Think
    so he was [ ]
    the young men, with the pink cheeks
    who now beside her [ ] ask the [ ]
        And she was so [ ] &
            so [ ]

[59]

[The following 2 folio pages come from a notebook in the Berg Collection of the New York Public Library dated 22 November 1924. The page numbers follow those originally assigned by the Berg's curator.]

She was Clarissa's greatest friend. What had become of her.
Where had she vanished, the [ ] Sally, the romantic Sally,
who mocked ~~w~~ & laughed, & ran along the terrace
barefoot & wrote poetry, reams of it, all very
bad wh. she read [ ] in the cabbage garden?
Where had she gone?

And Clarissa with her little hardness, & her air
of being injured & hurt, got up & went out the room, turning
her back on him, [ ] he felt, as if she knew
that he was saying, oh ~~her so~~ the death of the soul, &
as she opened the door, in came that great shaggy
dog wh. used to run after sheep, & she flung
herself upon him & kissed him & went into
raptures, and she said to ~~Peter (it is~~
him, to ~~Peter,~~ himself, "I know you thought me a [ ]
just now; I know you're criticising me; but see
how extraordinarily by [ ] I can see
how I lose my shot". And then she went;
~~she~~ & ~~he had~~ they had quarrelled. Yes; for he had
not forgiven her; he had not looked at her; he had
sat looking glum. And why? Why did it all
matter? What did it mean? And they,
of course, directly she shut the door, ~~he~~ it seemed

all useless, quite useless, going on being in love going on
quarrelling going on making it up. And he had
wandered off to the stables alone; he had
wandered; he had tried to forget; And what was the old
coachman's name? Moody, Goody, some such name,
not that the Parrys were well off; but they had
old servants; the stables were rather ramshackle:
Clarissa had a horse. There was an old nurse too,
one visited, with photographs and bird cages.

But it was an awful evening! Awful! He
could not see her he could not explain to her;
there were people about & that woodeness
in her that impenetrability—she would
go on as if nothing had happened: he
had felt it ~~ev~~ this morning; virginity;
coldness: Yet ~~she~~ she had some queer
power too: fiddled on his nerves yes; turned
~~on~~ his nerves to fiddle strings. Still
she did that—

And so he went in to dinner
very late. He went & sat down by her
old Aunt in her cashmere
shawl, old Mrs. Parry, Aunt Helena
that was her name—there & he
sat with his head against

Appendix Three

Drafts of Essays and Reviews from the Reversed Pages of Notebook 3 of "The Hours"

[177-176]: Draft of "The Pastons and Chaucer."

[175-152]: Draft of "Joseph Conrad."

[151-147]: Draft of "The Pastons and Chaucer."

[145-143]: Draft of "Rambling Round Evelyn."

[141-140]: Notes for "Modern Fiction."

[139]: Draft of "Lives of the Obscure."

[137]: Draft review of *The Passing Years* by Lord Willoughby de Broke.

[136-131, 126-125]: Draft review of *Figures in Modern Literature* by J.B. Priestley, published as "Appreciations" in *Nation & Athenaeum*, 27 September 1924.

[130]: Sketch of a porpoise named Peter in the aquarium at Brighton.

[129-128]: "Possible Little Articles"—list, including, but not limited to, suggestions for what was to become "The Russian Frame of Mind," and revisions to "Joseph Conrad," and, perhaps, "Modern Fiction."

[124-120]: Draft of "On Re-reading Novels."

[119-117, 115-114]: Draft of review of *Restoration Comedy* by Bonamy Dobree and *The Life of William Congreve* by Edmund Gosse, published in *Nation & Athenaeum*, 18 October 1924.

[116]: Draft of paragraph beginning "The cheapening of motor cars . . . ." published in *Nation & Athenaeum*, 18 October 1924.

[113]: Draft of paragraph beginning "Not the least pitiable . . . ." published in *Nation & Athenaeum*, 18 October 1924.

[112-109]: Draft of review of *A Nineteenth Century Childhood* by Mary MacCarthy, published as "The Schoolroom Floor" in the *Times Literary Supplement*, 2 October 1924.

[108]: Draft of review of *Smoke Rings and Roundelays*, compiled by Wilfred Partington, published in *Nation & Athenaeum*, 25 October 1924.

[107]: Draft of review of *Richard Hakluyt* by Foster Watson, published in *Nation & Athenaeum*, 25 October 1924.

CPSIA information can be obtained at www.ICGtesting.com
Printed in the USA
BVOW041043220212

283524BV00007B/22/P